Contents

01
Work at Height Regulations

Contents

Supporting information

GT 700 Toolbox talks

Overview

Falls due to working at height still remain the biggest cause of fatal and specified injury accidents in the construction industry. Many falls are from less than two metres high.

Many accidents are caused by the poor selection and use of access equipment, because no fall prevention measures had been provided, or due to workers not using the work equipment provided in a safe manner.

This chapter outlines what the regulations are about, what they require, what needs to be done and by whom.

1.1 Introduction

The purpose of the regulations is to reduce the number of deaths, injuries and personal suffering resulting from falls from height, and so improve the safety performance of the industry. The Work at Height Regulations came into force in 2005 and were amended in 2007. They implement the EC Temporary Work at Height Directive and apply to all work at height where there is a risk of falling a distance liable to cause personal injury.

The regulations cover all circumstances where a person is working at height, is gaining access to, or egress from, such a place of work, at, above or below ground, or could fall a distance liable to cause personal injury (that is, any distance whatsoever).

These regulations do not apply to fixed staircases.

Common examples of tasks carried out within the construction industry classified as work at height are shown below.

- ☑ Working on a scaffold.
- ☑ Working from a mobile elevating work platform (MEWP).
- ☑ Standing on, or working from, the back of a lorry.
- ☑ Working close to an excavation's leading edge.
- ☑ Working on staging or trestles.
- ☑ Using a mobile access tower (MAT).
- ☑ Using ladders or stepladders.

Many other jobs in the construction industry also involve working at height and are covered by the Work at Height Regulations.

The evaluation by the Health and Safety Executive (HSE) of reports of accidents that occurred through working at height show that common contributory factors include the failure of the following.

- ☑ All parties to recognise that there was a problem.
- ☑ Management to provide a safe system of work (SSoW).
- ☑ Management to ensure that the safe system of work was followed.
- ☑ Management to provide adequate information, instruction, training or supervision.
- ☑ The injured worker to use appropriate equipment.
- ☑ Management to provide safe plant and equipment.
- ☑ Collective protection to take priority over personal protection.

Falls from height – 2013-14 statistics

- ☑ Falls from height were the most common cause of fatalities in the construction industry, accounting for 45% of fatal injuries to workers (RIDDOR).
- ☑ The construction industry had the most specified injury accidents of any construction sector, accounting for 31% of the total reported (581 out of 2,457).
- ☑ In 2012-13 the HSE prosecuted 97 cases under the Work at Height Regulations. There were 83 convictions with an average fine of over £10,000.

While the number of fatal injuries has generally fallen over the past decade, the percentage of fatal injuries due to falls from height has not decreased.

The HSE website has many resources, including a dedicated work at height section that includes information on the Work at Height Regulations, including INDG401 (Rev 2) *Working at height: a brief guide.*

1.2 Important points

- ☑ Falls from height are the main cause of fatalities and injuries to construction workers.
- ☑ Falls from low heights (below two metres) are the cause of many deaths and injuries.
- ☑ Working at height is defined as working at any height from which, if measures are not taken, a fall could occur and cause personal injury.
- ☑ Work at height must be carried out in accordance with the Work at Height Regulations, which require that such work is:
  - avoided if it is reasonably practicable to do the job another way and thereby avoid working at height
  - carried out using appropriate equipment to prevent falls
  - organised so that the distance and possible consequence of any fall are minimised
  - risk-assessment based
  - properly planned and supervised by a competent person(s)
  - carried out by competent operatives
  - collective protection (for example, guard-rails) to take priority over personal protection (safety harnesses) at all times.

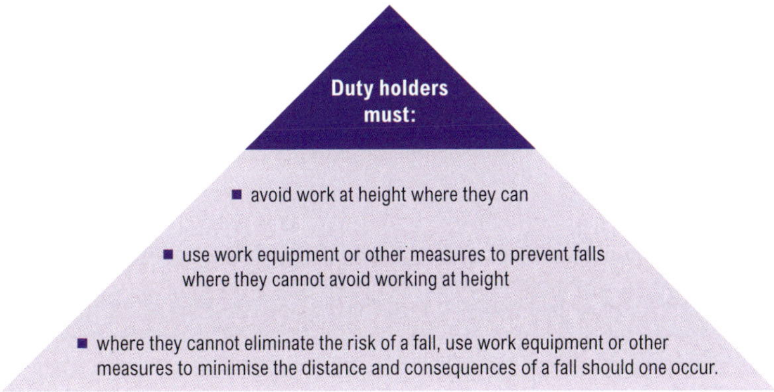

The HSE has developed a *Work at height access equipment information toolkit* (WAIT), developed to help workers at height understand the key factors to consider when selecting the safest and most appropriate types of access equipment.

The Access Industry forum website contains information and guidance, including a working at height video knowledge base, which includes a series of online videos of experts explaining the requirements for various topics (such as edge protection and fall prevention, scaffolding, MEWPs, safety nets, ladders and mobile access towers). It also contains a series of video toolbox talks.

1.3 Requirements, interpretation and duties (Regulations 2 and 3)

1.3.1 Requirements of the regulations

The main provisions of the regulations for employers is to ensure the following.

- ☑ Where it is reasonably practicable, avoid the need to carry out work at height.
- ☑ Where such work cannot be avoided, select the most appropriate equipment for the work and to prevent falls.
- ☑ Reduce the distance of, and potential consequences of, any fall.
- ☑ That the work is properly planned, including planning for an emergency. It must be risk-assessment based and carried out safely.
- ☑ The work is carried out by trained and competent persons who are adequately supervised.

The use of a ladder or stepladder is not prohibited by the regulations; however, a greater degree of consideration must be given to using an alternative means of access before selecting a ladder or stepladder for use. A decision to use this type of access equipment must be justified by the findings of a risk assessment that clearly shows that, given all of the circumstances, it is reasonable to use such equipment rather than safer types of access equipment and that any such work is short duration and low risk.

D
01

For further information refer to the HSE guidance document *Safe use of ladders and stepladders: a brief guide* (INDG455).

Some clients, contractors and principal contractors are explicit in their views by not allowing ladders or stepladders on their sites, as they see this as importing an unnecessary risk into a situation where more suitable and ultimately safer equipment may be used with a small degree of pre-planning. The tendency of some contractors and sub-contractors to turn up at site with a ladder or stepladder with which to do their work, without justifying why safer alternative equipment is not to be used, is being increasingly discouraged.

These regulations are a further stimulus to architects and designers to design out work at height for the construction and ongoing maintenance of buildings, or at least make safe working at height easier, to further contribute to safety in the industry.

1.3.2 Interpretation of the regulations (Regulation 2)

Below are the most important definitions from within the regulations.

- *Access and egress* includes ascent and descent.
- *Fragile surface* means a surface which would be liable to fail if any reasonable foreseeable load were to be applied to it. This includes the weight of a person or any work equipment or materials.
- *Ladder* includes any fixed ladder or stepladder.
- *Personal fall protection system* means:
  - a fall prevention, work restraint, work positioning fall arrest or rescue system, other than a system in which the only safeguards are collective safeguards
  - rope access and positioning systems.
- *Suitable* means suitable in any respect, which it is reasonably foreseeable that will affect the safety of any person.
- *Work at height* means work in any place, including a place at, below or above ground level, along with access to it and egress from it (except by a staircase in a permanent workplace) where, if the measures required by these regulations were not taken, a person could fall a distance liable to cause personal injury.
- *Working platform*:
  - means any platform used as a place of work or as a means of access to or egress from a place of work
  - includes any scaffold, suspended scaffold, cradle, mobile platform, trestle, gangway, gantry and stairway, which is used as a place of work.

Reasonably practicable

The term *reasonably practicable* is used in the regulations. It has the same meaning as it does in the Health and Safety at Work Act and elsewhere. Therefore, an employer can look at what the risks in a task involving work at height actually are, and what it would cost in terms of time, trouble and effort to avoid them. If it would cost a great deal of money or use of other resources to avoid a very small risk, then it may not be reasonably practicable to avoid it.

1.3.3 Application and duty of employer (Regulation 3)

The requirements of the regulations that are imposed:

- on an **employer** apply to work carried out by their employees or by any other person(s) under the employer's control, to the extent of that control
- apply to **self-employed** persons, together with persons under their control, to the extent of that control
- apply to persons who are **not self-employed**, in relation to work being carried out for them and under their control, to the extent of their control.

This last provision relates to clients and customers who are having work carried out for them, and the degree to which this duty applies. This depends upon the degree and extent of control that they have over the person(s) carrying out the work. A major client would obviously have more control over a contractor or sub-contractor than would a domestic customer who is perhaps having a roof retiled or gutters cleaned.

1.3.4 Duties of employees

The regulations also place a duty on employees in that they have specific duties under Regulation 14. These duties are similar, and in addition to, their duties under other acts and regulations (such as Section 7 of the Health and Safety at Work etc. Act). In particular, in these regulations, employees must:

Unsafe work at height – many factors could have led to these employees thinking it was an acceptable risk

- ☑ report any activity or defect relating to work at height that they know is likely to endanger the safety of themselves or that of any other person
- ☑ use any work equipment or safety device provided for work at height in accordance with any training and/or instructions that they have received.

Given the legal status of health and safety regulations, failure by an employee to comply with the above requirement is an offence that could, in the appropriate circumstances, be dealt with in a court of law or by way of enforcement action.

1.4 Organisation and planning of work (Regulation 4)

It is the responsibility of every employer to ensure that all work at height is properly planned, appropriately supervised and carried out in a safe manner, taking into account weather conditions that could jeopardise the health and safety of employees and others that may be affected by the activity.. Planning must include the selection of appropriate work equipment, and planning for any emergencies or any rescue.

An employer will probably meet most of the requirements of this regulation if they have carried out and properly implemented the control measures identified within a suitable and sufficient risk assessment.

For a work at height flowchart refer to Appendix A.

Falling from height

A site supervisor was fined after a 24-year old temporary employee suffered multiple injuries and was left paralysed after falling 10 metres from the roof of a warehouse. The temporary worker fell from an unprotected and fragile roof after the supervisor allowed workers who were removing cement sheets to go onto the roof, ignoring the company's safety policy.

The employer, who had a contract to remove asbestos cement roofs from a number of warehouses at the site, had identified them as fragile. The company had agreed a system of work where its employees would use scissor lifts to remove the roof sheets from the underside. However, when the task became difficult the supervisor did not bring this to the attention of the contracts manager, as required by the company procedure. Instead he allowed a change to the system of work, whereby he and other employees went onto the roof itself to carry out some of the work.

The HSE found the company's system of work was safe but by changing it the supervisor had sanctioned an unsafe system of work. The company was unaware of the changed way of working and the supervisor had failed to consult with them.

The supervisor pleaded guilty to breaching Regulation 4(1)(b) of the Work at Height Regulations, by failing to properly supervise work at height and make sure it was carried out safely. He was fined £1,000 and ordered to pay £9,765.88 costs.

The HSE inspector said: 'Those who supervise work at height have a responsibility to ensure that it is carried out in a manner that is safe and which guards against the risk of injury from a fall. Such injuries, if not fatal, may result in a lifelong disability for the injured person'.

For further information on fragile roofs refer to Chapter D02 Safe working at height.

D 01

1.5 Competence (Regulation 5)

Employers must ensure that no person takes part in any work at height activity, including being involved in the organisation, planning and supervision of the work and work equipment, unless they are competent to do so or, if they are being trained, that they are being supervised by a competent person.

The level of supervision is important. The supervisor will need to be able to intervene, physically or by virtue of their authority, if an unsafe situation begins to develop and rectify the situation or stop the work in progress. The more inexperienced an employee is in relation to working at height, the greater will be the appropriate level of supervision required.

While there is no definition of *competence* in the regulations it may be taken to mean the following.

- A person who has practical and theoretical knowledge of the appropriate aspects of work at heights, together with actual experience of what they are to do, which will enable them to ensure that all necessary planning and assessments have been prepared, and safety precautions taken, so that the work may be carried out safely, or that they may work safely. This person must also be able to understand and recognise their own personal limitations.

If they will be inspecting work equipment then *competence* may be taken to mean the following.

- A person who has practical and theoretical knowledge, together with actual experience of what they are to examine, which will enable them to detect errors, defects, faults or weaknesses that it is the purpose of the examination or inspection to discover and to assess the importance of any such discovery. This person must also know their limitations and must not put themselves or others at risk during the inspection of work equipment.

Training is an element of the competence necessary to work at height safely. Similarly, those who deliver such training must also be competent to do so.

To assist trainers in this respect British Standards published the *Code of Practice for the delivery of training and education for work at height and rescue* (BS 8454).

1.6 Avoidance of risks from work at height (Regulation 6)

This is one of the main regulations and specifically requires employers to ensure that risk assessments take account of work carried out at height in accordance with Regulation 3 of the Management of Health and Safety at Work Regulations.

For further information refer to Chapter A05 Risk assessments and method statements.

In addition, the regulation requires that: 'every employer shall ensure that work is not carried out at height where it is reasonably practicable to carry out the work safely otherwise than at height'.

This clearly requires the employer to carry out a detailed study or assessment of all the ways in which the work could be carried out. If work can be carried out without the need to work at height, then the employer should do so, provided that it is reasonably practicable.

Eliminating the need to work at height

A good example of this was demonstrated during the construction of an over-bridge. The bridge deck was completed on flat ground before the spoil was excavated from below it. This virtually eliminated the need for working at height and reduced the height at which people had to work when constructing the upper parts of the structure.

Ground-level fabrication is another way of eliminating, or at least reducing, some tasks that have been traditionally carried out at height.

The fact that falls from height often result in fatal or serious injuries should weigh heavily in any risk assessment in deciding if an alternative to working at height is reasonably practicable.

When assessing risk or developing a safe system of work, the hierarchy in the flowchart opposite must be followed.

1.6.1 Hierarchy for working at height

Step 1. Avoid working at height

e.g. assemble on the ground and crane up, use extendable handles on equipment.

Only if this can't be avoided then:

Step 2. Use an existing safe place of work

e.g. parapet walls, defined access points, staircases.

Only if this can't be done then:

Step 3. Provide work equipment to prevent falls

e.g. scaffolding, edge protection, handrails, podiums, mobile towers, MEWPs.

Only if this can't be provided then:

Step 4. Mitigate distance and consequence of a fall

e.g. safety netting, airbags, crash decks
(harnesses must only be used as a last resort).

Step 5. Provide instruction, training and/or other means

e.g. PASMA training for mobile towers, IPAF training for MEWPs,
using ladders (the last resort).

1.7 Selection of equipment for work at height (Regulation 7)

In selecting work equipment for use in work at height there is an absolute requirement for the employer to select work equipment or other measures that will give collective protection to employees as a whole, rather than just individual personal protection for one person. For example, a guard-rail will protect everyone (collective), whereas a safety harness and lanyard only protects the wearer (personal).

The Personal Protective Equipment at Work Regulations requires that employers follow current good industry practice when selecting equipment for work at height. In particular, employers are required to take account of the following elements.

- ☑ Working conditions and risks to the safety of persons at their place of work.
- ☑ Access and egress and distances to be negotiated.
- ☑ Distance and consequences of any potential fall.
- ☑ Duration and frequency of use of the work equipment.
- ☑ Need for and ease of evacuation and rescue in any emergency.
- ☑ Any additional risks posed by the installation, use, or removal of the work equipment, any evacuation or by any rescue from it.
- ☑ Any other provisions of the regulations.

Any work equipment which is selected must meet the following requirements.

- ☑ Be appropriate for the work intended to be carried out and the foreseeable loadings.
- ☑ Allow the safe passage of persons and materials without risk.
- ☑ Be the most suitable equipment for avoiding risks while working at height.

Where a trade or occupation has historically used ladders, stepladders, trestles and other similar work equipment, the regulations do not prohibit their continued use provided that the provisions of the Work at Height Regulations and the Management of Health and Safety at Work Regulations are fully considered and complied with.

D 01

In such circumstances employers will have to be in a position to demonstrate the following.

- The work at height has been properly planned and cannot be avoided or done any other way that is reasonably practicable.
- The most suitable work equipment is proposed to be used, and a risk assessment shows that the remaining risks are low.
- Appropriate steps have been taken to mitigate the effects of any fall, should one occur (for example, safety harnesses or safety nets).
- Employees are competent and properly supervised.

Risk assessments should be very thorough but proportionate to the risks inherent in the work that is to be done.

It may, however, be the case that a client or contractor, or principal contractor where appointed, will not allow, or will control through a permit system, certain types of access equipment (such as ladders, stepladders or some types of trestles) on their premises or site. This requirement may form part of the client's or contractor's own policies and procedures in relation to the use of this form of access equipment. It may mean that an alternative form of access equipment is used.

1.8 Requirements for particular work equipment (Regulation 8)

This regulation and Schedules 2 to 6 of the regulations cover the following provisions.

- Guard-rails, toe-boards, barriers and similar means of protection.
- Working platforms (such as scaffolds and trestles).
- Safety nets, airbags and other collective means of arresting falls.
- Personal fall protection systems.
- Work positioning systems.
- Rope access and positioning systems.
- Fall-arrest systems.
- Work restraint systems.
- Ladders.

In respect of guard-rails, the main guard-rail must be installed to at least 950 mm above the work surface or the edge from which a person may fall.

Members of the public should be protected from items falling form height

Although there is no statutory minimum height for toe-boards, both BS EN 12811-1 and TG20:13, which relates to scaffolding good practice, recommend a minimum of 150 mm. They must be suitable and sufficient to prevent the fall of persons or materials. In line with current industry practice it is anticipated that scaffold boards on edges will continue to be used in most circumstances.

The maximum distance or gap between the top of a toe-board and the mid guard-rail, or between the mid guard-rail and the top guard-rail, is 470 mm.

Where brick guards or similar items are used as a means of protection, then they must meet the following criteria.

- Be placed so as to prevent the fall of persons or materials.
- Be of a suitable size and strength.
- Be placed or secured so that they do not become accidentally displaced.
- Be inspected at regular intervals.

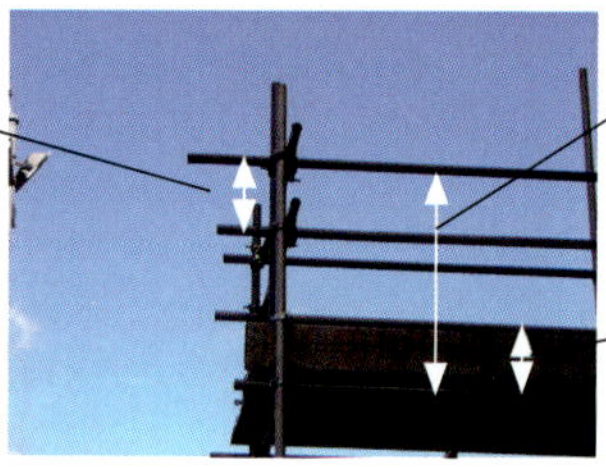

Guard-rails may be removed on a temporary basis for the movement of materials, provided that suitable and effective alternative fall protection measures are put in place for the duration of the work, and that the guard-rails are replaced as soon as possible after the work is completed.

There is also provision in the regulations for danger areas (*refer to Regulation 11*). Where a workplace contains an area where there is a risk of injury to any person at work falling, or being struck by a falling object, measures should be taken to prevent unauthorised access and the danger area must be clearly indicated. This would generally mean the provision of an exclusion zone, supported by safety signage. The safety signage must comply with the Health and Safety (Safety Signs and Signals) Regulations.

Where employers can demonstrate that they are complying fully with current industry good practice and HSE Codes of Practice or guidance, then in the majority of situations they will meet most of the requirements of the Work at Height Regulations. Their risk assessments for working at height will then essentially be a comparison between what they are already doing to control the risks and what is regarded as good practice, then implementing further control measures if necessary.

1.8.1 Use of scaffolds

The current industry guidance is based on the content of the British Standard: *Temporary work equipment. Part 1. Scaffold – Performance requirements and general design* (BS EN 12811-1).

Additional practical guidance is produced by the National Access and Scaffolding Confederation (NASC), which produces the *Guide to good practice for scaffolding with tubes and fittings* (TG20) and *Preventing falls in scaffolding* (SG4). Both of these documents are accepted by the scaffolding industry and the HSE as essential in ensuring that scaffolding is designed and erected in a safe manner, and in compliance with the Work at Height Regulations.

www.

NASC has a large number of technical (TG) and safety (SG) guidance notes that are accepted by the HSE as scaffolding industry good practice. These are available to purchase online.

1.8.2 Use of ladders, stepladders and trestles

Ladders may be used for access to and egress from the place of work. Ladders, stepladders and trestles may be used to work from, provided that all of the requirements of the Work at Height Regulations are fully complied with.

The primary objective of the regulations is to eliminate work at height (and so the possibility of falls) and, where that is not possible, to ensure that all work at height is carried out safely and that the work equipment being used (such as a ladder or stepladder) is appropriate, suitable and safe for the work and the environment in which they are to be used.

In deciding to use a ladder for access or egress, or a ladder, stepladder or trestle for work at height, the employer must have carried out an assessment and found that it is not reasonably practicable to use any safer means, and that a risk assessment has shown that the risks from using the ladder, stepladder or trestle are low.

Ladders should be used in accordance with manufacturers' instructions. They must be the right ladder for the job, positioned at the correct angle, placed on a firm level surface, and secured or otherwise prevented from slipping or moving. Users should face the ladder at all times when climbing up or down, have both hands free, and not be carrying anything that would interfere with their safety or balance.

Ladders may be used as a place of work, subject to the above, and if it is light work and of short duration. Users should be trained in how to work safely on ladders (for example, not to overreach).

When stepladders are to be used to carry out work they should be of a suitable size and type. Generally, stepladders should be placed facing the work. They should not be used side-on to the work in any situation where a sideways load could be applied. Again, the work should be light and of short duration.

Pre-fabricated access equipment (such as podium steps) are a product that was developed as a result of the implementation of the Work at Height Regulations and, in simple terms, are a stepladder with a secure working platform with guard-rails and toe-boards in place. They are available in various sizes and heights and many are fitted with castors to make them more mobile. This type of access equipment provides a safe working platform and collective means of fall protection.

Trestles should be of sound construction, and properly set up on a surface that will bear their weight, as well as any loading of persons or materials. Trestle boards must be supported at a distance specified by the manufacturer. If they are adjustable, using telescopic adjustment, they should have high tensile pins in the adjusters. If they are fitted with wheels or castors, they should have brakes or other suitable devices on the wheels or castors. Employees who install and use trestles should be trained how to do so safely.

Trestles should be fitted with guard-rails and toe-boards, where appropriate.

www.

The Ladder Association in consultation with the HSE and with the support of the DTI has produced *Risk assessment guidelines for leaning ladders and for stepladders.*

For further information on the use of ladders refer to Chapter D03 Common access equipment.

1.9 Fragile surfaces (Regulation 9)

The general requirement is that employers must ensure that no person passes across or near, or works on, from or near any fragile surface when it is reasonably practicable to carry out the work safely without their having to do so.

Where this requirement cannot be met, then the employer must:

- provide and ensure that there are suitable and sufficient platforms, coverings, guard-rails or other similar means of support or protection, which must be capable of supporting any foreseeable load or loading
- where the risk of a fall still remains, take suitable and sufficient steps to minimise the distance and consequences of any fall, should it occur
- place prominent warning notices at the approach(es) to any fragile material
- where such notices cannot be used, ensure that employees (and others as appropriate) are made aware of the fragile materials by other means.

1.10 Falling objects (Regulation 10)

Along with much else in the Work at Height Regulations, the requirement in this regulation follows current good practice in that employers must take suitable and sufficient steps (including prohibiting the throwing down of materials) to prevent, so far as is reasonably practicable, the fall of any materials or objects that are likely to cause any injury to any person. Suitable steps will include the use of such items as brick guards, toe-boards and debris nets.

Where such falls cannot be prevented, or in the interests of safety, suitable and sufficient measures must be taken to prevent persons from being hit by falling objects or materials. This will cover the use of protective fans, boarded or roofed walkways and exclusion zones at ground level, which must all be supported with the appropriate level of safety signage.

Materials on scaffolds and working platforms must be stored so that they cannot fall or pose a risk of injury to anyone by their collapse, overturning or unintended movement.

1.11 Danger areas (Regulation 11)

Following on from Regulation 10 and building on its requirements, in any workplace where there is a risk of any person falling or of persons being struck by falling objects, then employers must take all reasonably practicable steps to prevent any unauthorised access to that area (such as putting up physical barriers and appropriate warning signs). Any signs must comply with the Health and Safety (Safety Signs and Signals) Regulations.

1.12 Inspection of work equipment (Regulation 12)

This regulation only applies to work equipment to which Regulation 8 and Schedules 2–6 apply, and closely follows the current requirements in the Provision and Use of Work Equipment Regulations (PUWER) as regards the inspection of work equipment.

Where the safety of work equipment used for working at height (for example, a scaffold) depends upon how it has been installed or assembled, then it must not be used in that place or elsewhere until after it has been inspected by a competent person. Throughout the regulations, *inspection* means any visual or more rigorous inspection, and any appropriate testing that a competent person decides is necessary.

All work equipment exposed to conditions causing deterioration that may result in dangerous situations must be inspected. This will ensure that it remains safe and that any deterioration can be detected and remedied.

Inspections must take place at suitable intervals and after each time that exceptional circumstances have occurred that are liable to have jeopardised the safety of the work equipment.

In addition to these requirements, any working platform that is used for construction work, and from which a person could fall more than two metres, must not be used unless it has been inspected in that position within the previous seven days. A mobile working platform (such as a mobile scaffold tower or a MEWP) must have been inspected within the previous seven days.

Employers must ensure that no work equipment (other than lifting equipment for which an identical provision applies under the Lifting Operations and Lifting Equipment Regulations (LOLER)), whether it is purchased, brought in or hired in, is used unless they have evidence that the last inspection required by this regulation was carried out.

If there is no evidence of the last inspection then the work equipment cannot be used on site until an inspection is carried out by a competent person. These formal inspection(s) should not be regarded as a substitute for any routine pre-use checks that should be carried out by the user.

What is a suitable interval should be decided by a competent person, based on the results of risk assessments, and then be reviewed in the light of experience.

The purpose of an inspection is to identify whether the work equipment is safe to use, and that any defect or deterioration is detected and repaired. If this is not possible, the work equipment should be removed from service before it becomes an unacceptable risk.

The results of every inspection must be recorded and kept on site until the construction work is completed, and after that they must be kept at one of the company offices for three months. The detail of the inspection must be recorded before the end of the working day, in accordance with the particulars given in Schedule 7, and the report delivered within 24 hours. Lifting equipment that has had a thorough examination under the provisions of LOLER is treated as having had an inspection under these regulations.

Provided that the required information is recorded, and is readily available, then an employer may adopt their own recording system. Any computer-based system should be secure and cannot be interfered with. Systems may also be in the form of a register.

1.13 Inspection of places of work at height (Regulation 13)

So far as is reasonably practicable, every employer must ensure that the surface and every parapet permanent rail or other such fall protection measure be inspected visually prior to each use. While there is no requirement to record such inspections, a simple record would provide evidence that the risk has been identified and appropriate inspections carried out.

1.14 Schedules 1 to 8

There are eight schedules to the regulations. Much of the information contained in the schedules is virtually identical to current requirements and/or guidance so if employers are actively working to current standards and guidance then there is little extra for them to do.

1.14.1 Schedule 1. Regulation 6(4)(a)

The requirement in this schedule is for existing places of work at height and means of access or egress to and from such places to be stable, of sufficient size and strength and with suitable edge protection as necessary. Ladders in particular must rest on stable, strong surfaces.

A place of work is to be properly constructed, used and maintained so as to prevent the risk of tripping, slipping or being trapped between it and adjacent surfaces. It should have no gaps through which materials could fall and injure someone below.

1.14.2 Schedule 2. Regulation 8(a)

This covers the requirements for guard-rails, toe-boards, barriers or similar means of protection *(refer to Regulation 8)*. The remainder of the requirements are unchanged other than the fact that the top guard-rail must now be at least 950 mm above the edge from which any person might fall (with the provision of 910 mm for guard-rails that were in place at the time the Work at Height Regulations came into force), and the removal of any specific height at which guard-rails and toe-boards must be fitted.

1.14.3 Schedule 3. Regulation 8(b)

This covers the requirements for working platforms. Part 1 deals with requirements for all working platforms, and Part 2 covers the additional requirements for scaffolding.

Part 1. All working platforms must be erected and used so that components cannot become displaced and cause danger to anyone. They must be suitable for the work, and of sufficient strength and rigidity. If they are altered or modified (by a competent person) they must remain safe and stable.

A supporting structure means any structure used for the purpose of supporting a working platform and includes any plant used for that purpose. It must be suitable and of sufficient strength and stability while being erected, used or dismantled. It must be prevented from slipping or moving, and if it has wheels or castors, they must be capable of being locked or similar. Working platforms and supporting structures must not be overloaded.

Part 2. As regards the **additional requirements for scaffolding** strength and stability, calculations must be carried out unless it is being assembled in conformity with generally recognised standard configurations (for example, a TG20 compliant scaffold, erected in accordance with a TG20 compliance sheet). If the scaffold is not a TG20 compliant scaffold then design calculations will need to be provided by the scaffolding contractor. Such calculations are usually supported by the provision of detailed drawings, to assist scaffolders during construction and inspection of the scaffold.

If prefabricated scaffolding materials are being used, (for example, ladder beams and hop-up platforms) then the manufacturer's data will be required to confirm that these products may be used in conjunction with the scaffold in question.

Depending on the complexity of the scaffold, an assembly, use and dismantling plan (commonly referred to as a method statement) shall be drawn up by a competent person. This may be a standard or generic plan, supplemented with specific details as appropriate. A copy of the plan must be kept for the use of any persons concerned with the erection, use or dismantling of the scaffold.

The size and layout of the scaffold must be appropriate and suitable for the work to be performed, and it must also permit the work and passage of persons to happen safely. (NASC TG20 gives details on specific scaffold dimensions, layouts and load bearing capacities.)

When a scaffold is not available for use during erection, alteration and/or dismantlement, then warning signs in accordance with the Health and Safety (Safety Signs and Signals) Regulations need to be displayed (scaffold tagging systems are available that will help fulfil this requirement). Physical barriers must also be put in place to prevent access to the scaffold, or any unsafe or incomplete parts of the scaffold.

Scaffolding may only be assembled, dismantled or significantly altered under the supervision of a competent person and by persons who have received appropriate and specific training.

The Construction Industry Scaffolders Record Scheme (CISRS) has a card scheme in place for people working in the scaffolding industry, including scaffolders, trainee scaffolders, labourers and supervisors.

1.14.4 Schedule 4. Regulation 8(c)

This schedule covers the requirements for collective safeguards for arresting falls. Collective safeguards include safety nets, airbags, landing mats and any similar devices or arrangements. All must be suitable and of sufficient strength to be able to safely arrest or cushion a fall and may only be used in the following situations.

- Where a risk assessment has shown that the work to be done can be carried out safely while the safeguard is being used, and without influencing its effectiveness.
- Where the use of safer work equipment is not reasonably practicable.
- If a sufficient number of employees (or others) have received adequate training specific to the safeguard, including rescue procedures.

An important requirement is that if the safeguard is designed to be attached to a building or a structure then the safeguard, the structure and all anchorages must be suitable and of sufficient strength for any foreseeable load that a fall might impose on it.

Airbags and landing mats must be suitable for the purpose intended, and they must be stable.

If a safeguard is designed to distort when arresting a fall, it must give sufficient clearance from the ground or adjacent structures to avoid injury to a person whose fall is being arrested.

1.14.5 Schedule 5. Regulation 8(d)

This schedule covers the requirements for personal fall protection systems (Part 1), work positioning systems (Part 2), rope access and positioning techniques (Part 3), fall-arrest systems (Part 4) and work restraint systems (Part 5).

Much of the information in this schedule is technical in nature and it is of paramount importance that employees are fully trained in the use of any of the fall protection systems available to them. There is insufficient detail within this brief explanation of the schedule to train a person on the requirements, or for them to gain sufficient knowledge to be regarded as competent.

All safety harnesses, lanyards and other fall prevention or fall-arrest equipment must comply with the appropriate British and European standards.

Part 1 deals with the requirements for all personal fall protection systems. See 'Interpretation of the regulations' *(refer to 1.3.2)* for the definition of personal fall protection systems.

Current guidance is that the requirements set out in this schedule apply to all rope-based activities for work at height, including industrial rope systems and any other similar activity when carried out as a work activity. The following points are requirements of the schedule.

- A personal fall protection system shall only be used if a risk assessment has shown that the work can be done safely while it is being used, and that the use of other, safer work equipment is not reasonably practicable.
- The user and a sufficient number of others have been trained in its use and in rescue procedures.
- It shall be suitable and of sufficient strength for the purpose for which it is to be used and will withstand any foreseeable loading.
- It fits the wearer and is correctly fitted or worn.
- It is designed to minimise injury to the user in the event of a fall, and is such that the user will not fall or slip out of it should they fall.
- It is designed, installed and used so as to prevent unplanned or uncontrolled movement of the user.

Any anchorage point must be suitable and of sufficient strength to support any foreseeable loading. If designed to do so, the equipment must be securely attached to at least one such anchorage point when in use.

Part 2 deals with the additional requirements for work positioning systems. They may only be used in the following instances.

- If the system includes a suitable backup system for preventing or arresting a fall.
- If the system includes a line as a backup system and the user is connected to it.
- Where it is not reasonably practicable to do either of the above, then other suitable measures are taken to prevent or arrest a fall.

Part 3 deals with the additional requirements for rope access and positioning techniques, which may only be used in the following instances.

- ☑ If it has two separate lines: the working line and a safety line.
- ☑ If the user has a safety harness that is connected to both the working line and the safety line.
- ☑ When the working line has safe means of ascent and descent, and a self-locking device to prevent falling.
- ☑ When the safety line has a mobile fall protection system that is connected to, and travels with, the user.
- ☑ Subject to the type and duration of work, and the findings of a risk assessment, it has a seat with appropriate accessories. However, if a risk assessment has demonstrated that a second line would entail a higher risk to the user, then, provided that appropriate safety measures have been taken, a single rope may be used.

Part 4 deals with the additional requirements for fall-arrest systems. It requires that they must have a suitable energy absorber (often called a shock absorber and which is usually either a folded metal strip that deforms, or tear-away stitched webbing), or other suitable means of limiting the force applied to the user's body in the event of a fall. In addition, a fall-arrest system must not be used if there is any risk of a line (a rope or a lanyard) being cut, or where there is no safety zone or clear zone to allow for any swinging or pendulum effect after a fall, or in a way that hinders the system's safety performance or makes its use unsafe.

Part 5 deals with the additional requirements for work restraint systems (often a safety harness with a very short lanyard), and requires that they are designed so that they are used correctly to prevent the user from getting into a position where they could fall.

1.14.6 Schedule 6. Regulation 8(e)

This schedule contains a specific requirement on the use of ladders and stepladders for work at height. Employers and the self-employed must ensure that a ladder or stepladder is only used for work at height if a risk assessment has shown that the use of more suitable work equipment is not justified because of the low risk and the short duration of the work, or because of existing features on site that cannot be altered.

The remainder of the schedule is in line with current industry good practice. The requirements are shown in brief below.

- ☑ The surface on which a ladder rests must be stable and of sufficient strength.
- ☑ The ladder is strong enough for loads that may be put on it.
- ☑ The ladder is placed so that it is stable during use.
- ☑ A suspended ladder is attached in a secure manner so that it does not swing.
- ☑ Portable ladders are prevented from slipping by being secured at or near their top or bottom, or with anti-slip or stability devices, or other effective means.
- ☑ Access ladders are long enough to provide a handhold when getting off at the top, unless other handholds have been provided.
- ☑ Sections on interlocking or extension ladders are prevented from movement while in use.
- ☑ Mobile ladders are prevented from moving before being stepped on.
- ☑ Where reasonably practicable, rest platforms are provided where a run of ladders rises a vertical distance of more than nine metres.
- ☑ Ladders are used in such a way that a secure handhold and secure support are always available to the user.
- ☑ The user can maintain a safe handhold while carrying a load.

This last point is qualified for stepladders in that:

> **...in the case of a stepladder the maintenance of a handhold is not practical when a load is carried, and a risk assessment has demonstrated that the use of a stepladder is justified because of the low risk and the short duration of the work.**

> **For advice on footing ladders, refer to Chapter D03 Common access equipment.**

1.14.7 Schedule 7. Regulation 12(7)

This schedule states the details (shown below) to be recorded in a work equipment inspection report (for example, scaffold inspection).

- The name and address of the person for whom the inspection was carried out.
- The location of the work equipment inspected.
- A description of the work equipment inspected.
- The date and time of the inspection.
- Details of any matter identified that could give rise to a risk to the health or safety of any person.
- Details of any action taken as a result of any matter identified in the point above.
- Details of any further actions considered necessary.
- The name and position of the person making the report.

Reports of inspection have to be kept on site until construction work is completed and then at the employer's offices for three months.

1.14.8 Schedule 8. Regulation 19

This schedule outlines various other regulations or parts of them that are revoked by the coming into force of the Work at Height Regulations.

Appendix A – Work at height flowchart

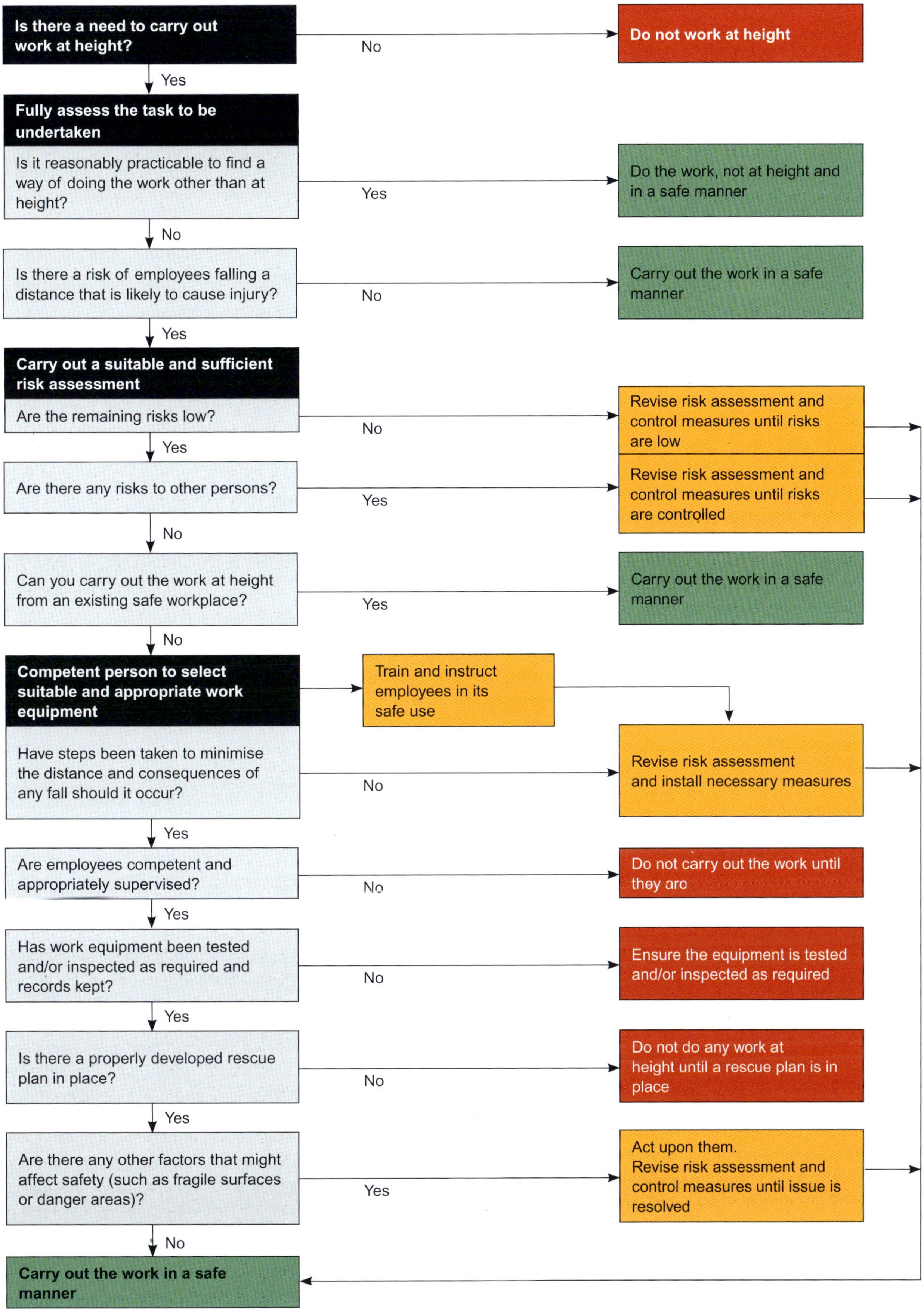

D
01

02

Safe working at height

Contents

Supporting information

GT 700 Toolbox talks

D
02

Overview

There is no such thing as a safe height; anyone who is off the ground is at risk of falling. The hazard exists on working platforms, scaffolds, ladders, flat and pitched roofs, open steelwork and any area where work is being done in proximity to fragile materials, openings, holes and roof edges.

Ladders, stepladders and trestles (or lightweight staging) are among the most commonly used pieces of access equipment on site and, perhaps, the most misused.

Most building and construction workers have used them at some time and it is essential that safe working practices should be followed if accidents are to be avoided.

2.1 Introduction

Before reading this chapter, it is strongly recommended that readers familiarise themselves with Chapter D01 Work at Height Regulations. There have been a number of major improvements in safety standards and practices, with regard to working at height. For example, the almost standard practice of profile roofing workers using safety nets on new build, along with the use of powered access for steel workers, have been significant steps forward in construction health and safety.

Every year, however, work at height remains by far the largest cause of death in the construction industry. Roof work, in particular, including work on fragile roofing materials, gives rise to a substantial number of fatal and serious accidents. These invariably affect lives and livelihoods.

It needs to be emphasised, however, that there is not just the actual roof working to be considered, but the whole process: planning the job, creating a safe access, the safe storage of equipment and materials, and so on.

There is no such thing as a safe height; anyone who is off the ground is at risk of falling. The hazard exists on working platforms, scaffolds, ladders, flat and pitched roofs, open steelwork and any area where work is being done in proximity to fragile materials, openings, holes and roof edges.

Various work at height solutions

In many respects, maintenance, repair and working for domestic clients may offer greater challenges to providing a safe working environment. The work is typically of shorter duration than new build, and often carried out directly for a client who may not be aware of the required standards. This does not lessen either the need for safe working methods or compliance with the law.

Compliance with well-established safety procedures and existing legislation could save many lives and prevent many injuries. Most accidents could be avoided, given the provision of appropriate equipment and the adequate information, instruction, training and supervision of those who use it.

The photo shows various work at height solutions in practice, including proprietary edge protection mesh barriers and scaffold guard-rails.

Guard-rails and toe-boards are required on all working platforms where a risk assessment indicates that any person would be injured as a result of the fall.

For additional information refer to:

- ☑ **Chapter D01 Work at Height Regulations**
- ☑ **Chapter D03 Common access equipment**
- ☑ **Chapter D04 Scaffolding**
- ☑ **Chapter D05 Fall arrest and suspension equipment**
- ☑ **Chapter F05 Working over or near to water.**

For further sources of information and guidance relating to roof work refer to the following websites.

- ☑ **Advisory Committee for Roofsafety (ACR).**
- ☑ **National Federation of Roofing Contractors (NFRC).**
- ☑ **Access Industry Federation (AIF).**
- ☑ **National Access and Scaffolding Confederation (NASC).**
- ☑ **Health and Safety Executive (HSE).**
- ☑ **British Constructional Steelwork Association.**

2.2 Important points

- Those who work on roofs are, by the nature of their work, at risk of falling if appropriate measures are not taken.
- Those who plan, supervise or carry out roof work must be competent to do so.
- A risk assessment and, where considered necessary, a method statement, should be compiled for all such work.
- Integral features of roofs (such as a steep pitch, valleys, fragile cladding or roof lights) can increase the risk of falling.
- Falls through fragile roofing materials continue to be the cause of many deaths and injuries.
- Bad weather can have a significant impact on the risk control measures that have to be taken.
- Ideally, work will be carried out from a stable working platform, fitted with guard-rails and toe-boards, all of which comply with the requirements of the Work at Height Regulations.
- If safe working platforms cannot be provided, then harnesses with work restraint systems should be used to prevent falls.
- Where such fall prevention measures cannot be used, effective fall-arrest measures must be put in place, ideally collective measures (such as safety nets or other soft-landing systems).
- Those who work on roofs must also take into consideration the safety of anyone passing below to protect them from falling materials or tools.
- Access equipment (such as powered access (MEWP), scaffolding, ladders, stepladders and lightweight stagings) are all easily transported means of access to work at height. They can all be used safely in certain conditions.
- The danger often comes when access equipment is used for a job for which it is not suitable; this particularly applies to ladders and stepladders.
- All persons that are working at height must have received adequate training in systems of work and any equipment that they are planning to use for access.
- The nature and duration of the job will be significant factors in determining the most appropriate type of access equipment to use for work at height.
- The Health and Safety Executive's (HSE) evaluation of accidents resulting from work at height shows that inappropriate access equipment, provided by management and used by workers, is a significant factor.
- Falls from low levels (such as a height below two metres) are the cause of many injuries and fatalities.
- All holes in floors must be protected with secured guard-rails, toe-boards, coverings or similar barriers and be clearly marked with warning signs.

2.3 Stages of a roofing project

The various stages of a roofing project are shown below.

- Design.
- Selection of contractors and staff.
- Planning.
- Carrying out the work.
- Post-completion information (at the end).

2.3.1 Stage 1. Design

Designers have duties under the Construction (Design and Management) Regulations to eliminate, reduce or control foreseeable health and safety risks that may arise during construction, use and future maintenance of roof structures. Where residual hazards remain in the design, these should be communicated in the planning so that suitable precautions (such as those shown below) can be taken.

- The ability to safely construct a roof.
- Specification of materials and construction methods, including fragility.
- Future access for maintenance and repair.

Anyone in the planning or construction process who changes a specification or construction method assumes responsibility for design.

For further information refer to Chapter A03 Construction (Design and Management) Regulations.

2.3.2 Stage 2. Selection of contractors and staff

Where a company is using its own employees to carry out roof work, it is essential that several factors are taken into consideration. Operational work on roofs can be both hazardous and strenuous, often involving:

- ☑ work at considerable heights for long periods of time
- ☑ work outdoors, including adverse weather conditions (such as hot, cold or wet weather, high winds, snow, ice and fog affecting visibility).
- ☑ repetitive materials handling
- ☑ reaching, stretching and maintaining balance in awkward postures whilst carrying loads on varying roof terrains.

This means that fitness to work is particularly important and needs to be considered by the employers. The ACR suggests that it is vital that people working on roofs do not suffer from the following conditions.

- ☑ Any neurological condition likely to cause seizures.
- ☑ Weakness of limbs.
- ☑ Loss of balance, including vertigo (dizziness from being at height).
- ☑ Any heart or lung condition likely to be aggravated by strenuous work.
- ☑ Any disability or impairment of limb function.
- ☑ Any other disease, disability or the effects of medication, alcohol, drugs or toxic substances (lead and so on) likely to impair mental or physical activity, especially at a height.
- ☑ Temporary ailments (such as influenza) or other conditions that may affect judgement.
- ☑ Uncorrected sight problems.
- ☑ A physique that would be unsuitable for the work.

Obviously an employer needs to be aware of the provisions of the Equality Act with regard to the above. It is very strongly suggested that employers should establish a policy on fitness for work, and ideally that this should be implemented before taking on any new staff. So-called fitness to work medicals are not new and many sectors already use them for their staff (for example, holders of PSV driving licences, such as bus drivers). Often a local GP can carry out these medicals or a specialist occupational health service provider.

www.

For further information refer to the ACR's *Guidance note for competence and general fitness requirements to work on roofs.*

2.3.3 Stage 3. Planning

Planning the work should include consideration of the progression of the work with regard to the following.

- ☑ Site-specific hazards and risks.
- ☑ Weather conditions.
- ☑ Emergencies (including rescue).
- ☑ Safe means of access and egress.
- ☑ Materials handling and storage.
- ☑ Personnel involved, including competence and supervision.

2.3.3.1 Site-specific hazards and risks

The site-specific hazards could include the following.

- ☑ Working above public areas (such as shopping malls or public streets).
- ☑ The difficulties in delivering materials and transferring them to roof level.
- ☑ The presence of site traffic or road traffic on a public road.
- ☑ Awkward working environments (such as occupied houses or factories).
- ☑ Emergency situations (such as rescuing someone who has fallen and is suspended at high level in a safety harness or recovering an injured worker from height).
- ☑ Vent pipes that may suddenly shower unsuspecting roof workers with anything ranging from high pressure steam to noxious chemicals.
- ☑ Nesting birds that will aggressively defend their territory.
- ☑ The presence of accumulated pigeon droppings *(refer to Chapter B01 Management of health).*

2.3.3.2 Weather conditions

It goes without saying that the weather can have a significant impact upon the intention to carry out roof work and may ultimately be the reason for the start of a job being delayed, or it being suspended part-way through.

Heavy rain, high winds, frost, snow or fog might make it unsafe for operatives to work at height.

Five-day weather forecasts that include temperature, wind speed and direction are available from several websites.

Typical hand-held wind meter (anemometer)
(Image supplied by Kestrel Weather & Environmental Meters by NK)

Wind speeds and temperatures quoted in weather forecasts can differ considerably at height (for example, if installing a glass atrium roof on top of a multistorey tower block).

If a roofing job has started and the weather is forecast to be changeable, with perhaps extremes of conditions, it will be essential to monitor the forecast and conditions so that work can be halted before it becomes unsafe to continue.

Wind speeds in excess of 25 mph can create unsafe working conditions. Winds can funnel and eddy around buildings, causing turbulence, which again may make working places unsafe. In cold weather conditions, the wind will effectively lower the temperature considerably – this is known as the wind chill factor.

Work involving the handling of sheeting and cladding requires extra care in windy conditions, when a sheet may act like a sail, causing the person holding it to lose their balance.

Guidance from the National Federation of Roofing Contractors (NFRC) suggests that the following work should cease when the average wind speeds shown are exceeded.

- ☑ **17 mph** – handling lightweight materials and any materials over five metres long or rolls of felt.
- ☑ **23 mph** – general roofing work.

Beaufort wind scale for use on land (numbers 1-9)

Windforce number	Description of wind	Wind locally	Speed mph	Speed m/sec
0	Calm	Calm, smoke rises vertically.	1	0–1
1	Light air	Direction of wind shown by smoke drift, but not by wind or weather vanes.	1–3	1–2
2	Light breeze	Wind felt on face. Leaves rustle. Wind or weather vanes move.	4–7	2–3
3	Gentle breeze	Leaves and small twigs in constant motion. Wind extends light flags.	8–12	3–5
4	Moderate breeze	Wind raises dust and loose paper. Small branches move.	13–18	5–8
5	Fresh breeze	Small trees in leaf begin to sway. Little crested wavelets form on inland waters.	19–24	8–11
6	Strong breeze	Large branches in motion. Umbrellas used with some difficulty.	25–31	11–14
7	Near gale	Whole trees in motion. Becoming difficult to walk against the wind.	32–38	14–17
8	Gale	Twigs break off trees. Progress is generally impeded.	39–46	17–21
9	Strong gale	Chimney pots, slates and tiles may be blown off.	47–54	21–24

The Beaufort scale provides management and workers with indicators of prevailing wind conditions. However, managers and supervisors can use fixed or hand-held anemometers (wind velocity meters).

For detailed guidance on wind speed advice for different roof work refer to the HSE guidance *Health and safety in roof work* (HSG33).

For further information refer to the National Federation of Roofing Contractors' guidance booklet *Roofing and cladding in windy conditions.*

2.3.3.3 Emergencies (including rescue)

Emergencies (such as a fire or gas leak) could occur either at ground level or at height, which requires that an emergency evacuation of the whole site or the roof work be carried out. For this reason the planning stage must ensure that safe access and egress will be available at all times. Depending upon the nature of the job it may be necessary to have more than one access and/or egress route.

If the nature of the work and site layout necessitates that the asphalt or bitumen boiler, or other forms of hot work, has to be sited on the roof, then this must be considered as part of the fire risk assessment, local hot-work procedure and emergency arrangements.

For further information refer to the HSE guidance *Fire safety in construction* (HSG168).

It may be necessary to deal with medical emergencies where someone becomes incapacitated at height through illness or injury and is unable to make their way back to ground level. In such circumstances, the local fire and rescue service (FRS) may have to be involved to affect a safe rescue. Consider emergency arrangements when selecting the method of roof access (for example, it may be easier to evacuate a casualty via a passenger hoist or stairway, rather than ladder access).

Carrying out roof work will often involve the use of fall-arrest equipment (such as safety nets or safety harness and lanyard). Anyone who falls will have to be rescued promptly, particularly if they are suspended in a harness.

Where MEWPs are used to carry out the work it is essential that an effective emergency plan is produced, rehearsed and implemented. This will include familiarisation with ground controls. There must always be someone at ground level who is able to take action in the event of an emergency while a MEWP is in use.

For further information refer to Chapter D05 Fall arrest and suspension equipment.

2.3.3.4 Safe means of access and egress

The means of gaining access to height and safely working there will depend upon many factors (such as the nature of the roof structure, whether there is room to erect a scaffold or bring in a MEWP, and even the length of time that the job is expected to take).

Some common means of gaining access to height or actually working at height are listed below.

- Ladders.
- Mobile access equipment.
- Fixed or mobile towers.
- Stair towers.
- Independent scaffolds.

Before using an existing access and working platform (such as a permanently installed ladder or stairway and surface) it should be inspected by a competent person to ensure its stability. Additional temporary measures may be necessary to meet the requirements of the Work at Height Regulations for working platforms (for example, a parapet wall less than 950 mm high could require additional guard-rails).

2.3.3.5 Materials handling and storage

The planning process will involve taking decisions on the following.

- What roofing materials are required and possibly where they can be stored safely at ground level.
- A safe means of transferring roofing materials to height and in what quantities, pack size and load (weight).
- Avoiding the overloading of any part of the roof by stacking materials prior to installation, including the integrity of steelwork members.
- The safe storage of sheet materials if they are to be stored for any length of time, particularly during windy weather.
- The safe distribution of materials around the roof during installation.
- The safe transfer of waste materials back to ground level.

Further notes on the safe stacking of materials on roofs are included later in this chapter. *(Refer to 2.8 Handling and storage of roofing materials.)*

2.3.4 Stage 4. Carrying out the work

To a large extent, the risks of doing the job, the risk-control measures that will be necessary and therefore the way in which the work is carried out will depend upon the type of roof and nature of work to be undertaken.

Short duration means a matter of minutes rather than hours. It includes jobs such as brief inspections or minor adjustments (for example, minor adjustments to a television aerial).

Work on a flat roof is still dangerous, even if it lasts a short time. Appropriate safety measures remain essential.

It may not be reasonable to provide full edge protection for short duration work but something will need to be provided in its place. The minimum requirements for short duration work on a roof are safe means of access to and egress from the roof level and safe means of working on the roof (such as a properly constructed and supported roof ladder for sloping roofs, or a fall-restraint system for flat roofs) that prevents the wearer reaching a position where they could fall.

Mobile access equipment (such as scaffold towers or MEWPs) or proprietary access systems can provide a suitable working platform for some short duration tasks.

2.3.5 Stage 5. Post-completion information

Where there is more than one contractor on a project, the principal designer must ensure the health and safety file is prepared, developed and reviewed as the project progresses.

At the end of the project the principal designer must pass the file to the client. If the principal designer's appointment finishes before the end of the project, they must pass the file to the principal contractor, who must take responsibility for it.

The purpose of this document is to provide useful health and safety related information for anyone who, at a later date, has to carry out subsequent work (such as maintenance, cleaning, refurbishment or demolition).

In accordance with the CDM Regulations it will be necessary for the roofing contractor to provide the principal designer with relevant health and safety information about the roof structure and materials used, as requested.

2.4 Types of roof work

2.4.1 Flat roofs

On flat roofs, falls most frequently occur from:

- the edge of a completed roof
- from the leading edge where work is being carried out
- through openings or gaps
- through fragile material.

A roof with a pitch of less than 10 degrees is classed as a flat roof. Safe access to the roof, and to any working place on that roof, must be provided and maintained.

If there is no parapet or similar barrier to stop anyone from falling, edge protection must be provided. This may take the form of standard guard-rails and toe-boards or, providing nobody will approach the edge, a suitable physical barrier set back from the edge. All demarcation barriers should be positioned at least 2 m from a leading edge, to prevent workers from accessing danger areas where they would be exposed to a risk of falling. Demarcation barriers should also be secured to prevent them becoming displaced (such as in high winds). Warning signs should be displayed on the barriers.

Where works are to be undertaken that could result in materials or equipment falling onto people passing below, protective measures must be taken. This can range from adding netting, close boarding or debris fans, to scaffolds or establishing exclusion zones with fenced-off areas and warning signs to stop people from accessing the drop zone at critical times.

There could be circumstances when operatives need to work at exposed leading edges but it is not reasonably practical to install guard-rails or other collective fall prevention measures. In these circumstances, it will be necessary to use personal work restraint systems or collective fall-arrest systems. The most suitable type of fall-arrest system will be indicated by a risk assessment. Where safety nets, airbags or other soft-landing systems are used, they will provide collective fall protection for anyone working above them who falls.

Alternatively, it may be decided that operatives should use a personal fall-arrest system, such as a safety harness with a lanyard clipped to a suitable anchor point or a horizontal running line. The effectiveness of this system depends upon the training and personal discipline of operatives. Adequate supervision is required to ensure the system is effective (such as the operatives actually clipping on). Employers should consider work restraint systems where the lanyard should be sufficiently short or adjusted so that it prevents the wearer from reaching a position from which they could fall.

Temporary anchorage for a fall-restraint system

When a safety harness and lanyard is used, consideration must be given to the position of the anchor point, which ideally will be above the head-height of the user. Where the anchor point is at ankle level, for example, there will be more slack in the lanyard and the fall will be further before it is arrested. It is important to note that when using this form of fall-arrest system the anchor point and self-retracting lifeline (SRL) is as high as possible to ensure that the fall factor, which provides an indication of the length and severity of fall, is kept as low as possible.

As a guide, when using a 2 m length lanyard, the fall distance required (to provide adequate clearance to the fallen operative) is 5.2 m when attached above head height, 5.75 m when connected at shoulder height and 6.75 m when attached at foot level.

Inertia reel blocks are designed to be used vertically with a restricted horizontal movement. If the inertia reel moves through angles it will become less effective. Users should ensure they refer to the manufacturer's instructions to ensure inertia reels are used correctly. If not, they can create a pendulum effect (swing fall risk) and, as well as not stopping the fall, they can expose the user to additional hazards.

For further information refer to Chapter D05 Fall arrest and suspension equipment.

The use of this type of equipment has become more common as it is not as restrictive as a fixed line system.

Sometimes, guard-rails have to be moved or removed to enable work to be undertaken. Consider using proprietary edge protection systems that are especially designed to allow adjustments without compromising the guard-rail protection (for example, raising a guard-rail post to allow access to the roof surface). If temporary removal of a guard-rail is unavoidable then the following precautions should be followed.

- An equally effective safe system of work must be in place and maintained, which will prevent falls of persons or materials.
- The guard-rails must be replaced or re-erected as soon as practical.

Some flat roofing systems will involve the use of various chemicals or hot works and the liberation of fumes or solvents may occur. Consideration to the Control of Substances Hazardous to Health (COSHH) Regulations and the manufacturer's information should be given as well as the significant possibility of fire, explosion or burns from hot bitumen.

2.4.2 Traditional pitched roofs

Working at height in a safe environment

Catch barrier

On traditional pitched roofs, most falls occur:

- from the eaves or ridge, by slipping down then falling from the roof
- into the structure during truss erection
- from unprotected gable ends
- through fragile roofing materials, particularly fragile roof lights.

A sloping roof is defined as any roof having a pitch of more than 10 degrees.

Work on pitched roofs should only be carried out in the following circumstances.

- By persons who are physically capable and adequately trained.
- Using roof ladders or a temporary work platform equipped with guard-rails and toe-boards as necessary and securely fixed to prevent it slipping. (The use of homemade or improvised roofing ladders should be prohibited.)
- Providing that either a suitable catch barrier or a working platform with guard-rails is erected at the eaves of the building.

This requirement applies to any work on a sloping roof, including access to, and egress from, other workplaces.

A steeper roof pitch increases the risk of slipping down the roof surface. The European Standard: BS EN 13374 provides guidance and a specification for edge protection depending upon the slope of the roof and potential fall distance. Working platforms should be provided where the slope of the roof prevents a secure foothold. Alternatively, work restraint systems or rope access techniques may need to be considered.

2.4.3 Curved roofs

Curved roof surfaces (such as a barrel-vault structure) may be used as a working platform, but this will depend upon the radius of the curve, as to whether a secure foothold can be safely maintained (similar to steeper pitched roofs). The more acute the curve the greater the risk of slipping and falling down the roof. Therefore, it is often necessary to employ rope access techniques (such as work positioning or abseiling). It is essential that any such system incorporates lines secured to the apex or other suitable anchor point and a self-locking device to prevent the uncontrolled descent of anyone who loses their footing.

Additionally, proprietary rubber steps are available that follow the exact contour of a curved roof, with sections being joined to extend the overall length. These steps must be regarded as a foothold only, as they are not equipped with a handrail. They must therefore only be used in conjunction with another form of fall protection (such as a fall-arrest block).

Where there is a risk of falling through a curved roof, fall-arrest safety netting or similar protection should be installed. Special measures are required when rigging safety nets to curved type roofs.

2.4.4 Profiled roofs

These range from a single asbestos cement sheet on an outside toilet to the latest continuously extruded system formed in situ to cover large portal frame buildings. The systems will differ in complexity and range from single skin and multiple skin (build-up type) through to composite factory-produced sheeting units.

New build profiled installation will normally be carried out over a system of safety nets that provide fall protection.

For further information refer to Chapter D05 Fall arrest and suspension equipment.

Other systems include temporary leading edge devices (such as stages with guard-rails) and trolley systems that are designed to run along purlins. However, installation, use and moving of these systems can be high risk and will normally require the use of additional fall protection measures (such as safety nets or a safety harness system). The HSE recommends that trolley systems should only be used where there is no safer option.

Designers who specify roofing materials should consider fragility and provide precise information on fixing configurations and load-bearing capacity, so that contractors can prepare safe systems of work.

Composite roof sheet systems are often immediately load bearing, independent of fixings. However, safe systems of work should be developed for handling these heavier sheets.

Edge protection on a steel structure

If a build-up roof system is being installed, the inner sheet or liner tray must be securely fixed before it can be stood on. Metal profile roof sheets are therefore still fragile until they have been fixed. Furthermore, many roof-light assemblies, which are often installed as part of a profiled roof system, may also be fragile. This will necessitate proprietary work platforms (such as stagings) that are used to enable safe access and an additional means of fall protection (such as safety nets).

Edge protection should be provided in accordance with BS EN 13374 (practical method of providing edge protection for working on roofs).

Any working platform must comply with the Work at Height Regulations and be ideally a minimum of 600 mm wide with handrails on one or both sides, depending on whether a fall can occur. This does create practical difficulties in terms of moving them, due to their bulk and weight.

For further information refer to *Solar panel installation* (GS001).

2.4.5 Trussed roofs

The placement and installation of roof trusses and their associated bracing has the potential to be a very hazardous activity and a safe system of access and protection must be planned and implemented. The risk assessment should have considered these and all other aspects of the work.

Proprietary decking system providing internal fall protection

The design of safe access into a roof truss system should be undertaken by the truss designer or the architect, and information passed to the contractor. This will then form part of the overall risk assessment.

A safe working platform around the perimeter of the roof should be erected and, where access is required within the trusses, safe access provided. The most common fall protection systems typically used for internal falls when handling, positioning and constructing a trussed roof include the following.

- ☑ Proprietary decking systems.
- ☑ Interior birdcage scaffolding.
- ☑ Boarding out the bottom chord of the trusses (as long as they are stable and capable of taking the imposed loads).
- ☑ Soft-landing systems (such as air bags or bean/foam bag types).

Safety nets can be used, provided a safe clearance distance can be achieved below the net and a suitable anchorage is provided.

2.4.6 Solar panel installation and maintenance

The installation and maintenance of solar energy PV panels (photovoltaic) on roofs presents the same inherent risks to health and safety as roof work itself and, therefore, the same levels of protection need to be adopted.

Consideration should be given to the following points.

- Safe access to the roof surface (such as scaffolding work platforms or edge protection), for fixing rails, brackets, PV panels, and so on, as a priority before resorting to personal fall protection (such as harnesses and work restraints).
- Working on or near fragile roofing materials.
- Raising and handling heavy PV panels at height.
- Future access for repairs or maintenance.

2.5 Fragile roofs and surfaces

All roofs, once fixed, should be treated as fragile material until a competent person has confirmed otherwise.

Falls through fragile surfaces account for 22% of all fatal injuries of falls from height.

The following are likely to be fragile.

- Fragile cement sheeting (non-reinforced sheets, irrespective of profile type, for example asbestos).
- Roof lights (difficult to see in certain light conditions or hidden when painted).
- Liner panels, on built up sheet roofing.
- Metal sheets, where corroded.
- Glass, including wired glass.
- Chipboard, or similar materials, where rotted or not sufficiently supported.
- Others, including wood wool slabs, slates and tiles.

As far as the strength of the materials is concerned, the appearance of fragile roofs is often misleading. Surface coatings, dirt or moss may conceal the fragile nature of the material, thereby giving a false appearance of soundness to glass, plastic, asbestos, and so on. Even if the roof is clad in a load-bearing material, roof lights can often be fragile.

Asbestos and various plastic materials are particularly brittle and will shatter without warning.

Falls from roofs

- A 50-year-old roofer was killed when he fell from the edge of a pitched roof. He was understood to have been carrying out extensive work to repair the roof following storm damage. There was no edge protection and the access ladder was not secured.
- A 60-year-old employee was killed when he fell through a fragile roof as he was helping to install a ventilation duct for a spray booth.
- A self-employed builder, aged 52, fell while he was trying to repair damage to the asbestos cement roof of an industrial unit. He fell through a fragile roof light.

Many deaths and serious injuries have occurred as a result of roof workers falling through fragile surfaces. Most of the falls could have been easily prevented had a risk assessment been carried out and a safe system of work developed. Even if the falls did occur, the deaths and injuries could have been prevented or mitigated by the use of safety nets or another soft-landing system.

Effective precautions are required for all work on or near fragile surfaces, no matter how short the duration, whether the work concerns construction, maintenance, repair, cleaning or demolition.

Ideally, find another way of carrying out the job that does not require anyone to work on or near to fragile roofing materials. However, in many cases, this may not be practical.

Temporary working platform

Fragile materials should be protected when anyone passes by or works near to them. They should be securely covered and a warning notice displayed if people are working within 2 m of the risk. Appropriate precautions should be taken when installing protection (such as the use of netting, birdcage scaffold or a harness system).

Sometimes it will not be reasonably practicable to provide such protection, usually if the proximity to fragile materials is irregular and of short duration (such as a matter of minutes). Safety harnesses will usually be the most appropriate solution and may be used in conjunction with any permanently installed running line systems.

Boundaries can be established using demarcation barriers to identify safe areas within the workplace and routes to and from them. The safe area boundary should be at least 2 m from the nearest fragile material and leading edge. It does not need to comply with full edge protection standards, but there should be a continuous physical barrier (a painted line or bunting is **not** acceptable), and discipline is essential to ensure that everyone stays inside the safe area at all times.

Rooftop walkway with guard-rails to prevent access to a leading edge of fragile materials
(Image supplied by Kee Safety Ltd)

If it is necessary to pass across a fragile roof, a roof-board complete with a guard-rail should be used to spread the weight and provide a good handhold. Depending upon the job, it may be necessary to use more than one roof-board: one to support the person, whilst the other is moved to a new position. In such cases additional fall protection may be necessary (such as fall-arrest netting or a safety harness system) if there remains a risk of a fall through a fragile roof surface.

The practice of trying to walk the line of the bolts or the line of the purlins is very dangerous and must not be attempted. Where walkways with a handrail are not an integral part of the roof structure, a safe system of work must be devised.

Walkways near fragile surfaces (in valleys, parapets, gutters or channels) must be provided with suitable guard-rails or, if not, the fragile surface should be overlaid with a load-bearing material to prevent the possibility of anyone falling through.

Warning signs must be fixed at all approaches to roofs constructed with fragile materials. This is a requirement of the Work at Height Regulations. Such signs must comply with the Health and Safety (Safety Signs and Signals) Regulations.

Where such signs are not fixed in place, it is essential that the presence of fragile material is identified in advance and those doing the job are made aware of it by other means.

Refer to the HSE publication *Health and safety in roof work* (HSG33) (paragraphs 170-202) and *Fragile roofs* (GEIS5) for details of the dangers presented by fragile surfaces.

Fatal fall through a skylight

A scaffolding firm was ordered to pay more than £100,000 in fines and costs following the death of an employee who plunged 13 metres through the roof of a warehouse.

The deceased stepped onto a skylight, which broke and gave way. There were around 80 fragile skylights on half of the roof measuring 1 m x 2 m. However, the company failed to arrange for covers to be put on the skylight nearest to where they were working.

Things to consider

Avoidance. Plan and organise work to keep people away from fragile surfaces, so far as possible (for example, undertake work from below the surface in a mobile elevating work platform).

Control. Working on or near fragile surfaces requires a combination of staging, guard-rails, fall restraints, fall arrests and safety nets slung beneath.

Communication. Fix warning notices to the approach of any fragile surface. Workers must be trained, competent and instructed in the use of the precautions required.

Co-operation. On business premises contractors should work closely with the client and agree the arrangements for managing work.

2.6 Managing asbestos in roof work

Asbestos-containing materials have been widely used in UK roof construction for many years. It is a legal requirement of the Control of Asbestos Regulations (CAR) (Regulation 10) that anyone liable to disturb asbestos during their work, or who supervises such employees, receives the correct level of information, instruction and training.

- Category A – Asbestos awareness.
- Category B – Non-licensed work.
- Category C – Licensed asbestos work.

HSE maintains a list of accreditation bodies for training organisations that can deliver training of this nature.

The HSE has produced *Asbestos essentials*, a task manual for building, maintenance and allied trades on how to safely carry out non-licensed work involving asbestos.

A method statement, also known as a plan of work, will be required for any work with asbestos and this requirement makes no exception for the number of employees. The method statement must be written by someone who is deemed competent with regard to asbestos and who understands the requirements of CAR.

Safe access over a fragile roof

All asbestos-containing materials removed from roofs will be classed as hazardous waste (special waste in Scotland) and will need to be disposed of by a registered waste carrier to a licensed tip under a hazardous waste consignment note.

Whilst the construction of a new roof will not pose any asbestos problems, the replacement, repair, refurbishment or demolition of an existing roof might well have asbestos implications.

Under CAR an employer must assume all materials are asbestos-containing unless they can prove otherwise (for example, by reference to the asbestos survey undertaken to meet the requirements of *Asbestos: the survey guide* (HSG264) and by extension of CAR). Whilst it is not difficult to recognise asbestos cement roof sheet, determining if a particular existing roofing felt contains asbestos and whether soffits are asbestos cement or asbestos insulation board is normally more problematic. All commercial clients have a duty to be able to provide information on the presence of asbestos and should be able to give both designers and contractors a copy of their asbestos register and/or asbestos survey report. Domestic clients have no such obligation and it is down to the contractor to find out if there are any asbestos-containing materials present, prior to the commencement of work. This would facilitate the need for a survey in line with the requirements of HSG264, identified above.

All asbestos removal work must be undertaken in accordance with CAR, by those competent to do so.

For further information refer to Chapter B09 Asbestos.

2.7 Access arrangements

2.7.1 Stair towers

Stair towers are an effective and safe means of access. They help speed up access, production and enable the workforce to carry materials and equipment far more safely than ladder access. Many companies now default to stair towers, unless a risk assessment deems that ladder access is suitable for the situation (such as short or low risk access).

A purpose-built scaffold stair tower

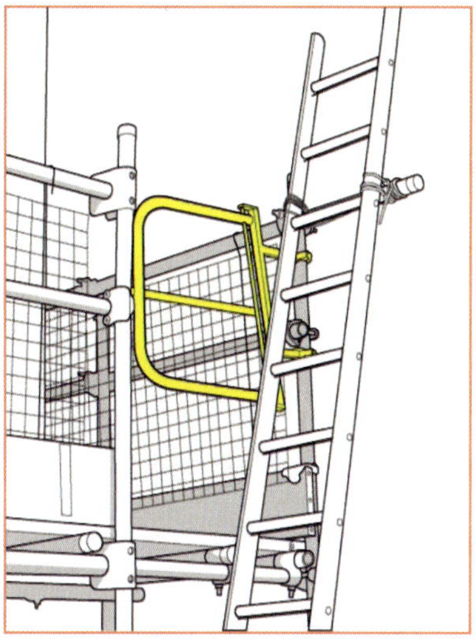

External scaffold access with safety gate

2.7.2 Ladders

Ideally, access to a scaffold or roof will be via a purpose-built stair tower. However, where the decision is taken to use a ladder, the scaffold should be constructed to incorporate internal ladders and protected ladder traps. If an external ladder is used it should be positioned along the face of the scaffold rather than at right-angles to it. Ladder gates should be installed at access points.

A ladder must not be used as an access to, or egress from, a workplace unless it is reasonable to do so, taking into account the work being carried out, its duration and the risks to the safety of any person arising from the use of the ladder.

If the vertical height of a ladder is over 9 m, safe landing areas or rest platforms should be provided at suitable intervals.

Competence is vital

Demonstration of competence is a vital requirement of the Work at Height Regulations, and successful completion of the Ladder Association's industry standard training course contributes significantly to providing proof of competence when working with ladders and stepladders.

www.

For further information on this course, and the regulations, refer to the Ladder Association and legislation websites.

2.7.3 Landing places

All landing places must be of adequate dimensions.

If a person is liable to fall from a height that would result in injury, landing places must be provided with the following.

- A guard-rail at a height of not less than 950 mm.
- An intermediate guard-rail.
- A toe-board.
- A gap not exceeding 470 mm between the toe-board and guard-rail, or between any two guard-rails.

D
02

2.7.4 Roof ladders

A proprietary roof ladder

Roofers should not walk directly on slates or tiles on sloping roofs, as they do not normally provide a suitable foothold, especially when wet.

Roof ladders should be used. These should be designed for the purpose and secured by means of a ridge hook over the ridge tiles, bearing on the opposite roof pitch.

The ridge tile or gutter should not be used to support roof ladders, as they can become accidentally displaced.

2.7.5 Edge protection

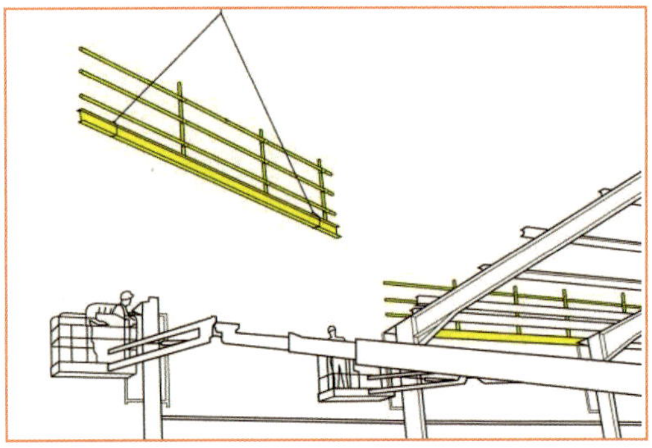

Temporary edge protection pre-fixed to steelwork before installation

Falls from the edge of the roof should be protected by perimeter scaffolding or an edge protection system fixed to the building structure. Designers of new buildings should consider how edge protection may be secured to the building for construction and future maintenance.

Edge protection to prevent the fall of people and materials should be provided in accordance with the Work at Height Regulations and BS EN 13374 for construction and maintenance work. This British and European standard is not generally suitable for the public, other workers, vehicles or mobile plant equipment or bulk materials (such as packs of roofing materials). The classification of edge protection systems are selected primarily based on the gradient of the surface and the potential fall distance down the roof for which they are to provide protection.

The performance requirements for the various classes are detailed within the standard BS EN 13374.

- **Class A** provides protection to flat surfaces and slopes generally up to 10 degrees. It provides resistance to static loads and is based on the requirements to support a person leaning against, walking beside, and possibly stumbling against the edge protection.
- **Class B** provides protection to flat surfaces and slopes, generally up to 30 degrees, and to even steeper slopes with short slope lengths. It provides resistance to both static and low dynamic loads and is based on the requirements to support a person leaning against, walking beside, possibly stumbling against and sliding down a sloping surface towards the edge protection.
- **Class C** provides protection to steeply sloping surfaces, generally up to 45 degrees, and up to 60 degrees for 5 m slopes. It provides resistance to high dynamic loads only and is based on the requirements to contain a person sliding down a steeply sloping surface.

All edge protection systems should be adequately secured so that they cannot become accidentally displaced in their intended use (loading as per BS EN 13374 or, in the case of scaffolding, BS EN 12811).

Scaffolding edge protection installed from a MEWP

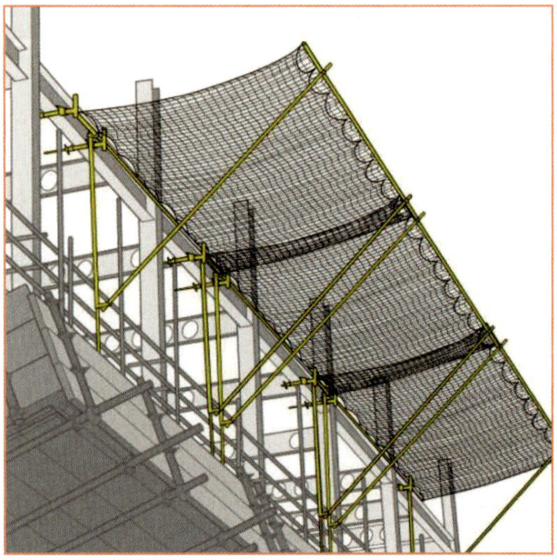

A proprietary safety net fan system provides fall protection so perimeter guard-rails can be erected above without MEWP access

Safe systems of work must be established for the installation and removal of temporary edge protection. Where possible, edge protection installed to the building structure should be accessed by a MEWP. Where MEWP access is not practical, collective fall-arrest fans or fall-restraint systems should be used.

Counterweight temporary edge protection system
(Image supplied by Kee Safety Ltd)

Proprietary net barrier temporary edge protection system (Class C)

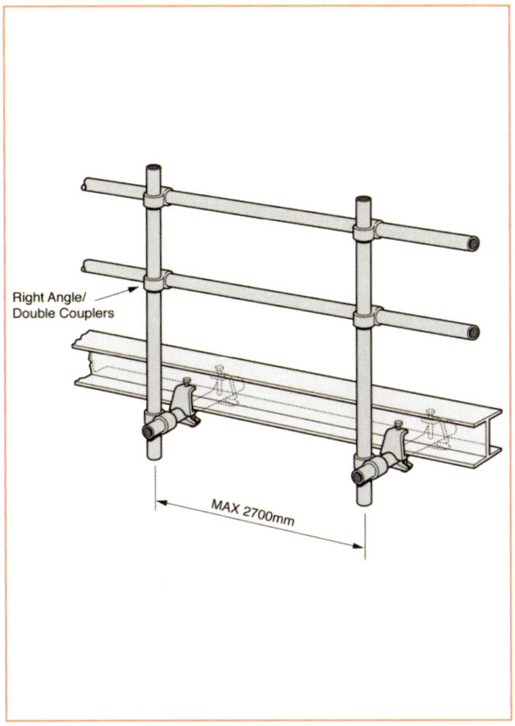

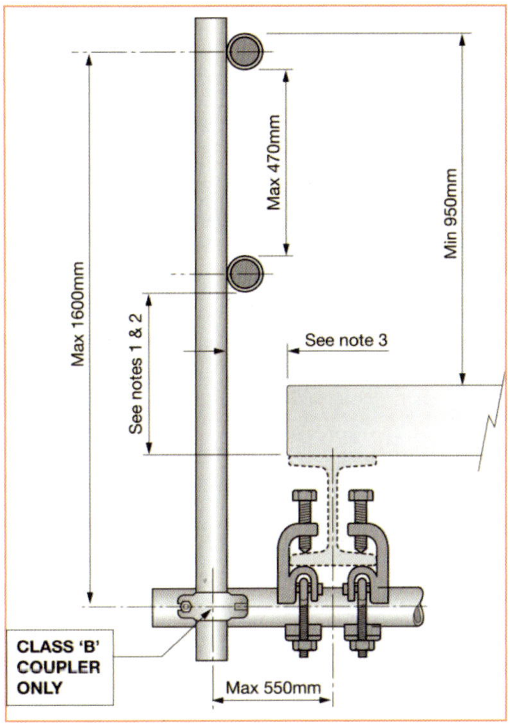

Temporary edge protection on open steelwork (Class A)

Edge protection on a sloping roof

Where scaffolding is used with a working platform, guard-rails and toe-boards, to provide roof edge protection, it should be positioned close to the eaves to minimise the potential fall distance to the platform. This should be ideally no more than 300-450 mm below the eaves or roof edge. However, sometimes access may also be required to the eaves (for example, facia and soffit) where the fall distance may be slightly greater (up to 600 mm) but avoids unnecessary scaffold adaptions. In such cases the increased risk of injury must be assessed so that the fall distance is minimised and consideration given for safe access and egress to the roof surface and the possible need for an additional guard-rail for increased fall protection (for example, internal guard-rails to the eaves or an additional, third guard-rail above the main platform guard-rail).

It is recommended that the platform should be wide enough to provide a suitable catchment area should someone fall from a sloped roof. Ideally the platform should extend 2 m past the work area on the roof, or guard-rails should be installed on the roof to contain the workers within the protection offered by the scaffolding.

Special consideration should be given in the following situations.

- When workers can access within 2 m of the verge, where guard-rails or gable-end scaffolding may be required.
- If there is a risk of workers falling down the opposite side of a ridge and unprotected eaves. Edge protection to the opposite eaves should be provided or a work restraint system used.
- When workers can encroach within 2 m of an opening or fragile surface within the roof surface.

2.7.6 Access to chimney stacks

Construction and maintenance of chimney stacks should always be undertaken from a properly constructed working platform with safe access. Traditionally, scaffolding to chimney stacks offers the safest option. However, risks involved during erection and dismantling also need to be considered.

Example of a TG20 compliant chimney stack and access scaffold

NASC TG20 offers a range of compliant scaffolding configurations for roof access and working platforms for chimney stacks. Where the position of the chimney on a roof structure or the nature of the work is not covered by these standard configurations then design advice must be sought.

There are various purpose-designed, lightweight stagings and access systems available for work on or around chimney stacks. MEWP access may also be a practical solution for short duration or inspection work before resorting to ladders.

Consideration should be given to the roof structure and load imposed by the access equipment. If in doubt engineering advice should be sought.

For further information on scaffolding refer to Chapter D04 and the NASC website.

2.7.7 Powered access

Powered access covers a wide range of mechanical access equipment, such as those listed below.

A mobile elevating work platform

- Mobile elevating work platforms (MEWPs).
- Mast climbing work platforms (MCWPs).
- Suspended cradles.
- Man-rider platforms.

Mobile access platforms are often used as an alternative to ladders, scaffolds and cradles.

Each of these types of equipment can be suitable for carrying out particular types of roof work (for example, using a telescopic boom MEWP (also known as a cherry picker) might be a suitable and safe way of accessing a job that would otherwise require someone having to cross a fragile roof). This is particularly important for inspection or short duration maintenance work. Truck-mounted MEWPs now have sufficient reach to enable inspection of many building types to be made without having to directly access the roof.

2.7.7.1 Mobile elevating work platforms

- All MEWPs must conform to *Mobile elevating work platforms. Design calculations. Stability criteria. Construction. Safety. Examinations and tests* (BS EN 280).
- MEWPs must be operated by authorised and trained persons who hold the appropriate International Powered Access Federation (IPAF) powered access licence (PAL) for the type of MEWP to be used.
- Operators must be familiar with the model of MEWP and maintain a log book to record experience.
- Safety harnesses with fall restraint lanyards must be used in boom-type MEWPs (except when working over water), to prevent operatives from accessing a position where they could fall.
- Only use suitable anchor points, as specified by the manufacturer.
- Fall restraint lanyards must be adjusted to the shortest practical length necessary for the platform, ideally no more than 1.5 m long.

  Note: *adjustable or suitable length fall-arrest lanyards can be used in a fall restraint mode, as the energy absorbers will not deploy until a load of 3 kN or more is applied.*
- When working in a MEWP harnesses should not be used in a fall-arrest scenario as the dynamic loads imposed could be beyond the capacity of the MEWP and cause overturning or collapse.
- Never exceed the safe load rating of the MEWP. Specially designed devices are available for handling materials within a MEWP (such as cladding installation systems). Seek advice from the supplier.
- Never use a MEWP as a hoist, crane or prop, unless it is designed for the purpose.
- MEWPs must be used in accordance with the *Operator's safety guide* (IPAF) and *Safe use of MEWPs – Code of Practice* (BS 8460).
- Care should be taken to avoid trapping and crushing people in the platform.
- MEWPs must be maintained in accordance with the manufacturer's recommendations and subject to LOLER inspections every six months.
- Planning for emergencies must include how rescue and recovery from a MEWP is to be carried out, including the competence of the rescuer(s).

IPAF powered access licence

IPAF operators' safety guide

For further information refer to the following.

- **International Powered Access Federation website.**
- ***Avoiding trapping/crushing injuries to people in the platform* – Strategic Forum Plant Safety Group, Best practice guidance for MEWPs.**

2.7.7.2 Mast climbing work platforms

Mast climbing work platforms (MCWPs) are not commonly used or suitable for roof access or edge protection; as their primary function is to provide a movable façade access to buildings that, when repositioned, will leave the leading edge exposed.

With this equipment, the platform or cradle rises up one or more static masts in a similar way to a hoist, providing a temporary work platform at height, usually on the side of a building. Some procedures to be observed in the erection of mast climbers are described below.

- ☑ Installers must be trained, in accordance with the manufacturer's instructions.
- ☑ MCWPs should be operated by authorised and trained persons who hold the International Powered Access Federation (IPAF) powered access licence (PAL) special category for MCWPs.
- ☑ MCWPS must be inspected daily before use, by the user.
- ☑ MCWPs must be regularly inspected by a competent person and records maintained of the inspection. They must be thoroughly examined every six months.
- ☑ The safe working load and the permitted number of persons allowed on the platform at each configuration must be clearly marked on the MCWP. They should not be used as a substitute for using stairs or a passenger lift for travelling to higher levels.
- ☑ Planning should consider the interface with building features that could impede the working envelope of the MCWP and present trapping or shear points to the users or residents of occupied buildings (such as opening windows and balconies).
- ☑ All MCWPs must conform to the *Code of Practice for the installation, maintenance, thorough examination and safe use of mast climbers* (BS 7981) and *Lifting platforms. Mast climbing work platforms* (BS EN 1495).

www. **For further information refer to the International Powered Access Federation website.**

2.7.7.3 Suspended cradles

This section covers suspended working platforms commonly referred to as cradles. As with MCWPs, cradles are not commonly used or suitable for roof access or edge protection, as their primary function is for façade access.

Permanently installed cradle system for future building maintenance used during construction operations

- ☑ All proprietary cradle systems must conform to *Safety requirements on suspended access equipment. Design calculations, stability criteria, construction. Tests* (BS EN 1808).
- ☑ Temporary suspended cradles and scaffolds must conform to the *Code of Practice for temporarily installed suspended scaffolds and access equipment* (BS 5974).
- ☑ The design, inspection, testing and use of suspended cradles must be in accordance with the Specialist Access Engineering and Maintenance Association (SAEMA) guidance.
- ☑ Installers of proprietary cradle systems must be trained in accordance with the manufacturer's instructions.
- ☑ Users of suspended cradles must use personal fall protection equipment and be attached to a designated anchor point within the cradle or line system.
- ☑ The use of permanently installed cradle systems for access during building construction, designed for future maintenance use, may be a practical option. However, consideration should be given to the nature of use and advice should be sought from the manufacturer.

www. **For further information refer to the Specialist Access Engineering and Maintenance Association website.**

2.7.7.4 Man-rider platforms

Man-rider platforms (or baskets) are not powered access equipment. However, they are designed to be used with cranes or lift trucks and, when combined, provide a means of powered access. Consideration should be given to a MEWP, or similar purposely designed access equipment, before resorting to man-rider platforms.

Lift truck mounted and crane slung man-rider platform

The use of man-rider baskets with rough terrain or telescopic type lift trucks in construction increases the risks to users and therefore safer alternatives (such as MEWPs) should always be considered first.

- ☑ Man-rider baskets provide specific hazards, as the user is reliant on the operator of the crane or lift truck. Therefore, there must be an effective means of communication and a signaller used, as per other lifting operations.
- ☑ The use of a man-rider platform must be planned, managed and operated, the same as any lifting operations under the Lifting Operations and Lifting Equipment Regulations (LOLER).
- ☑ The type of man-rider platform must conform to *Cranes. Equipment for lifting of persons. Suspended* (BS EN 14502).
- ☑ The lifting device (crane or lift truck) must be suitable and have the correct load rating.
- ☑ The man-riding platform must be slung and/or secured to the lifting device, as per the manufacturer's instructions.
- ☑ Passengers in the man-riding platform must use personal fall protection equipment and be attached to a designated anchor point within the platform or the lifting equipment (for example, a crane hook).
- ☑ Due consideration must be given to the thorough examination requirements of LOLER when mobile work equipment is used to lift people, including the accessory itself, as follows.
  - Six months, for lifting equipment and any associated accessories used to lift people.
  - Six months, for all lifting accessories and 12 months for all other lifting equipment.

For further information refer to:

- ☑ **Chapter D05 Fall arrest and suspension equipment**
- ☑ **Chapter C05 Plant and work equipment**
- ☑ **Chapter C07 Lifting operations.**

2.7.8 Safety nets

For most industrial and commercial roofing and flooring construction, properly rigged fall-arrest safety nets and perimeter edge protection is the preferred solution. Nets provide workers with maximum freedom of movement, as long as they do not access beyond the protected area.

Example of a remote rigged safety net

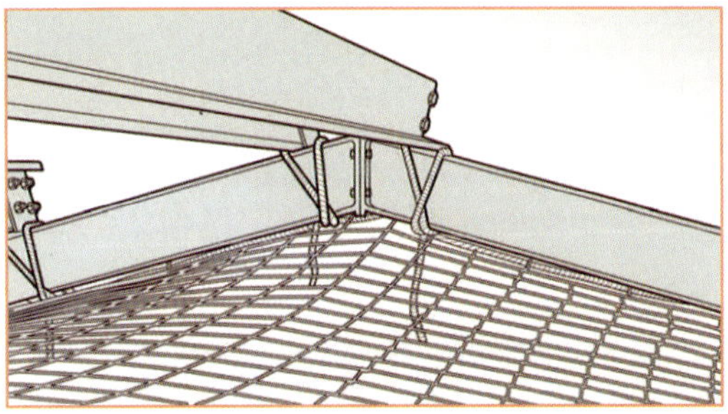

Example of a rigged safety net

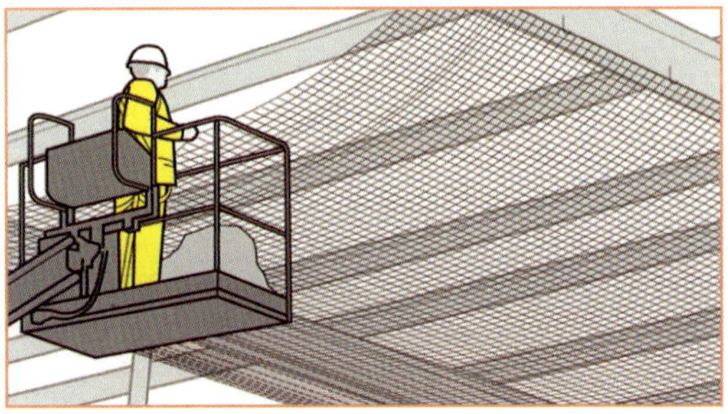

Typical method of rigging a roof safety net via a MEWP

- Nets must be supplied in accordance with BS EN 1263 Part 1 and rigged in accordance with BS EN 1263 Part 2 and BS 8411 *Code of Practice for safety nets on construction sites and other works.*
- All nets must be patch tested by a competent person within 12 months prior to use.
- Only competent and trained riggers are permitted to rig, alter or de-rig safety nets, ideally in accordance with the *Fall arrest safety equipment training* (FASET) scheme, or equivalent.
- Anchorage for safety nets must be capable of withstanding 6 kN of force. Therefore safety netting must be tied to a suitable structure. Never fix nets to scaffolding unless it has been designed for the purpose.
- Ensure the most suitable method of access is used for rigging and de-rigging safety nets, in accordance with the FASET safety guidance notes.
- Remote methods of rigging and de-rigging should be used wherever possible.
- Rescue plans must consider recovery of a casualty from the safety nets.
- Nets can be rigged with debris netting for light debris containment.
- Net repairs must be tagged by a competent person, in accordance with FASET recommendations.
- Never store materials below safety nets that reduce clearance distances.
- Nets must be inspected by a trained safety net rigger or inspector, before use, every seven days, and after any event likely to jeopardise the safe condition of the nets.
- A safety net inspection register must be maintained.

Alternative methods of access for rigging safety nets where MEWP access is not a practical option

www.

For further information refer to the following.

- **FASET website.**
- ***The Blue book – Recommended practice for the use of safety nets for roof work*, published by the Advisory Committee for Roofsafety.**

2.7.8.1 Working platform nets

Tensioned netting systems that can be used as a working platform are a relatively new innovation. They are currently being used in the construction industry for roofing operations and must be subject to a specific design scheme.

- Installation and use must be properly planned, risk assessed and a detailed method statement produced.
- They must be installed, inspected, used and maintained in accordance with FASET recommendations and specific design.
- The design must determine the maximum loading and the load imposed on the supporting structure.
- A methodology for the safe use must be established for the management of this work at height access system as part of the scheme.
- As a minimum, working platform nets should be inspected to the same standard as fall-arrest safety nets.

2.8 Handling and storage of roofing materials

Care must be taken at all times when stacking bulk material on or at roof level. Attention should be given to the following points.

- ☑ Size of the load involved.
- ☑ Types of material involved.
- ☑ Methods of raising the load, whether manually or mechanically.
- ☑ Means of communication (signals) and the competence of the slinger or signaller.
- ☑ Position authorised for stacking materials.
- ☑ Distribution of the loads (loading plan).
- ☑ Maximum load or stack size.
- ☑ Loading limitations of the roof.
- ☑ Adequate support or packing to the truss.
- ☑ Provision of exclusion zones at ground level.
- ☑ Careful stacking of materials on roofs.
- ☑ Protection of the existing roof surface and any weatherproofing.
- ☑ Prevention of the displacement of loads that should be secured against:
  - the wind, especially split bundles and sheets
  - sliding down sloping roofs (sheet stop).

Manual handling of materials needs to be considered by roofing contractors as part of the risk assessment process, especially heavy or unwieldy sheeting materials and adverse weather conditions.

www.

For further information refer to *Health and safety in roof work* (HSG33) and the NFRC guidance for handling roofing sheets and recommended safe wind speeds.

Mechanical handling equipment should be used where possible for handling bulk materials. Specially strengthened sections of scaffolding or loading bays may be required. Where roofing materials are being stripped from an existing roof and stored on a scaffold for reuse, they must be stacked safely, not overloading the structure, and there should be sufficient space for working and safe passage.

The risks from falling materials and other objects in roof work must be considered and suitable controls established to prevent and protect against falling objects.

Where the risk of falling objects cannot be completely eliminated, the risk must be managed. Some precautions are shown below.

- ☑ Toe-boards on working platforms.
- ☑ The use of brick-guards.
- ☑ Protections fans *(refer to Chapter D04 Scaffolding)*.
- ☑ Containment sheeting and debris netting, including overlay debris netting for fall-arrest netting.
- ☑ Pedestrian gantries with crash decking.
- ☑ Debris chutes for removal of waste materials from the roof.
- ☑ Segregating the area below as a designated danger area and preventing unauthorised access with physical barriers and displaying warning signs.

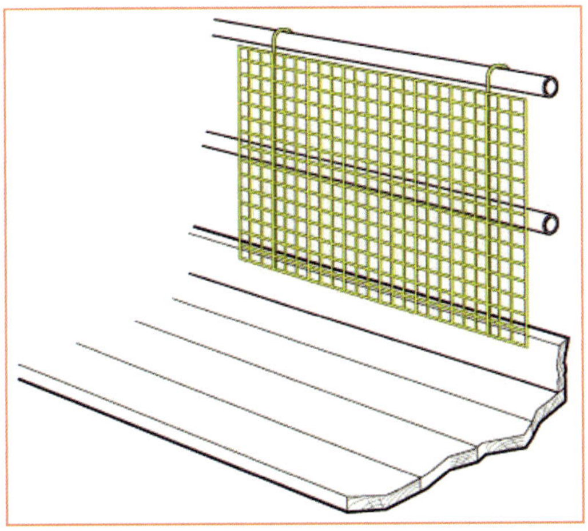

Example of a brick-guard

Example of a debris chute

2.9 Other considerations

This section is primarily focused on roof work. However, work at height and associated risks are present in a wide range of construction, refurbishment and maintenance activities. Employers must ensure all work at height is properly planned and managed in accordance with the Work at Height Regulations.

2.9.1 Danger areas

Under the Work at Height Regulations there is a specific legal requirement to ensure the safety of those working at height (from falls), and others who may be working or passing below (from falling objects), by the creation of danger areas, either around the high-level workplace and/or below it.

This is achieved by preventing unauthorised access into any danger area, so far as is reasonably practicable, by the use of equipment (such as barriers and appropriate signs) placed at vantage points.

It is essential that an effective means of communication be established between those working at height and the workers controlling the danger area, whilst also giving due consideration to others reasonably affected.

2.9.2 Presence of bats

Bats commonly roost in roof space and it is vital that contractors are aware of their obligations.

All species of bat and their breeding sites or resting places (roosts) are protected under the Conservation of Habitats and Species Regulations and the Wildlife and Countryside Act.

It is an offence for anyone intentionally to kill, injure or handle a bat, to possess a bat (whether live or dead), disturb a roosting bat, or sell or offer a bat for sale without a licence. It is also an offence to damage, destroy or obstruct access to any place used by bats for shelter, whether they are present or not.

If bats are discovered during the course of the work, work in that area should be stopped and specialist advice sought. This should include consultation with the client.

2.9.3 Presence of pigeons

The accumulated droppings of pigeons, if disturbed into airborne dust and then inhaled, can cause severe respiratory problems. It is anticipated that this will mainly be a problem during refurbishment and repair work, or demolition.

If during the early visits to site it is evident that pigeons have been, or are present, measures must be taken to clean up the droppings before work starts, using a safe system of work, and to discourage the return of the birds.

2.10 Legislative requirements

2.10.1 Work at Height Regulations

The relevant requirements of these regulations with regard to roof work are considered to be as follows.

- Employers should ensure that work at height is planned, supervised and carried out in a safe manner by trained and competent persons.
- Work at height must be carried out using appropriate work equipment, particularly that which provides collective fall protection.
- Suitable and sufficient steps should be taken to prevent falling objects that are likely to cause injury to any person.
- Consideration needs to be given to the weather conditions.
- Where appropriate, the need to plan how to rescue someone who has fallen but is suspended.
- Where there is a risk of a person falling or being struck by a falling object, steps need to be taken to prevent unauthorised access into that area.

There are a number of trade associations for roofing companies (listed below) that could be consulted or comment upon queries on competence.

- National Federation of Roofing Contractors (NFRC).
- Flat Roofing Alliance (FRA).
- Single Ply Roofing Association (SPRA).
- Mastic Asphalt Council (MAC).
- Rural and Industrial Design and Building Association (RIDBA).

Whilst membership of these organisations by itself does not guarantee either good health and safety practices or quality, they do all vet members and operate a dispute resolution service, which may be a useful facility.

The Advisory Committee for Roofwork is a body dedicated to making working on roofs safer. It was established in 1998 and is made up of nominees from HSE, trade associations and organisations involved in roof work that provide the experience of many years of involvement in working on roofs in the advice given in their documents.

Refer to the Access Industry forum website for some useful online videos.

In the context of roof work, the definition of **personal protective equipment** (PPE) includes items of fall-arrest equipment (such as safety harnesses and lanyards).

In deciding which type to issue, the employer must take into account the risk that the PPE is being used for, and also ensure that the PPE will fit the wearer and allow them to work comfortably.

The employer must ensure that employees have been given adequate and appropriate information, instruction and training to enable them to understand the risks being protected against, the purpose of the PPE and the manner in which it is to be used.

Whilst the employer must take reasonable steps to ensure that any PPE supplied is used, the employee in turn must use the equipment provided in accordance with instruction and training given and know the procedures for reporting loss or defects to their employer.

2.10.2 Construction (Design and Management) Regulations

The regulations place legal duties on duty holders, each of which has the potential to reduce the risks to health and safety during and after the construction phase.

For additional information and resources refer to the HSE website.

2.10.2.1 Designers

The definition of *designer* under the CDM Regulations is extremely wide. It can include architects, consulting engineers, quantity surveyors, interior designers, temporary work engineers, chartered surveyors, technicians or anyone who specifies or alters a design. Therefore, principal contractors and specialist contractors could also be designers. A common scenario would be where the client simply asks the contractor to sort out a leaking roof and the contractor designs the solution. A commercial client who becomes actively involved in designing their project may also be considered to be a designer.

Whoever prepares or modifies a design for a construction project (including temporary works) or instructs someone else to do so will be considered as the designer. This is very important as the designer has a legal duty to consider health and safety issues in relation to not only carrying out the work, but also the maintenance, cleaning and eventual removal (demolition) of the roof.

In common with all aspects of design, the person carrying out the design should be sufficiently knowledgeable of the construction process to specify how the work can be carried out safely.

Roofers working on industrial type buildings are commonly faced with the problem of fragility. This may be because the roof itself is made of a fragile material (such as asbestos cement sheets) or simply because the roof lights are not load bearing. As the standard specification for roof lights is 10% by area, this represents a significant amount of fragile roof surface.

The HSE states quite categorically that stringent effort should be made by designers to ensure that fragile roof lights are not specified. The Advisory Committee for Roofwork (ACR), which is the lead authority in the UK on roof work health and safety and represents all the relevant trade associations, has published jointly with the HSE definitive guidance on what constitutes fragile material.

This is found in the *Red book – Test for non-fragility of profile sheeted roofing assemblies (ACR 001:2014)*. This book details tests that manufacturers should carry out on profiled roof sheets. Anyone who specifies this type of roofing must be aware of the contents of this book and ensure the materials they specify meet the standards where possible.

When designing roofs, designers should also consider such things as ongoing maintenance work (for example, how roof lights and gutters can be cleaned safely) and whether the safe access for this type of work can be designed-in at the design stage.

2.10.2.2 Clients

Under the regulations the client has the main duty for providing relevant pre-construction information to each designer (including the principal designer) and contractor (including the principal contractor) being considered for, or already appointed, to enable the job to be planned so that it can be carried out safely. For projects involving more than one contractor the client can expect help from the appointed principal designer.

The main type of information that would be relevant for roof work would be the presence of asbestos, areas of damage, loading limitations of the roofing material, the existence of fall-restraint systems, the location of safe access routes where known, as-built drawings where available and so on.

It should be noted that the client may not be aware of such factors as damaged areas of the roof or the existence (or lack) of safe access routes. The client may assume that the job will be carried out by a method that is neither practical nor safe. They commonly expect roofing contractors to be able to access places and do tasks that they would simply not allow their employees to do.

03
Common access equipment

Contents

Supporting information

G: Checklists and forms

GT 700 Toolbox talks

D
03

Overview

The purpose of this chapter is to give an understanding of the health and safety requirements when selecting and using common forms of access equipment (such as ladders, podium steps, mobile access towers and hop ups).

While the chapter provides relevant information, formal and recognised training in the actual access equipment system to be used will be necessary before a person can be regarded as competent.

It is important that anyone reading this chapter has a good understanding of the requirements of the Work at Height Regulations.

3.1 Introduction

Access equipment should only be erected, altered, used, dismantled or operated by a competent person.

In accordance with the Work at Height Regulations, all work at height should be avoided, where possible. When it cannot be avoided, the fall should be prevented by selecting the most appropriate form of access equipment for the particular environment and circumstances.

3.2 Important points

- ☑ When selecting suitable access equipment, the working at height hierarchy should be followed.
- ☑ Mobile towers and other forms of access equipment must be subject to a statutory inspection, with a report produced, where appropriate.
- ☑ All mobile towers must be properly erected. They must remain stable, be suitable for their purpose and be equipped with toe-boards and guard-rails on all working platforms.

www.

The Health and Safety Executive (HSE) has developed a *Work at height access equipment information toolkit* (WAIT).

This toolkit has been developed to help workers understand the key issues when working at height and the factors to consider when selecting the most appropriate and safest type of access equipment.

3.3 Ladders and stepladders

Traditionally, ladders and stepladders have been used as the way of getting up to or down from a place of work at height (for example, the means of access to a roof or scaffold). However, under the Work at Height Regulations, a ladder or stepladder that is being used to carry out an activity (for example, painting a first floor window) could now be considered as a place of work.

The Work at Height Regulations require that employers give adequate consideration to the safety of the user before selecting a ladder or stepladder as either a means of access to height or as a place of work at height.

In deciding whether or not a ladder or stepladder should be used, the employer must carry out a risk assessment and be able to demonstrate that it is not reasonably practicable to use an alternative, safer means of access and that the risks from using the ladder or stepladder are low.

HSE guidance is that ladders and stepladders should only be used as a place of work when the nature of the work meets the following criteria.

- ☑ Is of short duration (a maximum of 15-30 minutes).
- ☑ Is of a light (up to 10 kg) nature (requires no heavy lifting, carrying or a destabilising pressure applied by the user or equipment in carrying out the work – minimal manual handling).
- ☑ Allows one hand to be available at all times for holding on to the ladder or stepladder.
- ☑ Requires nothing to be carried that would cause instability of the ladder, stepladder or user.

Additionally, when stepladders are used as a place of work they should be positioned so that the user faces the work as the stepladder is climbed. A stepladder must not be positioned so that the user is side-on to the work, where the nature of the work would apply a sideways pressure and cause the stepladder to become unstable.

Ladders should:

- be set up at an angle of 75° (one metre out for every four metres up – a ratio of 1:4)
- be positioned on a firm, level surface
- not be vulnerable to impact by pedestrians or traffic
- be used in accordance with the manufacturer's instructions
- be the right ladder for the job. Remember that no single ladder will suit all applications
- be inspected before use to ensure there are no defects
- ideally, be lashed at or near the upper point of rest by the stiles, not the rungs
- extend at least one metre above the stepping-off place unless an alternative handhold is provided that enables a safe transfer between ladder and stepping-off place
- be secured at the bottom or footed* if lashing at the top is not possible
- not be rested against fragile or flexible items (such as plastic guttering); a ladder stay or stand-off device must be used, as necessary
- never be painted to an extent that the paint could conceal defects
- be subjected to a schedule of periodic inspections with written inspection reports kept, be individually identifiable and proof of inspection demonstrated
- be visually checked by the user for obvious defects before use and not used if found to be defective. If defective the ladder should be taken out of service and reported.

Users should face the ladder at all times when climbing up or down, and not carry anything that would interfere with their safety or balance.

** HSE research has shown that, to be most effective, the person footing a ladder should stand on the bottom rung with both feet at all times. Even then, footing is not an effective method of stopping a long ladder from slipping sideways. Ideally a ladder will only be footed when it is climbed for the first time for the purpose of tying it off.*

Footing a ladder is the last resort and should be avoided, where reasonably practicable, by the use of other access equipment.

For further information on the performance and effectiveness of ladder stability devices refer to the HSE website.

3.3.1 Types of ladder

Standing ladders are a single stage ladder up to six metres in length.

Pole ladders are a variant of the above type, but with the stiles having been made from a long, wooden pole cut centrally to give even strength and flexibility. Lengths can vary up to a maximum of 10 m.

The practice of shortening a pole ladder to fit a particular situation should be discouraged. Care must be taken to ensure that the fabric of the ladder remains stable if a tie wire is removed.

Extension ladders consist of two or three sections coupled together and extended by sliding over or inside each other. Longer multi-stage ladders are extended by means of a rope and pulley. The maximum reach of a single run ladder is 9 m. At this height and above, resting points must be provided.

Stepladders are of various types, have flat rectangular treads and are usually free standing.

Platform stepladders have a built in working platform, and newer models can have wheels for ease of movement, handrails and restraint chains. Due to the provision of a platform, these are usually a better option for work that is regularly carried out at the same height.

Roof ladders are ladders with a hook on the top end for securing over the ridge of a roof.

Aluminium and steel ladders are available in various types. Their main advantage is that they are light and weather resistant. They can be prone to slipping at the base if the rubber or wooden feet are not properly maintained.

3.3.2 Classes of ladder (BS 1129:1990, BS 2037:1994 and BS EN 131)

Portable ladders, steps, trestles and lightweight staging are covered by BS 1129:1990, BS 2037:1994 and BS EN 131.

A **duty rating** indicates their suitability of use.

- **Class 1. Industrial**. Heavy duty – can be used frequently and in the tough conditions that can be found on site. These are the only ladders that are recommended for use on site.
- **Class 2. Light trades**. Medium duty – can be used only in good conditions. Suitable for light trade purposes. (This class of ladder is now covered by BS EN 131.)
- **Class 3. Domestic**. Light duty – suitable only for domestic and household use.

Class 3 ladders are not recommended for general use on a construction site.

All ladders should be marked with a unique identification number and the class or duty rating. For more comprehensive guidance refer to the HSE guidance document *Safe use of ladders and stepladders* (INDG455).

3.3.3 Inspection of ladders

Every ladder should be inspected on a regular basis and should carry an identification mark, as detailed above. A written record should be kept of all inspections, defects and repairs.

The frequency of ladder inspections should be determined by considering the use, duration and environment in which they will be used. It is common for ladders that are used regularly to be thoroughly inspected every three months.

Ladders should not be used if defective in any way and, if damaged beyond repair, they should be destroyed.

Regulation 12 of the Work at Height Regulations requires work equipment (including ladders) to be inspected at regular intervals. It is also recommended that all ladders are inspected prior to use.

Some considerations for ladder inspections are shown below.

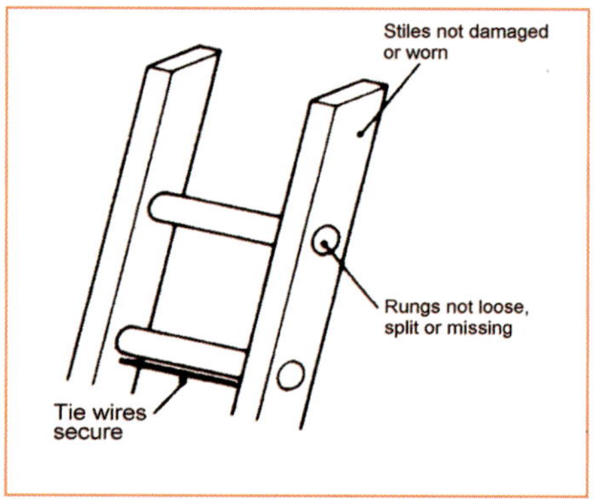

- ☑ There should not be any signs of splitting, cracking, splintering, warping or bruising.
- ☑ Metal ladders should not exhibit signs of mechanical damage or chemical attack.
- ☑ There must not be any undue wear or movement of the rungs.
- ☑ All rungs must be in place.
- ☑ Wedges and tie rods must be tight.
- ☑ Any metal reinforcements must be positioned correctly.
- ☑ Feet must not be split or frayed.
- ☑ Plastic inserts must be intact and not be excessively worn.
- ☑ There should not be any mud or grease on the rungs.
- ☑ Wooden ladders should be free from rot.
- ☑ Where repairs are required, if these are not possible the report should specify that the ladder should be scrapped.

The condition of any ropes and cords, along with pulleys, hinges and any other fittings, should be checked for fraying to ensure that they are all secure with no sign of damage.

3.3.4 Carrying a ladder

A short ladder may be carried comfortably by having it vertical against the shoulder and holding one of the lower rungs, using the other hand to hold the stile. Longer ladders should be carried horizontally by two people. Care should be taken in negotiating corners and obstacles.

Ladders must not be taken into the vicinity of overhead power lines (OHPL) unless a permit to work has been issued and/or a physical barrier is present, to provide a clearance distance between the overhead power line and ladder. Where any doubt arises the distribution network operator (DNO) should be contacted for further advice. This may include the installation of temporary protective overhead line covering (also known as shrouding) or isolation of the OHPL. Even then, extreme care is still advised.

Timber ladders generally do not conduct electricity (unless wet) but aluminium ladders are extremely conductive, and are dangerous to use in close proximity to OHPLs.

3.3.5 Erecting and lowering ladders

The procedure for erecting a ladder, when the ladder is flat on the ground, is as follows.

- ☑ Check there are no overhead obstructions in the vicinity.
- ☑ One person stands on the bottom rung while the other takes position at the head of the ladder and takes hold of the top rung, raising the ladder off the ground.
- ☑ Then, rung by rung, that person moves towards the foot of the ladder, lifting as they go. The person at the foot grasps the lower rungs as soon as possible and draws the ladder towards them, steadying it at the same time.
- ☑ The sequence is reversed when lowering.
- ☑ Short ladders may be raised by one person placing the foot of the ladder against a wall or fixture and pushing the ladder upwards, starting at the top, walking, under-running and raising the ladder as they go.

3.3.5.1 Extension ladders

Extension ladders are raised one section at a time and slotted into position. The minimum recommended overlap on extension ladders is shown in the table below.

Closed length	Approximate no. of rungs	Overlap of rungs
Under 5 m	Under 18	2
5–6 m	18–23	3
Over 6 m	Over 23	4

Latching hooks must be properly engaged.

Ladders must never be lashed, tied or spliced together in an attempt to make an extension ladder.

3.3.5.2 Roof ladders

Roof ladders should only be used when it has been established that the use of a safer alternative is not possible. Any work undertaken involving roof ladders must be of short duration and involve only low risk work.

Roof ladders should be erected as follows.

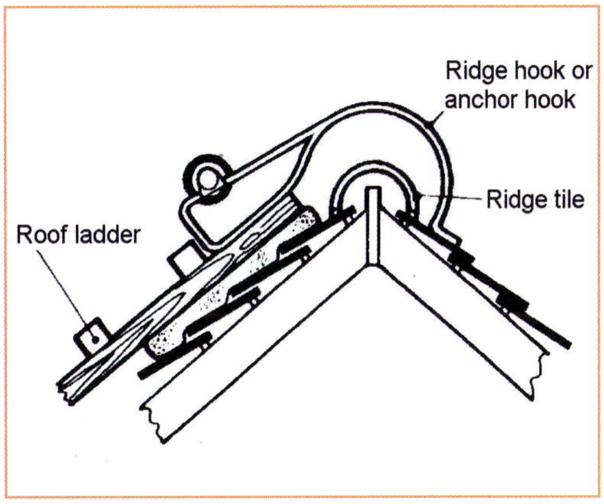

First, a standing ladder is erected for access to the eaves of the roof. It should extend at least one metre or five rungs above the eaves of the roof and be properly secured, but not to the guttering, downpipes or any other plastic or fragile material. Proprietary ladder anchors are available and these should be used in preference to other methods.

Adopting good manual handling, the roof ladder should then be passed up by an individual at ground level, before being brought up and pushed up the roof on its wheels, with the anchor hook or ridge hook uppermost.

Once over the ridge, the ladder is turned over and the hook engaged. It may be necessary to secure the ladder with a rope if ridge tiles are unsound. Three points of contact should be maintained at all times.

Ideally, where it is necessary to use a roof ladder, access to the lower end of it will be from a working platform at the eaves.

Where access is from a free-standing ladder, the points on ladder safety *(refer to 3.3 Ladders and stepladders)* must be observed.

Roof ladders must be:

- ☑ only used by persons who are competent to use them
- ☑ positioned to enable easy and safe transfer between:
  - any other ladder used to get to the eaves and the roof ladder
  - the roof ladder and the place of work
- ☑ designed for the purpose
- ☑ of good construction, strong enough to enable the planned work to be carried out and regularly inspected
- ☑ adequately supported to take the user's weight without damaging the roof
- ☑ securely fixed to the sloping part of the roof by means of a ridge hook placed over the ridge. Ridge hooks must not bear down on ridge tiles or capping tiles.

3.3.6 Storage of ladders

Ladders, especially if made of wood, deteriorate when exposed to the weather for prolonged periods. Where indoor storage is not available, they should be covered or stored in a protected, well-ventilated position. They should not be exposed to excessive heat, moisture or chemicals.

Ladders should be stored on racks, supported on the stiles only, with sufficient supports to prevent them from sagging. They must not be hung from the rungs or stiles.

Aluminium ladders should be kept away from wet lime or cement, as the chemical composition may result in corrosion of metallic components.

Pulleys and hinges should be lubricated and the condition of ropes and cords checked.

Any damage or deterioration should be noted and made good before further use.

3.3.7 Stepladders

Many of the general rules for the safe use of ladders also apply to stepladders. In addition, the following points should be considered.

Stepladder with integrated side guard-rails for additional protection

- ☑ Stepladders are not to be used if a fall from one would cause the user to be injured (based upon a risk assessment).
- ☑ The treads (or steps), hinges, bolts, screws and fixings must all be sound and secure.
- ☑ Retaining cords or hinges should be of equal length and in good condition.
- ☑ The stepladder must be stable when open and standing on a level base.
- ☑ The legs of stepladders should be positioned as far apart as the restraining mechanism allows, with all four legs firmly and squarely on the ground.
- ☑ Wherever possible, the stepladder should be positioned so that the person climbing it is facing the work to avoid twisting and unnecessary movement that can create instability.
- ☑ Unless the design permits, the knees of the person using the stepladder should be kept below the top step.
- ☑ The user should not work from the top third of a stepladder unless it has been designed for this purpose.

If it is not practicable to maintain a handhold when a load is being carried, a risk assessment must demonstrate that the use of the stepladder is justified because of the low risk and short duration use of the stepladder.

3.4 Podium steps, mini mobile towers and pop-ups

Podium steps provide low level height access, with adjustable height and guard-rails. The use of this type of equipment is preferred to stepladders in most circumstances as it provides a small but stable working platform, complete with guard-rails. This type of access equipment has the advantage over a stepladder in that it allows the user to work in a safer manner, facing any side of the working platform without it becoming unstable, and it also provides collective means of fall protection.

Podium steps and **mini mobile towers** are lightweight in construction and some types will fold flat for ease of transportation. Specific models are designed to be wheeled through a standard-sized door. Some types of this form of access equipment can be fitted with outriggers to increase stability.

Whilst providing a high degree of safety in most situations, there are a number of specific hazards with the use of this type of equipment and the employer should ensure the following precautions are considered in selecting and using podium steps.

There are many differing types of podium steps with different arrangements of use. Some are just wheeled platforms and others have specific installation requirements. The instructions for each individual podium must be available and understood by the user (for example, the manufacturer's instruction manual) and it is advised (through Regulation 5 of the Work at Height Regulations) that users of equipment of this nature are trained in its use. The PASMA low-level access course is one example of suitable training. Users should also ensure equipment is manufactured to PAS250.

- ☑ The height of the working platform should be assessed: too low and the user will not reach; too high and the user may be inclined to work from the steps rather than the platform.
- ☑ Where adjustable height platforms are in use, ensure that the user is trained in how to adjust the platform and handrails to ensure protection.
- ☑ Brakes must be used whilst the platform is in use and users must not be permitted to pull themselves along (surfing) from the top of the podium, as this can cause equipment of this nature to tip over.
- ☑ Podium steps, like any other access equipment, must have an individual identifying mark and be subject to frequent inspection.
- ☑ The manufacturer's instruction leaflet or hire company information leaflet should be available during the inspection to check that the low-level access equipment has been erected in line with these requirements. It is good practice to laminate and attach this information to the item of low-level access equipment being used.

Push around verticals, commonly called **pop-ups**, are an increasingly popular and versatile item of access equipment. These are a category covered by IPAF's PAL card (powered access licence).

Podium in use, correctly assembled and wheels locked

Example of a push around vertical (PAV)

www.

For further information about low-level access equipment and training refer to the PASMA website.

3.5 Lightweight staging and trestle scaffolds

Trestles can be used if the risk assessment shows that the risk of a person falling and injuring themselves is low and the work on top of the trestle is of short duration. Guard-rails and toe-boards should be installed on all trestle equipment, as per requirements of the Work at Height Regulations.

More modern trestles are similar in many ways to system scaffolding, including the fact that guard-rails and toe-boards are an integral part of the working platform. The spacing of the supports is fixed by the system design, which enables platform boards to fit snugly without overhanging or overlapping.

All lightweight staging should be marked with the maximum permitted distributed loading. This can be done by either specifying the maximum number of persons, allowing for their tools and equipment, or by specifying the maximum safe weight.

The following guidelines should be met.

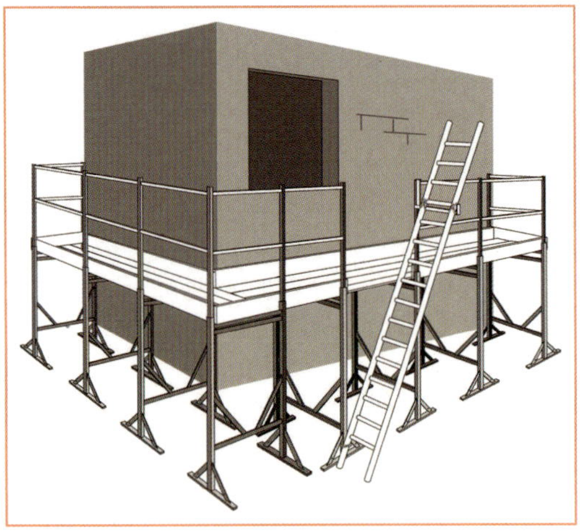

A modern trestle system with handrails, toe-boards and safe ladder access

- ☑ Trestles must be set on a firm, level base.
- ☑ Only one working platform is installed.
- ☑ Guard-rails, barriers and toe-boards are required where a fall would cause a personal injury, as indicated by a risk assessment.
- ☑ Trestles should be installed according to manufacturer's recommendations for use. This information should be readily available.
- ☑ Scaffold boards used on trestles to form a working platform must be of a consistent length and of equal thickness.
- ☑ The trestle assembly must be completely stable when in use.
- ☑ A safe means of access to the working platform must be provided (for example, a ladder that is of sufficient length, properly positioned and securely lashed).
- ☑ Where locating pins are used, they should be of the correct size and type and not rebar off-cuts or other makeshift items.
- ☑ Trestle based working platforms should be subject to a pre-use check. They should also have a formally documented inspection, which can be recorded (for example, on a scafftag).

The use of loose scaffold boards, supported on split-head trestles with no means of preventing falls that could cause an injury to the user, is totally unacceptable and should not be considered as an option for working at height.

3.6 Mobile access towers

The use of lightweight aluminium mobile towers on construction sites is a popular alternative to the use of traditional tube and fitting towers. However, these systems have some limitations and should only be used when they can satisfy both legislative and general site requirements.

Aluminium and thin-wall steel towers are light and can easily overturn if used incorrectly.

A mobile aluminium tower

Five different items make up a basic mobile aluminium tower.

- ☑ Frames.
- ☑ Braces.
- ☑ Platforms.
- ☑ Legs.
- ☑ Wheels or castors.

For further information on tower scaffolds refer to the HSE website.

3.6.1 General conditions and provisions

The same points that arise from the Work at Height Regulations in relation to the safe erection and use of system scaffolds apply to mobile access towers but, in addition, the following points should be particularly noted.

The Prefabricated Access Suppliers' and Manufacturers' Association (PASMA) has developed two methods of installing guard-rails that do not require the erector to stand on a working platform until the guard-rail frames have been installed.

- ☑ Advanced guard-rail system.
- ☑ Through-the-trap (3T method).

The **advanced guard-rail** system involves the use of specially manufactured, hinged guard-rail frames that can be raised and slotted into position from below. The progressive erection of guard-rails from a protected area at lower level ensures the operator is never exposed to the risk of falling from an unguarded platform.

The **3T method** involves the erector only passing through the platform trapdoor far enough to be able to locate the guard-rail frames in place. In many cases, safe erection of the guard-rail sections can be achieved with the erector sitting on the platform with their legs through the trap and their feet supported on the ladder section below.

Both of these methods are accepted by the HSE.

Fall protection equipment must not be attached to aluminium tower scaffolds.

3.6.2 Materials

Mobile access towers may be constructed from steel, but are principally aluminium.

All components must be free from any welding defects, dents, bends or distortion, or any corrosion that could prevent their safe use. Platform boards must be free from holes, cracks, splits or any delamination that would affect their safe use.

3.6.3 Competence

Any person erecting and dismantling a mobile access tower must be competent to do so, having received adequate training (such as that provided by PASMA). Always read and follow the manufacturer's instruction manual and never use the equipment beyond its limitations.

The tower must start off and remain vertical as it is built and used.

For further information about training in mobile towers refer to the PASMA website.

3.6.4 Maintenance

All aluminium mobile towers are work equipment and, as such, come under the requirements of the Provision and Use of Work Equipment Regulations (PUWER).

As such, mobile towers (including individual components) must be suitable for the job in hand and properly maintained.

3.6.5 Preparation and planning

A risk assessment should be carried out to determine whether or not a mobile aluminium tower scaffold is a suitable item of work equipment for the type of work that is to be carried out and the environment in which it is intended to be used.

Factors that should be considered when deciding whether or not it is safe to use a mobile tower are shown below.

3.6.5.1 Ground surface

Is the surface sufficiently level to use a mobile tower, if there is no adjustment on the legs for levelling the tower? A tower scaffold should not be erected if it cannot be levelled and therefore made stable.

Mobile towers only have a small area of each wheel in contact with the ground and therefore each wheel imposes a high loading at each point of contact. Is the surface strong enough to take the loading? It may be possible to use sole boards on soft ground to effectively spread the load and allow a mobile tower to be used, providing that there is no chance of the tower sinking, tilting or otherwise becoming unstable.

Are there any features (such as drain covers or underground pipes) that may not be able to take the direct or indirect loading imposed by one or more wheels?

3.6.5.2 Weather (outdoor use)

Aluminium tower scaffolds are lightweight structures that can become unstable in moderately high winds.

- ☑ Has a check of the weather been made for the period that the tower will be erected? (Consider the use of an anemometer or wind meter to measure the wind speed.)
- ☑ Is it possible to tie-in the tower to the structure against which it is to be erected?
- ☑ If any doubt exists on the limitations of the tower in high winds, has the manufacturer's or supplier's information been consulted?

3.6.5.3 Overhead power lines

Before starting the job identify any lines that are close enough to render the use of a metal scaffold unsafe.

Remember, it is not necessary to touch a high-voltage cable to get a shock. Many overhead power lines are not insulated and the electricity can arc through the air to an adjacent metal object.

If in any doubt, do not erect a tower until such time that the DNO has been contacted.

3.6.6 Pre-assembly inspection

The competent person who is to erect a mobile tower should check that all the components are present and undamaged and ensure that they are all from the same manufacturer/supplier, and are for the same type of tower.

A check should be made that the castors and wheels rotate and swivel freely and that they have a functioning locking device (brake).

3.6.7 Safety during use

3.6.7.1 Stability

Due to their lightweight nature, stability can be a problem with aluminium tower scaffolds, the more so the higher they are built.

Individual manufacturers carry out tests on their products to enable them to provide specific guidance on height-to-base ratios, including circumstances where the installation of outriggers will be necessary. Such guidance should be available to the competent person erecting the tower.

Safe working on a mobile tower, with toe-boards and both guard-rails in position and wheels locked

As general guidance, it should be assumed that stabilisers will be required if an aluminium tower is to have a working platform higher than three metres above ground level.

In addition to the dimensions of the erected tower scaffold, there are several other factors that can affect its stability.

- ☑ Ground conditions – bricks or building blocks should never be used to take the weight of any part of the tower.
- ☑ Sheeting (outside) – will increase the wind-loading on a tower scaffold. In many instances it will not be acceptable to sheet a tower scaffold unless it can be tied-in to the structure.
- ☑ Overreaching – if this is so severe that the centre of gravity is moved to a point outside the base area of the scaffold, it will overturn. It is far safer to move the tower scaffold.
- ☑ Work activity – any work that involves applying a sideways pressure to the adjacent structure (for example, water-jetting) at a point that is high on the tower will create an equal and opposite pressure that may overturn the tower. In many cases, tying-in the tower to the adjacent structure may overcome this problem.
- ☑ Hoisting materials – if heavy items are hoisted up the outside of the tower, it could become unstable and overturn. Again, tying-in the tower to the adjacent structure may overcome this problem.
- ☑ Climbing the tower – access to the working platform should be gained by using the built-in stair or ladder sections. If a vertical ladder is built into an end frame of the tower, the person climbing the ladder must **always** do so on the inside of the tower. Climbing the outside could overturn the tower. Never gain access to the working platform by leaning a ladder against the tower.

Towers should never be erected to heights above those recommended by the manufacturer.

3.6.7.2 Tying-in a tower scaffold

Care should be taken to avoid couplers causing damage to the aluminium tubing and only special couplers should be used. Advice on the horizontal and vertical frequency of ties will be supplied by the manufacturer or supplier or, in the case of substantial or linked towers, the scaffold designer.

3.6.7.3 The working platform

The access hatch to the working platform must be closed as soon as everyone working from the tower is on the working platform.

The working platform must be fully boarded unless a design feature of the scaffold enables safe access and egress and effective guard-rails and toe-boards to be installed around a partially boarded platform.

The Work at Height Regulations state that a working platform must be of sufficient dimensions for the safe passage of people, plant and materials with due regard to the type of work being carried out. However, BS EN 12811-1 recommends that platforms on all types of scaffold should not be less than 600 mm wide.

3.6.7.4 Gaining extra height

Placing stepladders and ladders on the working platform of a mobile tower to gain additional height is particularly dangerous and must be prohibited. Adjustable legs are only to be used for levelling, and not to gain additional height. If additional height is needed then a further lift should be added, providing this is within the manufacturer's guidelines relating to height limitations. In some situations the original equipment might not be suitable now for the task and an alternative form of equipment will be required.

3.6.7.5 Brakes

The wheel brakes must be locked in the ON position at all times when the tower is not being moved. The lightweight nature of aluminium tower scaffolds presents the potential for unattended towers to be moved by the wind if the brakes are not applied, particularly where they are used on exposed floor slabs at height.

3.6.7.6 Moving a tower scaffold

The tower must not be moved whilst anyone is on the working platform. Any item that could fall or cause the tower to be unstable whilst being moved, taking into account the condition of the floor surface, must also be removed. A tower scaffold must only be moved by pushing or pulling at the base. Movement should not take place in windy conditions and surfing is strictly prohibited. Towers in excess of four metres high should not be moved.

The tower must never be moved by towing it with a vehicle or by a person who is on the platform pulling the tower along using an adjacent structure (surfing).

3.6.7.7 Avoiding collisions

Suitable barriers should be erected to prevent people or vehicles from accidentally colliding with a tower scaffold, particularly where it is erected in a public place.

It may be necessary to create a safety zone around a tower simply because of the nature of the work being carried out above.

3.6.7.8 Loading capacity

The capacity of each platform and tower structure is often shown on labels attached to the frame of the mobile tower, or will be in the manufacturer's assembly guide. Never exceed the recommended loading levels as this may cause the tower to become unstable.

3.6.7.9 Incomplete towers

When a tower is in an incomplete or unsafe state, it should not be left unattended without the display of a notice stating 'Scaffold incomplete. Do not use'.

A new inspection and report is not required every time a mobile tower is moved to a new location on the same site. However, if guard-rails or other components have to be removed, to enable the tower to move past an obstruction, then a pre-use check must be undertaken by a trained and competent person to ensure the tower has been reinstated correctly.

3.6.7.10 Protecting the public

Extra caution is required when towers are used in public places.

- ☑ Erect barriers at ground level to prevent people walking into the tower or work area.
- ☑ Remove ladders or prevent access by physical means (for example, by using physical barriers) to prevent unauthorised access if the tower is to remain in position unattended. If this is not practical, the tower should be dismantled.

3.6.7.11 Wind strength

Aluminium structures are very vulnerable to the strength of the wind. It is recommended by many manufacturers that if the wind reaches a speed of 17 mph then all work should cease on the tower.

If the wind speed is likely to reach 25 mph, the tower should be tied-in to a rigid structure. If there is a possibility of the wind reaching speeds of 40 mph, the tower should be dismantled. The manufacturer's instructions should always be followed when using any tower in windy conditions.

Operators should be aware of the possibility of sudden high winds in exposed or gusty conditions.

It must be remembered that winds at high levels are often higher than at ground level. The wind speed can also increase as it funnels between buildings or other solid structures.

For further information on Beaufort wind scales refer to Chapter D02 Safe working at height.

3.6.8 Inspection and reporting

Where the tower constitutes a working platform, it must be inspected by a competent person, as shown below.

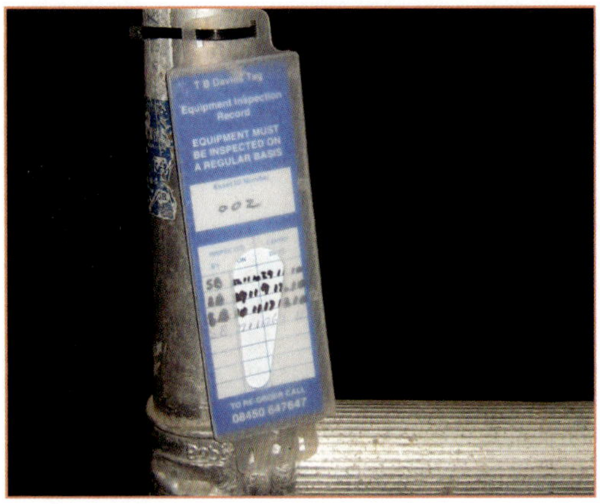

- After assembly but before being used for the first time.
- After any substantial addition, dismantling or other alteration and after any event that is likely to have affected its strength or stability.
- At regular intervals not exceeding seven days since the last inspection (towers with a platform at two metres or more).
- At suitable intervals, depending on the frequency and conditions of use (towers with a platform at less than two metres).

For towers with a platform at two metres or more, this written record must be more than simply a scafftag system and, in addition to the above requirements, they must also be inspected at intervals not exceeding seven days.

3.6.9 Training

Training for any operation on a construction or building site is a requirement of the Work at Height Regulations (Regulation 5 – Competence). Adequate training must be provided for those erecting, dismantling or modifying any mobile tower equipment or other equipment used for work at height.

Training courses are available from CITB, as well as from manufacturers and suppliers. Certificates should be provided as proof of training.

3.7 Other access equipment

There is a huge range of access equipment and solutions available to meet every need of the construction industry.

3.7.1 Proprietary access systems

A proprietary access system incorporating ladder access, working platform, guard-rails and hoist

Proprietary access systems are easy to transport between sites, quick to erect and provide good access.

They can be used as an alternative to fixed edge protection, where appropriate for the work being planned.

In some cases proprietary access systems can avoid the need for scaffolding. They are appropriate for short duration, minor work.

3.7.2 Hop ups

Dependant upon the results of the risk assessment, hop ups, up to 600 mm high, may be suitable for some applications, especially wet trades (such as plastering) that involve constant stepping up and down. Other solutions with handrails are available, but it is important to balance risk of falls against risk of musculoskeletal injuries if other solutions restrict or make movement awkward.

Hop up type platforms are for low-level access requirements.

3.7.3 Stilts

Fit out and finishing trades (such as dry lining, ceiling fixing and plastering) use professional stilts for low-level access. These should be designed and manufactured for professional use. However, there is not currently a British or European Standard applicable to these products.

Stilts can be used providing the following requirements are met.

- Following a risk assessment and method statement, and once the system of work has been agreed with the site management team.
- They have been inspected before use and maintained in good order.
- They are used in accordance with the manufacturer's instructions.
- Operatives can demonstrate that they have the skills and competence to use the stilts safely.
- The floor surface is level and clear from obstructions.

3.8 Work at Height Regulations

These regulations govern all work carried out at height in all industrial sectors and the schedules of the Work at Height Regulations contain a number of important dimensional and prescriptive requirements.

The regulations state that suitable and sufficient measures must be implemented to prevent, so far as is reasonably practicable, any person falling a distance liable to cause personal injury.

For more detailed information refer to D01 Work at Height Regulations.

3.9 Supporting information

There is a huge range of access equipment available to meet every need of the construction industry, and advice can be sought from a variety of means (such as the Access Industry forum). Members are listed below.

- ATLAS – Association of Technical Lightning and Access Specialists.
- BSIF – British Safety Industry Federation.
- EPF – Edge Protection Federation.
- FASET – Fall Arrest Safety Equipment Training.
- IPAF – International Powered Access Federation.
- IRATA – Industrial Rope Access Trade Association.
- Ladder Association.
- NASC – National Access and Scaffolding Confederation.
- PASMA – Prefabricated Access Suppliers' and Manufacturers' Association.
- SAEMA – Specialist Access Engineering and Maintenance Association (Suspended access).
- WAHSA – Work at Height Safety Association (Fall protection).

D
03

04
Scaffolding

Contents

Supporting information

G: Checklists and forms

GT 700 Toolbox talks

Overview

The purpose of this chapter is to give individuals an understanding of the safety issues that relate to the use of scaffolds, particularly where site managers or others have to manage scaffolding operations and assess the suitability of scaffolds that have been erected by others.

While its content will provide relevant basic information, training in the actual techniques of scaffolding will be necessary before a person can be regarded as competent in the erection, alteration or dismantling of any scaffolding whatsoever.

4.1 Introduction

It is very important that anyone reading this chapter has a thorough understanding of the Work at Height Regulations because they outline the legal requirements and sound principles of safely working at height.

The majority of guidelines for good practice in scaffolding can be found in the safety and technical guidance notes of the National Access and Scaffolding Confederation (NASC).

This chapter will provide you with a basic knowledge of what to look for in the scaffold contractors you employ and the scaffolds that are erected. It will not confer competence in scaffolding techniques or scaffold inspection.

Please refer to the Construction Industry Scaffolders' Record Scheme (CISRS) website for details of the UK recognised training scheme within the scaffolding industry.

The main British and European Standard for tube and fitting scaffolding is BS EN 12811 (Part 1) *Scaffolds – Performance requirements and general design.* Readers are directed to the range of NASC publications, particularly *A comprehensive guide to good practice for tube and fitting scaffold* (TG20).

Although this chapter applies to tube and fitting scaffolding, it is important to note that all proprietary scaffolding equipment (for example, system scaffolds, beams, modular transom units and hop-up brackets) must be manufactured and tested to the relevant British and European Standards (for example, BS EN 12810).

They must also be used in accordance with the manufacturers' instructions or the scaffold should be designed by a competent engineer.

The British and European Standards can be accessed via the British Standards Institution (BSI) website.

4.1.1 NASC technical guidance

Throughout this chapter, wherever TG20 appears in the text, it refers to the NASC suite of publications, which includes the following.

- ☑ *A comprehensive guide to good practice for tube and fitting scaffolding* (TG20:13 Operational guide).
- ☑ *Technical guidance on the use of BS EN 12811* (TG20:13 Design guide).
- ☑ *Good practice guide for tube and fitting scaffolding* (TG20:13 User guide).
- ☑ *Electronic software supplement for the operational guide* (TG20:13 eGuide).

Although this guidance is for tube and fitting scaffolding, some of the basic principles for managing scaffolding operations would be considered good practice for all types of scaffolding activities.

Please refer to the NASC website for details of guides and publications.

4.1.2 Training and competence

The term *competent person* is used in the Work at Height Regulations. However, there is no legal definition in the regulations for the word *competence* or the term *competent person*.

> **Competent person** (for the purposes of scaffold inspection)
>
> A competent person may be defined as a person who has practical and theoretical knowledge, scaffold inspection training and actual experience of what they are to examine, in respect of a scaffold, so as to enable them to detect errors, defects, faults or weaknesses, that it is the purpose of the examination or inspection to discover, and to assess the importance of any such discovery.

A competent person must understand and recognise their limitations.

> **Competence** (of individuals, for scaffold erection)
>
> As regards the competence of individuals in relation to scaffold erection, competence may be taken to mean a person who has practical and theoretical knowledge, together with actual experience of scaffolding, and has acquired, or who is being supervised while being trained to acquire, the recognised qualification in scaffolding.

This person must know their limitations and must not put themselves or others at risk.

The Work at Height Regulations requires scaffolders to demonstrate specific training for the erection, alteration and dismantling of scaffolding.

4.1.3 Record schemes

The CISRS record card is the industry recognised qualification for the scaffolding sector.

Users of proprietary (modular) products must also ensure that scaffolders have received appropriate training (such as manufacturer's training) or a recognised qualification (such as the system scaffold product training scheme (SSPTS)), which is endorsed on the CISRS record card.

4.1.3.1 Construction Industry Scaffolders' Record Scheme

CISRS is the oldest record card scheme in the UK. It is managed and administered by CISRS Ltd.

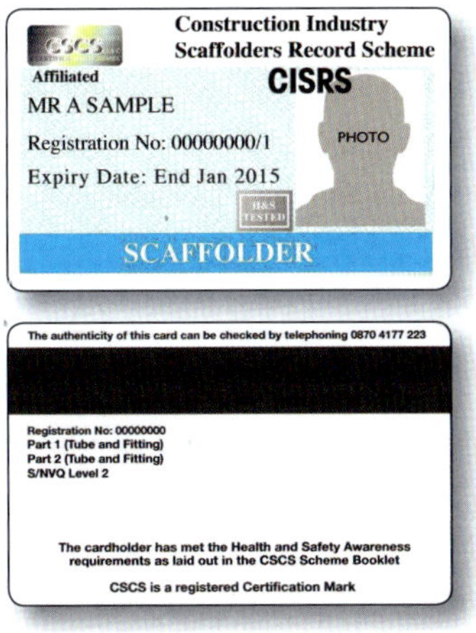

Record card processing is operated by CITB on behalf of CISRS. All registered scaffolders are issued with an identification card that details their grade qualifications.

The card scheme categories include scaffolding labourer, trainee, scaffolder, advanced scaffolder, scaffolding supervisor and scaffold inspection (basic and advanced) qualifications. Scaffolding apprenticeships are also available for new entrant scaffolders.

Options are available for tube and fitting scaffolding and system scaffolding.

The system scaffold product training scheme (SSPTS) is for existing scaffolders who use specific proprietary system scaffolding products and can have their record card endorsed to demonstrate this. The basic access systems erector (BASE) training is aimed at non-scaffolders who use system scaffold within a restricted scope of operation (for example, no public interface and a maximum height of 6 m).

The CISRS training makes it a requirement for any new entrant scaffolding trainee or scaffolding labourer to complete the CISRS construction operative training scheme (COTS) one-day course, before a card will be issued. Existing CISRS scaffolding labourer cardholders will be required to complete the COTS course upon expiry of their current card and prior to a new card being issued.

For further details refer to the CISRS website.

4.1.3.2 Other scaffolding training

Employers must demonstrate supervision by a competent person(s) and specific training for the use of proprietary products not covered by the CISRS scheme (such as temporary roofs, public access stairways, falsework and formwork systems).

4.2 Important points

- Scaffolding must only be erected, altered or dismantled by operatives who have been trained to do so or are under the direct supervision of a competent scaffolder.
- Employers who employ the services of scaffold contractors should look for proof of competence via the CISRS scheme.
- The main piece of legislation that applies to scaffolding is the Work at Height Regulations.
- Scaffolds are subject to statutory inspections, with reports of inspections raised where appropriate.
- All scaffolds must be properly erected, stable, tied to the structure as appropriate, suitable for their purpose and equipped with toe-boards and guard-rails on all working platforms.
- The BS EN 12811 series of standards were introduced in 2004 and are supported by TG20 and manufacturer's instructions.
- NASC's *Preventing falls in scaffolding* (SG4) is the accepted industry standard to which all scaffolding contractors should be working.
- SG4 is essential reading for site managers and safety professionals in order for them to understand how scaffolders should be erecting and dismantling structures safely.
- SG2 provides advice for scaffold contractors working with asbestos-containing materials and whether they need an ancillary asbestos licence.

NASC online video learning aids

- Overview of scaffolding terms (video).
- Explaining scaffold handover certificates and inspections (includes free online test).
- Explaining scaffold record cards and who can do what (includes free online test).
- The use of ladders in scaffolding (includes free online test).
- Preventing falls in scaffolding (SG4) (includes free online test).
- Introducing TG20 (includes an eGuide software demonstration).
- Recommended scaffolding criteria for pavement licences (includes free online test).

4.3 Planning and design

4.3.1 Planning for a scaffolding contract

When selecting a scaffolding contractor you should check that they are competent and consider the following.

- The competence of their management and operatives for the type of work.
- That they have a proven track record for the type of work.
- Their arrangements for managing health and safety (such as a recognised and auditable safety management system).
- Their past health and safety performance.
- That they have a positive safety culture.
- The allocation of sufficient physical and human resources to service the contract (for example, scaffolding equipment, transport, qualified scaffolders, supervision and designers).
- Whether they are regulated through membership of a recognised organisation (such as NASC).
- Whether they have any third-party health and safety accreditations (for example, ISO 18001 or CHAS).

Before engaging a specialist scaffolding contractor, it is advisable to prepare information on the intended use of the scaffolds for the contractor to take into account.

For further information refer to the planning and preparation, and the work on site sections of TG20.

Before the erection of any scaffold, the following points should be clearly defined.

Trainee scaffolder erecting scaffold in accordance with the design plan

- ☑ What is the scaffold going to be used for and how long will it be required?
- ☑ What dimensions are required for the scaffold?
- ☑ Is the scaffold TG20 compliant and covered by manufacturer's instructions, or is bespoke design input required?
- ☑ Exactly where is it to be erected? Consider environmental factors (such as interface with the public) and other areas (such as railway lines and overhead power lines).
- ☑ Can safe access be provided for the erection and use of the scaffold?
- ☑ How many working platforms will there be?
- ☑ Is the ground condition where the scaffold is to be erected suitable?
- ☑ How and where can the scaffold be stabilised (for example, ties)?
- ☑ What loadings will be imposed upon the working platforms, and on the scaffold as a whole?
- ☑ Will the scaffold be clad with sheeting, netting or other materials (such as advertising hoarding)?

A pre-contract site inspection should be completed to ascertain the nature of the site and as the first part of the risk assessment process to identify any significant hazards. This will allow suitable and sufficient control measures to be implemented, to ensure the safe and successful completion of the works.

4.3.2 Scaffold design

The Work at Height Regulations requires strength and stability calculations for all scaffolds unless constructed to a generally recognised standard configuration. TG20 provides definitions for TG20 compliant tube and fitting scaffolds, designed by structural calculation to BS EN 12811. System scaffolding should be planned and constructed in accordance with manufacturer's instructions, to BS EN 12811 and BS EN 12810, otherwise the scaffold must be subject to bespoke design and calculation by a competent engineer.

Site management responsible for controlling scaffolding operations should seek assurance that the planned scaffolding conforms to a standard configuration or a bespoke design and that calculations have been prepared.

The Code of Practice for temporary works procedures and the permissible stress design of falsework (BS 5975:2008 + A1:2011) provides guidance on the procedural management of temporary works, including scaffolding.

The TG20 design guide provides technical guidance for scaffolding design engineers on the application and interpretation of BS EN 12811 and related standards.

Scaffolding contractors and principal contractors should have suitable arrangements in place to manage and control the erection, alteration and commissioning of designed scaffolds (such as issuing drawings, managing variations to the design, inspection and handing over designed scaffolds).

www.

For further information, including a list of scaffold structures where bespoke design is recommended, refer to the HSE scaffold checklist.

4.3.3 TG20 compliance sheets

The TG20 operational guide contains a range of common scaffold configurations and scaffolding add-on features (Chapter 3) that do not require additional design. A TG20 compliance sheet can be used to demonstrate that a tube and fitting scaffold is TG20 compliant.

The TG20 eGuide software expands this range of scaffolding configurations and features. It can be used to produce TG20 compliance sheets or identify whether bespoke design is required. The sheets contain a brief summary of the criteria that must be met in order for the scaffold to be considered compliant. They should be read in conjunction with the detailed guidance in the TG20 operational guide.

Types of TG20 compliant scaffolding used in the construction industry are shown below.

- ☑ Tied independent scaffolding.
- ☑ Freestanding independent scaffolding.
- ☑ Tied putlog scaffolding.
- ☑ Tower scaffolding, including lift shaft access.
- ☑ Interior access birdcage scaffolding.
- ☑ Chimney-stack scaffolding.

TG20 scaffolding features are shown below for construction scaffolding.

- ☑ Loading bays.
- ☑ Ladder-access towers.
- ☑ Bridging with beams.
- ☑ Pavement lifts.
- ☑ Cantilevered platforms and protection fans.
- ☑ Prefabricated transoms and hop-up brackets.

TG20 compliance sheets can be used for various purposes, including quotations, scaffold plans, risk assessments and method statements. They are not intended to replace the scaffolding handover certificate or permit to load; however, they can be appended to these documents issued by the scaffolding contractor.

4.3.4 Fall prevention in scaffolding

Falling from height whilst erecting, altering or dismantling scaffolding presents a significant risk to all scaffolders. The NASC safety guidance *Preventing falls in scaffolding* (SG4) highlights basic requirements and principles of fall prevention and protection that should be taken by scaffolders.

SG4 states: scaffolding contractors should prevent falls by providing work platforms with suitable guard-rails or other collective measures, before resorting to fall-arrest equipment (safety harness).

Therefore, the use of temporary platforms with guard-rails would take priority when establishing safe systems of work. SG4 refers to such temporary working platforms as the scaffolders' safe zone.

A range of collective fall protection methods and equipment are recommended in the NASC guide (such as advanced guard-rail systems, step-ups and methods of working). These collective measures enable scaffolders to provide guard-rail protection in advance of erection and to maintain fall protection for alterations and dismantling. This then complies with the Work at Height Regulations heirarchy of control measures.

Such systems do not completely eliminate the risk of a fall in all circumstances and NASC still recommends the use of personal fall protection equipment. SG4 recognises that personal fall protection equipment should be worn by scaffolders working at height and provides guidance for use as part of the systems of work, including the use of suitable anchor points.

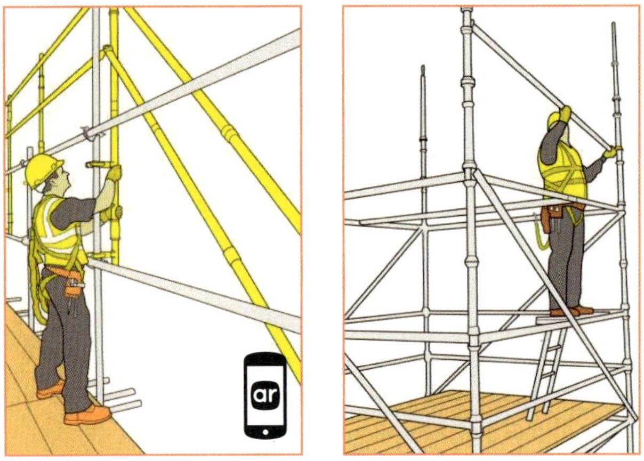

Examples of collective protection equipment and methods

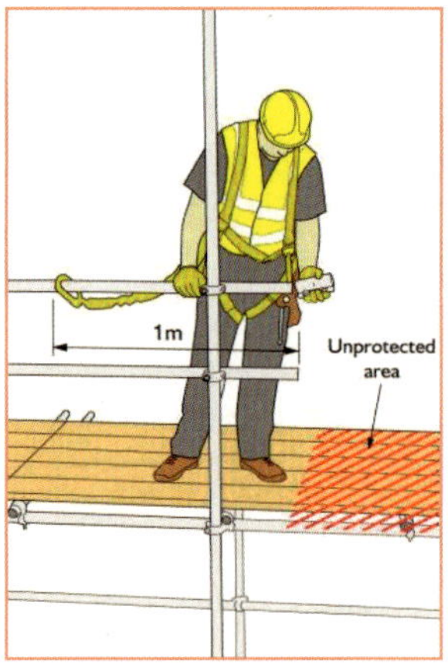

Use of personal protection

Personal fall protection equipment used for scaffolding should be inspected at the following intervals.

- ☑ By the user before use.
- ☑ Thoroughly by a competent person every three months and recorded.
- ☑ Thoroughly at other intervals if the need is identified via a risk assessment.

For further information on the management of fall protection equipment refer to the NASC Safety guidance note *Management of fall protection equipment* (SG16).

4.3.5 Rescue planning

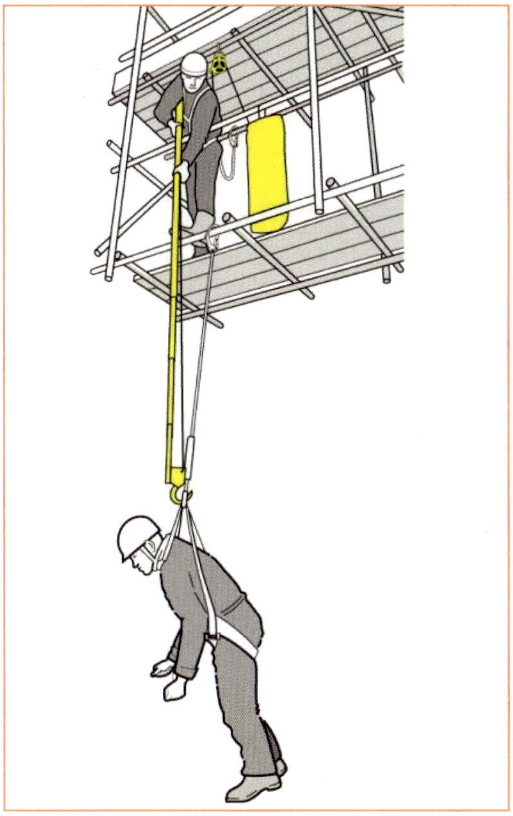

Specialist rescue equipment

The Work at Height Regulations requires employers to plan for emergencies and rescue for all work at height. These arrangements should not rely on the emergency services.

Scaffolding plans must also consider the rescue and recovery of a scaffolder suspended by their personal fall protection equipment.

To ensure compliance with the above requirements:

- ☑ scaffolders and their supervision should be trained in the requirements of SG4 (latest version) and the rescue plan, including the correct use of any specialist rescue equipment and techniques required
- ☑ site managers and others who run construction sites should check that the scaffold contractors coming on to their sites have adequately trained in the requirements of SG4 (latest version).

For further information on rescue planning refer to the NASC safety guidance notes (SG4 and SG19).

4.4 Basic independent scaffolding

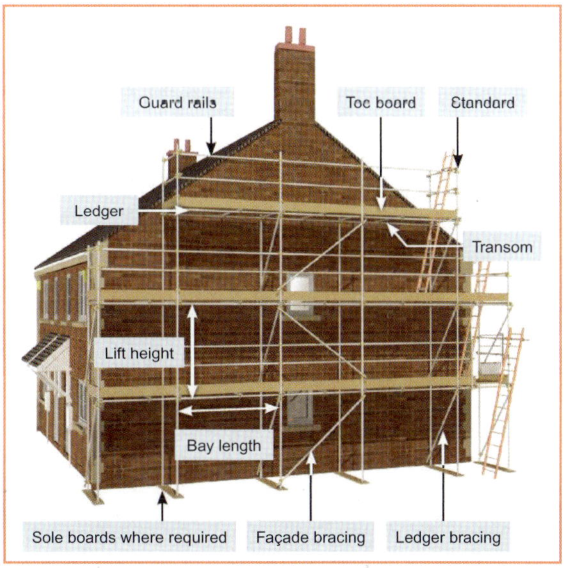

Scaffolding terminology

This section provides basic guidelines for independent scaffolding commonly used in the construction industry. For detailed guidance refer to NASC TG20 or the manufacturer's instructions for proprietary scaffolding equipment.

D
04

4.4.1 Common materials and components

4.4.1.1 Tubes

- ☑ BS EN 39 Type 4 galvanised steel tubes or equivalent, 48.3 mm diameter with a 4 mm wall thickness.
- ☑ High tensile thinner wall 3.2 mm tubes to BS EN 10210 or BS EN 10219.

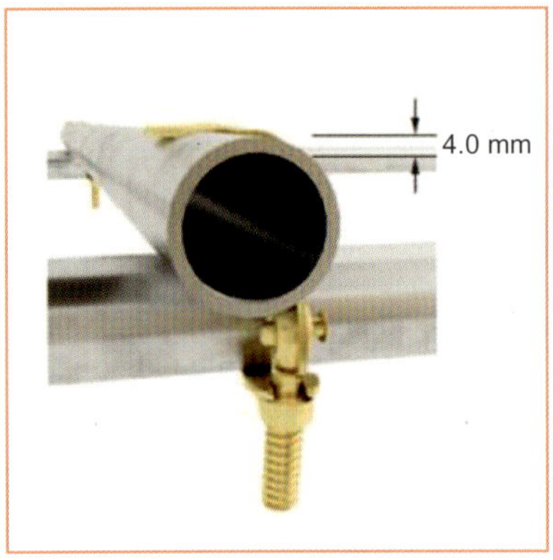

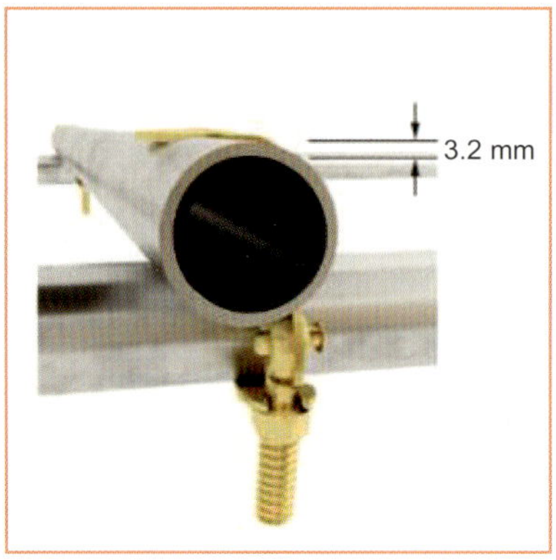

4.4.1.2 Fittings

- ☑ BS EN 74 couplers.
- ☑ Old stocks of BS 1139 coupler can still be used.

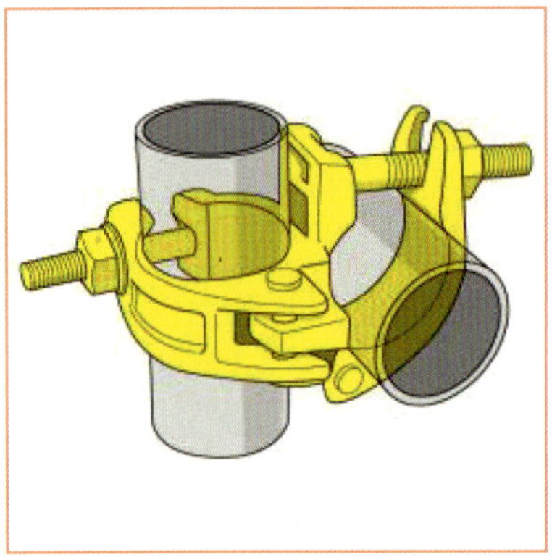

Right-angle coupler (double)

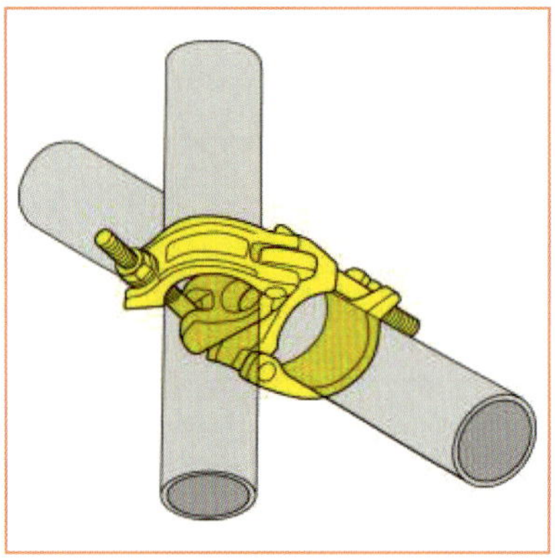

Swivel coupler

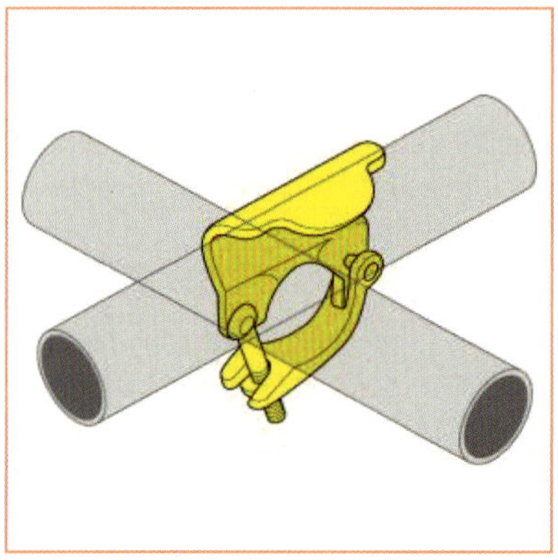

Putlog coupler (single)

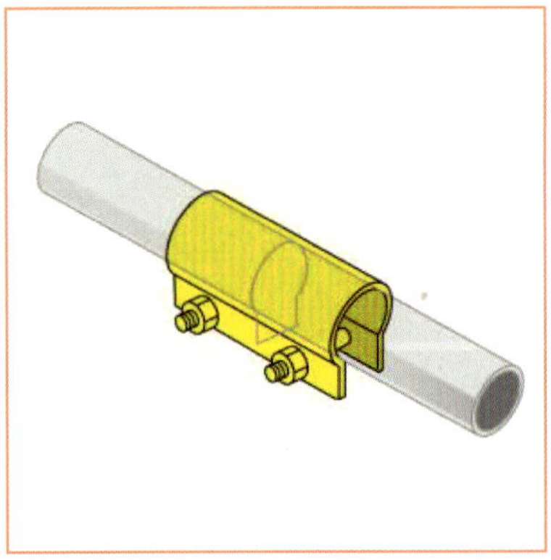

Sleeve coupler

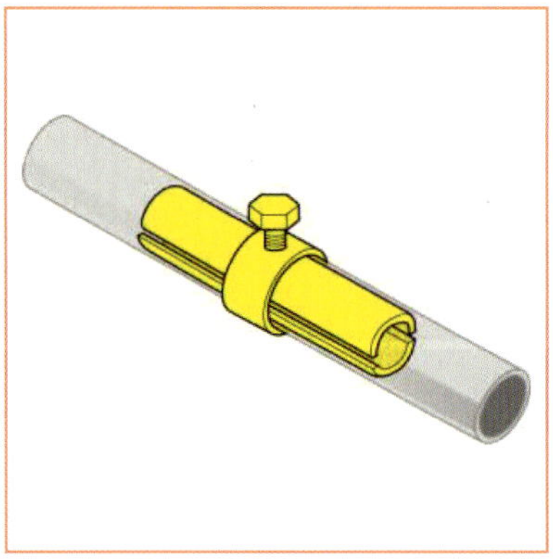

Spigot joint coupler

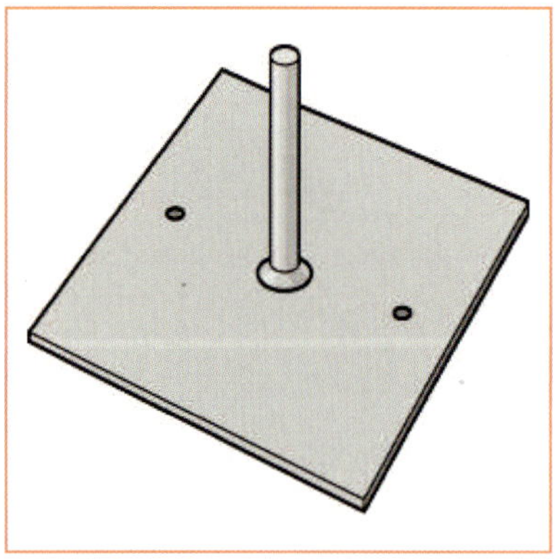

Base plate

4.4.1.3 Boards

- BS 2482 timber scaffold boards, 38 mm thickness, with a target span of at least 1.2 m.
- Laminated veneered lumber (LVL) or composite plastic decks may be used with a target span of 1.2 m and a unit weight not in excess of a 38 mm timber scaffold board.

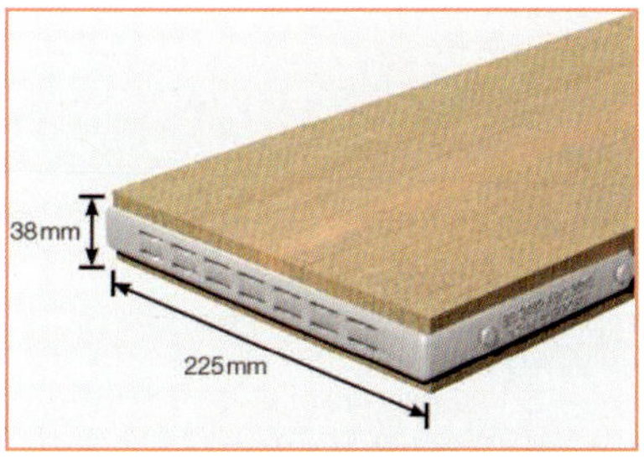

38 mm timber board (with end-bands)

38 mm timber board (with nail-plate option)

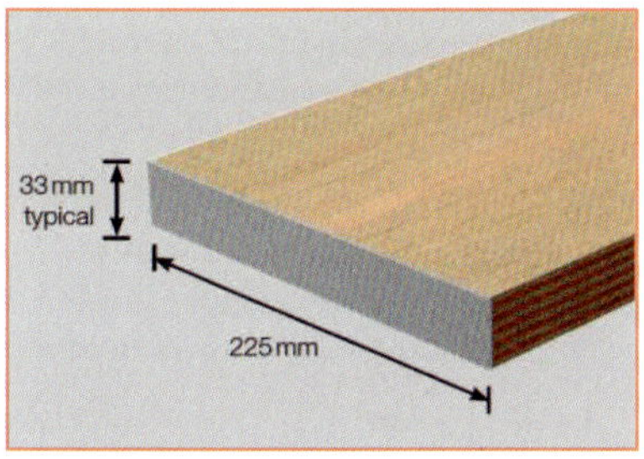

Laminated veneer lumber (LVL) board

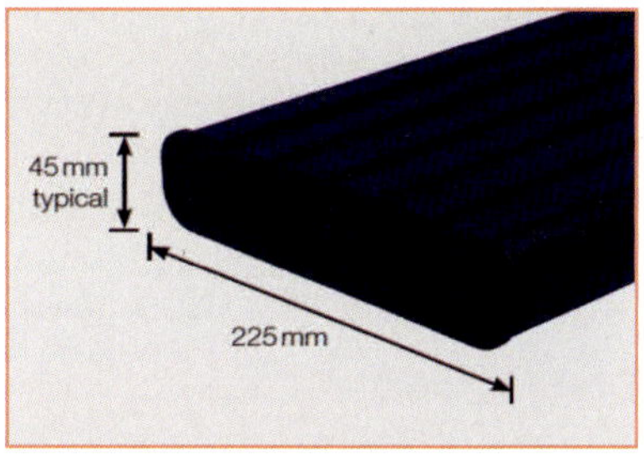

Composite plastic board

4.4.1.4 Ladders

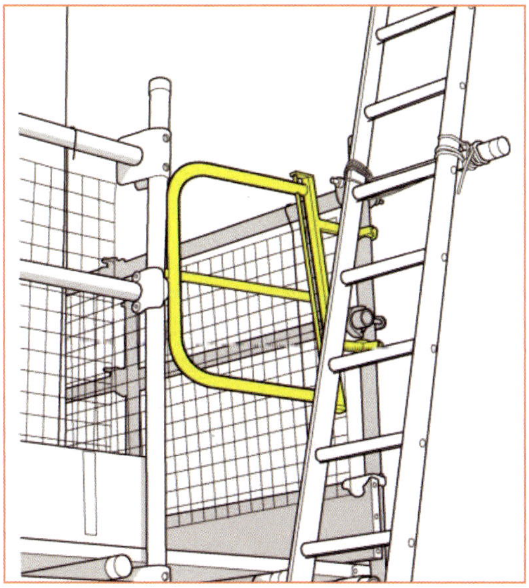

External scaffold ladder access with safety gate

- Ladders used with scaffolding should conform to BS EN 131 (Class 1 or 2).
- Timber ladders (BS 129) and metal ladders (BS 2037) may also be used with scaffolding.
- Domestic (Class 3) ladders should not be used.

4.4.1.5 Transom units

Prefabricated structural transom units can be used providing they are certified as TG20 compliant by the supplier.

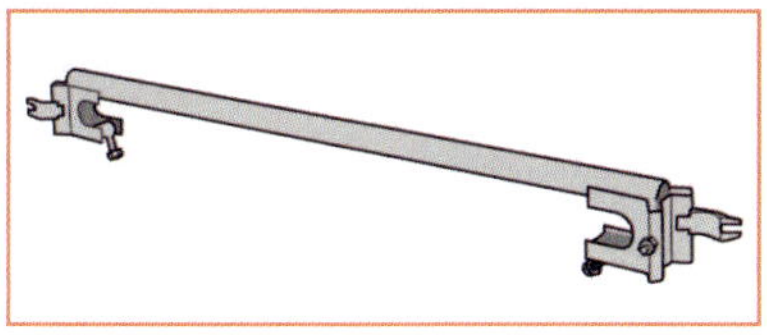

Prefabricated transom unit (Readylok, Easifix type)

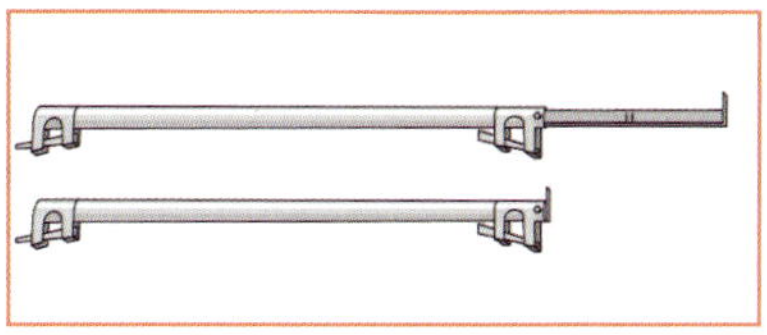

Prefabricated extending transoms

4.4.1.6 Beams

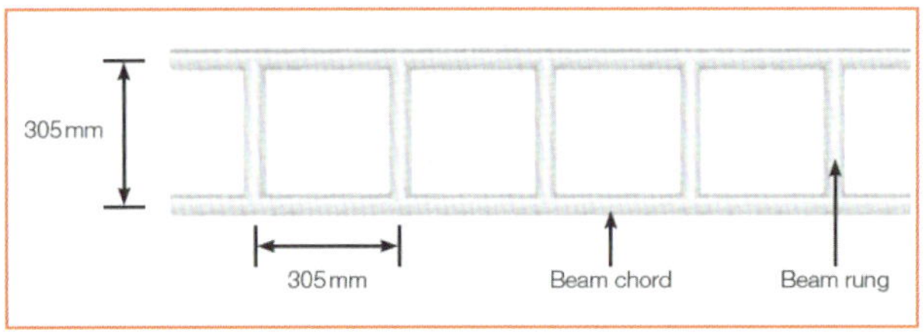

Steel ladder beam

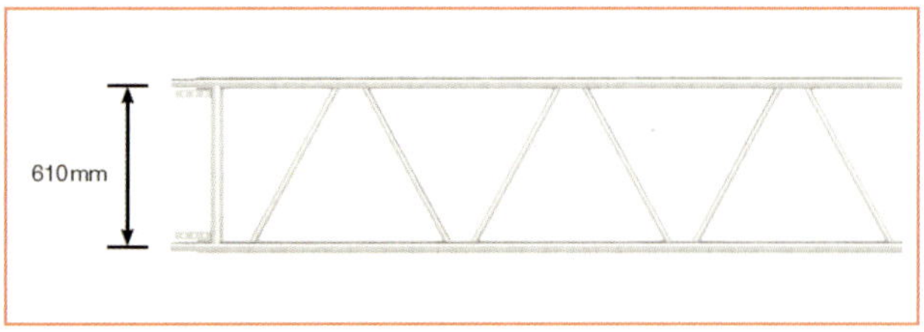

Steel unit beam

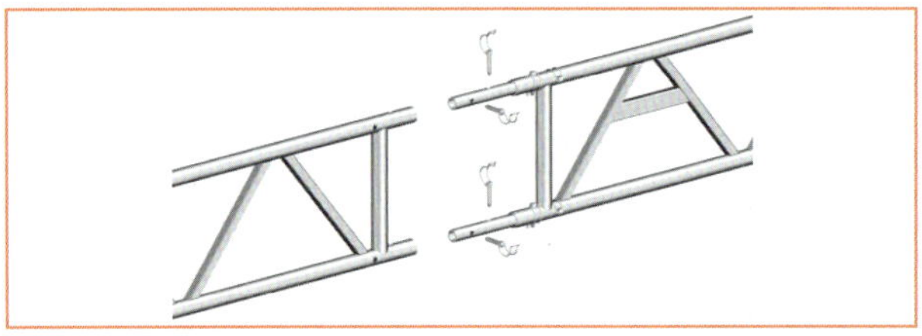

Aluminium unit beam

- ☑ TG20 states minimum structural properties for the use of steel or aluminium scaffolding beams.
- ☑ Check manufacturer's instructions for use with system scaffolding.
- ☑ Ensure the correct beams are used, as specified in bespoke designs.

4.4.2 Foundations

The foundations for all scaffolds must be of adequate strength to support and disperse the applied load. On hard surfaces (such as steel and concrete of sufficient strength and thickness) standards may be placed directly on the surface, although it is generally preferable to use a base plate that is 150 mm x 150 mm in size.

Sheeting or a proprietary plastic treader plate can also be used to protect sensitive floors from damage or marking. They also serve to highlight the base plate to pedestrians. TG20 restricts the height of scaffolds founded on treader plates to three lift independent scaffolds and four lift tower and birdcage scaffolds.

Plastic treader plate

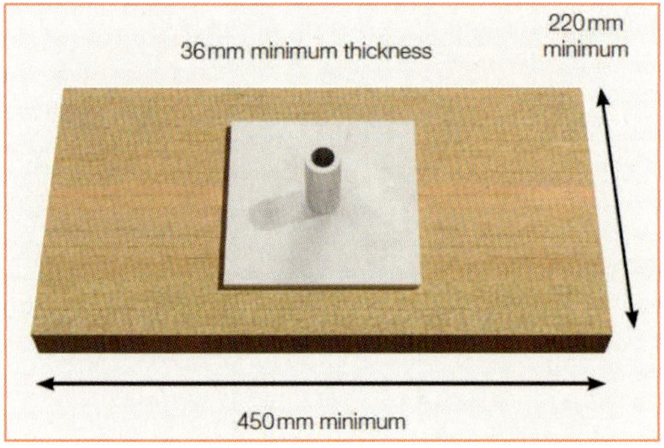

Minimum sole board dimensions

On other surfaces, the load should be spread by using base plates and sole boards. The soil or ground beneath the sole board should be level and properly compacted.

When a sole board is used on hard ground, the area beneath any one standard should be at least 0.1 m^2. If a timber sole board is used, it must be not less than 36 mm thick and a minimum dimension of 220 mm. Scaffold boards are typically used for this purpose.

On soft or disturbed ground, the sole board area should not be less than 17,000 mm^2. Each sole board should support two standards.

The system scaffold instructions or bespoke design should state the requirements for scaffolding foundations. Planning for scaffolding should consider the loads likely to be imposed to any surface by scaffolding; this may include seeking specialist engineering advice.

TG20 compliance sheets specify the requirements for scaffold foundations. This includes whether single or double sole boards are required and whether the scaffold requires double standards that may share sole boards. For double standards a minimum sole board dimension of 750 x 225 x 75 mm is required, unless each standard has it own sole board.

A foot lift (also referred to as a foot tie, locking lift or kicker lift) is considered good practice and helps stability of the scaffold, although not strictly necessary for most TG20 compliant scaffolds. This varies for system scaffolding, so refer to the manufacturer's instructions. TG20 compliance sheets may also specify a foot lift is required for taller scaffolds. A foot lift is also recommended for sloping ground with a gradient of more than 1:10.

Double sole board

Double standards sharing a sole board

Foot lift example

4.4.3 Bracing

For tube and fitting scaffolding the TG20 compliance sheets and TG20 operational guide specifies the requirements for bracing the various types of TG20 compliant scaffolds and scaffolding features (for example, pavement lifts, bridging with beams and loading bays). System scaffolding must be braced in accordance with the manufacturer's instructions. All other scaffold configurations must be braced in accordance with the bespoke design.

The following examples are for basic tube and fitting tied independent scaffolds.

4.4.3.1 Façade bracing

- Also referred to as face or sway bracing.
- Required on every elevation of scaffolding and every sixth bay horizontally. (Scaffolds more than 6-12 bays require two sets.)
- Can be fixed as single-bay, double-bay or continuous.
- Must be fixed with a right-angled coupler or swivels, no more than 300 mm from the intersection with the ledger and standard (node point), and at an angle of between 35 and 55 degrees.
- If jointed, it should ideally be with a Class B sleeve coupler.

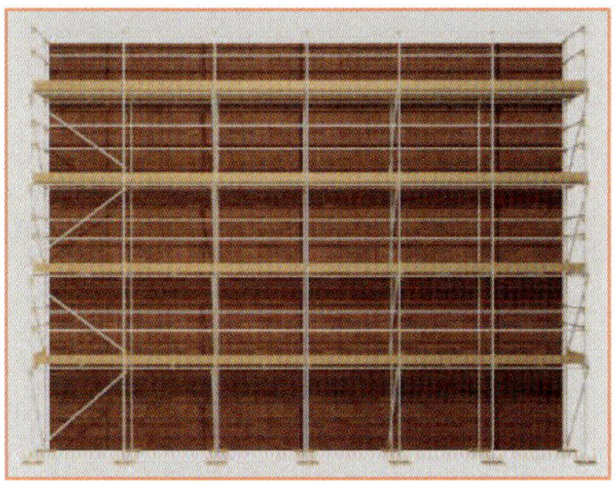

Single-bay façade brace

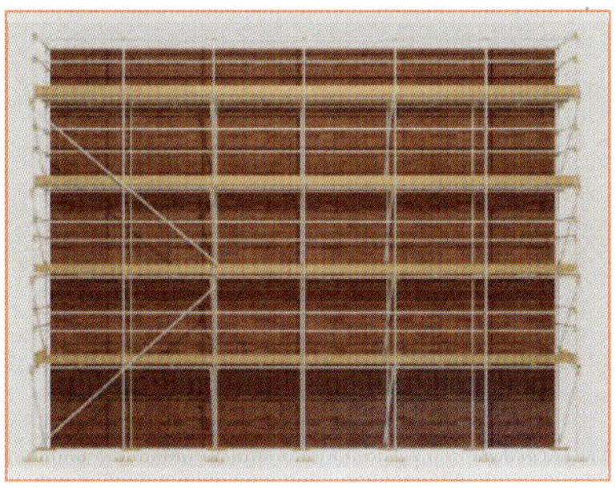

Double-bay façade brace

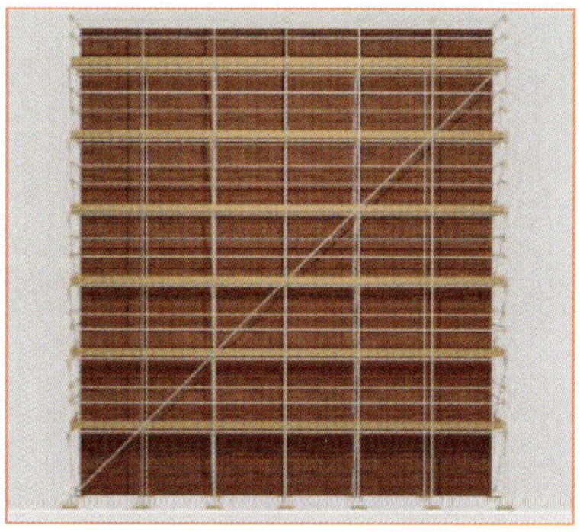

Continuous façade brace

4.4.3.2 Ledger bracing

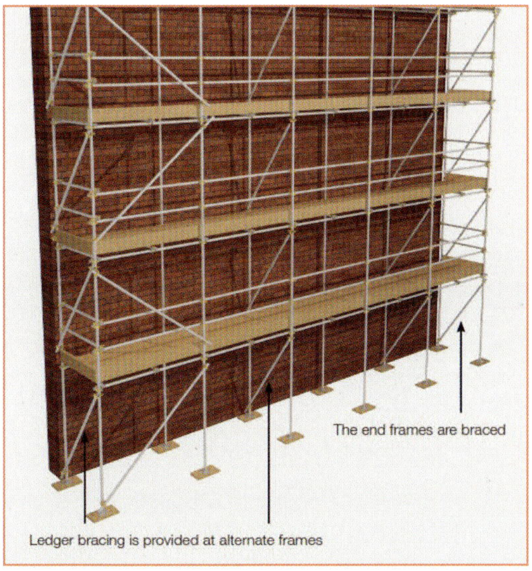

Ledger bracing

- Connects inner and outer standards to help stiffen and stabilise the scaffold.
- The first (end) pairs of standards and alternate pairs should be ledger braced at all lifts.
- Fixed with right-angled couplers to the ledgers or with swivel couplers to the standards, within 300 mm of the intersection with the ledger and standard (node point).
- TG20 provides exceptions to cases where ledger bracing may be omitted.

4.4.3.3 Plan bracing

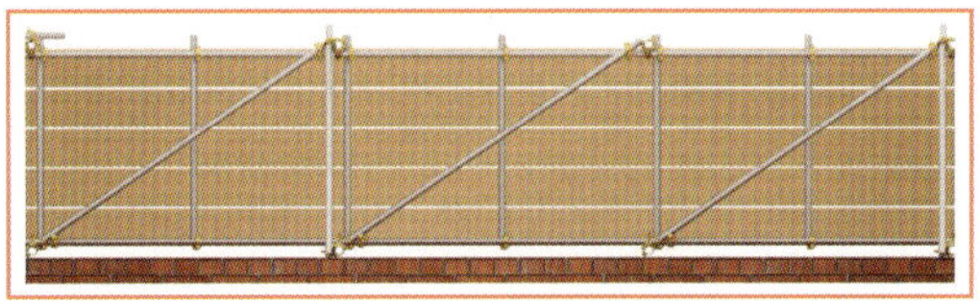

Plan bracing

- Not routinely required for basic independent scaffolds, unless specified on the compliance sheet or design.
- Some TG20 features routinely require plan bracing, including bridging, loading bays and pedestrian lifts.
- Fitted horizontally to right-angled or swivel couplers.

4.4.4 Ties

A tie secures the scaffold to the supporting structure and is provided to resist the inward (push) and outward (pull) movement of the scaffold and also to give some additional longitudinal stability (sway). Butting tubes may also be required to provide sway resistance.

TG20 operational guide (Chapter 7 – Ties to building façades) and TG4 Anchorage systems for scaffolding – provide comprehensive guidance on the selection, use and testing of ties.

D 04

Ties are generally designated as moveable or non-moveable, the terminology being self-explanatory. Where possible, ties should be left undisturbed until the scaffold is dismantled. Where it is necessary for ties to be removed, even for a short period, the scaffold will be less stable and the fitting of additional temporary ties will be necessary, unless the initial tie-pattern was designed to allow for the temporary removal of some ties.

Ties must not be removed by anyone other than a competent scaffolder or someone who is under the direct supervision of one. The removal of scaffold ties must be carried out in compliance with a safe system of work (such as a method statement and risk assessment).

TG20 compliance sheets provide details of the specification of ties to be used.

There are several methods of tying scaffolding to a building or other permanent structure, principally the assembly of tubes and fittings around structural features, or drilled or cast in anchors to the building material.

The capacity and load class of ties is stated in TG20 operational guide. Reference should be made to manufacturer's instructions for tying information of system scaffolding.

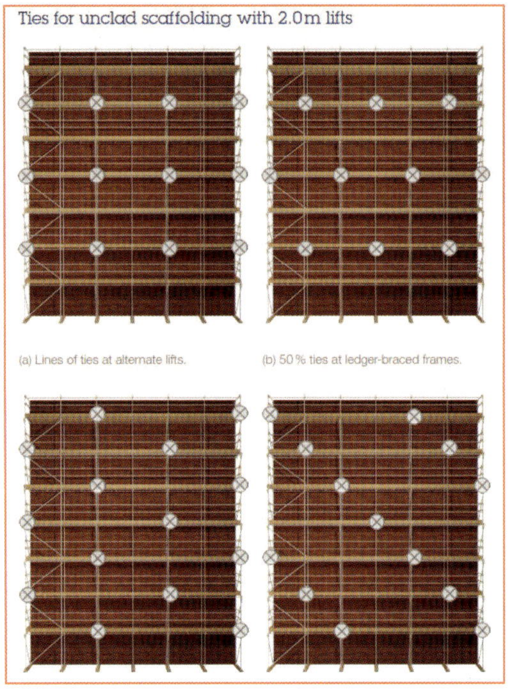

Typical tie patterns for unclad scaffolding with 2 m lifts

The frequency and capacity of the ties must be determined from the TG20 compliance sheet for tube and fitting scaffolding, system scaffolding manufacturer's instruction manual or a design drawing.

This will include the tie duty, frequency and maximum spacing of ties, which will vary due to the following factors.

- Location.
- Height.
- Load class.
- Lift height.
- Façade type.
- Cladding (brick guards netting or sheeting).
- Seasonal variations.

At least 50% of ties should be fixed to ledger braced standards.

Scaffolds erected around corners (returns) can provide stability and reduce the tying requirements. Refer to TG20 or the system manufacturer for details.

Some typical tying methods are shown below.

4.4.4.1 Box ties

Box tie

- ☑ Assemblies of tubes and fittings to form a square around a column or similar structural feature.
- ☑ Can be used for standard or heavy duty ties.
- ☑ Should be fixed with right-angled couplers.

4.4.4.2 Through ties

Through tie

- ☑ Fitted through windows or other façade openings.
- ☑ Suitable as a standard duty tie.
- ☑ Inner and outer tubes to resist movement and packing to protect the surfaces.
- ☑ Fixed with right-angled couplers.

4.4.4.3 Lip ties

Lip tie

- ☑ Can be used where it is not possible to form a box tie.
- ☑ Suitable as a standard duty tie.
- ☑ Opposing lip ties, butting tubes and/or sway transoms should be used to resist movement.

4.4.4.4 Reveal ties

Reveal tie

- ☑ Used where other forms of tie are not practical.
- ☑ Only suitable as a light duty tie.
- ☑ A maximum of 50% of ties in a façade may be reveal ties.
- ☑ Reveal pins should be regularly checked throughout the life of the scaffold to ensure they remain tight.

4.4.4.5 Masonry anchors

Masonry anchors

- ☑ Drilled or cast into the building fabric.
- ☑ Several types and methods of assembly (such as self-tapping screws and expanding plugs and sockets).
- ☑ Careful planning, selection, installation and testing are required for the correct use of masonry anchors. *(Refer to NASC guidance (TG20 and TG4) and manufacturer's instructions.)*
- ☑ Scaffolders installing and testing anchors must be trained to do so.

4.4.4.6 Girder clamps

Girder clamps

- ☑ Used to tie scaffolding to structural steelwork.
- ☑ Should be used in opposing pairs.
- ☑ The tie duty will depend upon their application and manufacturer's instructions.

4.4.5 Anchor testing

TG4 requires two levels of testing.

Typical anchor testing rig

- ☑ Preliminary testing – to check the suitability of the fixing for the tie load required.
- ☑ Proof testing – to check the installation and that the required tensile loads can be achieved.

A minimum of three ties must be tested and 5% (1 in 20) thereafter. Ties must be proof tested to 1.25 times (+25%) the required tensile load (for example, a standard duty Class A tie with a working load of 6.1 kN requires a 7.6 kN tensile test load).

If any anchor fails the test the cause must be investigated and recorded, then the test frequency increased to 10% and a minimum of six anchors. If two anchors fail the tests are doubled to 20% and 12 anchors. If more than two anchors fail then all of the ties must be tested (100%). A test report should be provided with the test results as part of the handover process.

The strength and pull-out capabilities of all cast or drilled anchorages must be confirmed before use.

4.4.6 Working platforms

The Work at Height Regulations and BS EN 12811 set out the minimum standards for working platforms for workers and users of scaffolding (Schedule 3 *Requirements for working platforms*). A higher standard is required for temporary scaffolding structures accessed by the general public and others (for example, temporary footbridge or fire escape) and specialist advice should be sought.

Lift heights of TG20 compliant scaffolds may be up to 3 m. However, they are typically 2 m for fully erected scaffolds and less for scaffolds progressively constructed (such as bricklaying lifts 1.35-1.5 m). A head clearance of 1.9 m should be maintained between lifts for personnel access. However, structural features (such as tie tubes or plan bracing) may reduce this to 1.75 m.

Working platforms should be assessed at planning stage to ensure there is sufficient space for access and working. BS 12811 stipulates a minimum width of 600 mm for work and 500 mm for access. TG20 recommends a minimum platform width of 800 mm for personnel and storage of materials. Where materials are stored on a working platform TG20 also recommends that a minimum clearance of 430 mm be maintained for access.

Suggested minimum clearance in TG20

Platforms are generally constructed using scaffold boards (BS 2482 or equivalent). Decking should be correctly supported, as recommended by TG20, the system scaffolding manufacturer's instructions or the design drawing. The spacing of transoms beneath scaffold boards is referred to as the target span and varies depending on the load class of the scaffold and specification of the board (for example, a visually graded BS 2482 board load Classes 1-3 are 1.2 m and load Class 4 is 0.9 m).

The ends of boards must be supported to allow for deflection and to avoid accidental tipping (known as trap ends). Transoms must be positioned a minimum of 50 mm and no more than 150 mm from the end of the boards. ***Note:*** *33 mm LVL boards have a maximum overhang of 130 mm.*

All short boards less than 2.13 m (7ft) must be secured at both ends. Rope, wire lashings or proprietary board clamps should be used.

Overlapping of boards should be avoided, except at corner returns. Where an overlap is unavoidable, the lapped board should be secured to prevent movement and, if necessary, bevelled pieces should be installed (known as a fillet).

Gaps in platforms should be avoided where possible, unless measures have been taken to prevent people from falling or falling objects from injuring someone. Where standards protrude through the platform (for example, between inside boards and the main platform) there will be a gap of approximately 50 mm. This gap is normally acceptable in construction. However, it may need to be covered following a risk assessment. There are several methods to cover such gaps. *(For further advice refer to NASC guidance TG20 and TG13 Non-standard boarded platforms.)*

The space between the inner edge of a working platform and the adjacent structure should be kept as small as possible to prevent falls. However, there can be circumstances in which this gap has to be wider. This is usually due to the nature of the work being carried out (for example, to enable the craning-in of sections of curtain wall between the scaffold and the building under construction or where there is only primary steelwork inside the scaffold). This is known as the service gap. In such circumstances, suitable protection measures must be taken if there is a risk of people falling, or people being struck by falling objects. *(For further information refer to TG20 and SG29.)*

It is recommended that where a service gap exceeds 225 m and a person could fall or suffer injury, double guard-rails and toe-boards should be installed or other suitable compensatory measures used *(see examples below)*.

- ☑ Use of inner guard-rails and toe-boards.
- ☑ Segregation of the areas below the scaffold and post warning signs.
- ☑ Areas of the scaffold designated as danger areas, where access is restricted by guard-rails and warning signs.
- ☑ Use of personal fall protection equipment (harnesses).

The space between scaffolding boards should be kept as small as possible and in any case should not exceed 25 mm.

Modern construction methods often require the use of inside boards to extend the width of the main platform. These inside platforms frequently need adapting to accommodate the construction work for various applications and trades (for example, they may require reducing to allow installation of the façade material). TG20 provides compliance sheets for scaffolds with 1-3 inside boards.

Inside boards can be supported by extending the main transoms, using telescopic transoms or using proprietary inside board brackets (known as hop ups). Inside board brackets may be raised or lowered by up to 500 mm from the main platform. The inner board may need to be secured if there is a risk of accidental displacement. ***Note:*** *inside boards are generally rated as a lower load capacity to the main platform (for example, TG20 states 0.75 kN/m^2 for inside boards).*

4.4.7 Guard-rails

All scaffolding working platforms must be protected with double guard-rails where there is a risk of a fall.

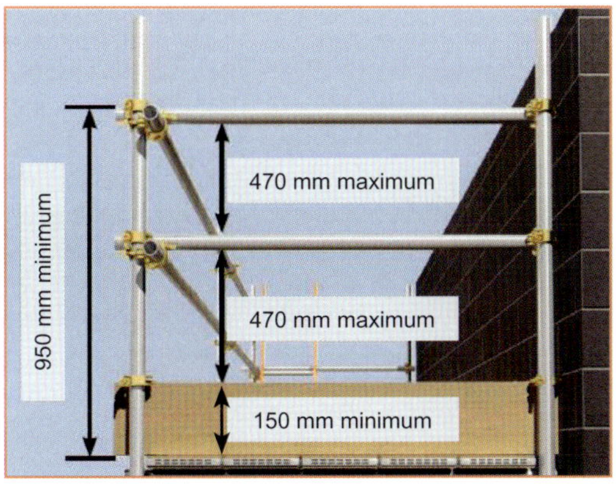

Work at Height Regulations guard-rail dimensions

The main or top guard-rail must be 950 mm above the edge (or above a working platform) from which any person is liable to fall.

An intermediate guard-rail (or mid guard-rail) may be placed approximately halfway between the top edge of the toe-board and the top guard-rail, so there is no gap larger than 470 mm between the guard-rails or the toe-board.

All guard-rails must be fixed inside the standards with right-angled couplers to each standard. The only exception to this rule is stop-end guard-rails (at the end of a single elevation with no corner return), which may be fixed on top of the main guard-rails with a putlog coupler. However, the other ends must be fixed with a right-angled coupler to the standard.

There will be occasions when it is possible to fall from the working platform into the structure under construction. In these cases, it will be necessary to consider installing guard-rails to the inner edge of working platforms or using other fall prevention or arrest measures.

Additional guard-rails may be required to maintain the minimum height of 950 mm for a raised inside board bracket and other scenarios identified through a risk assessment.

Where it is necessary to load out scaffolds with, for example, bulk materials, ideally there will be a purpose built loading bay with a lifting safety gate or similar. Where this is not the case, it is permissible to temporarily remove guard-rails and toe-boards in the following circumstances.

- ☑ Unless other work is stopped, other equally effective fall prevention or arrest measures are put in place (such as safety harnesses) whilst there is an exposed edge.
- ☑ Once the loading has been completed, the guard-rails and toe-boards are replaced immediately.

The removal and refitting of guard-rails and toe-boards must only be carried out by a competent scaffolder or someone who is under the direct supervision of a competent scaffolder.

Although unboarded lifts are not intended to be accessed by scaffold users, they should be protected by single main guard-rails for erecting, altering or dismantling, as part of the NASC SG4 system of work.

4.4.8 Toe-boards

Toe-boards should be fitted to all boarded platforms where there is a risk of material or a person falling. The minimum height of a toe-board (as per BS EN 12811) is 150 mm. However, they are typically 225 mm scaffold boards. Toe-boards should be fixed inside the standard, at a minimum of two positions.

4.4.9 Brick guards

Brick guards should be installed where there is a possibility of materials toppling from working platforms and where materials will be stacked higher than the toe-boards.

Wire brick guard with double guard-rails and toe-board

If using the common type of brick guard, intermediate guard-rails should also be fitted. TG20 compliance sheets take account of the use of brick guards and increased wind loading.

Brick guards are now available in various materials and colours (for example, wire or plastic). Colour allows missing brick guards to be easily identified from the ground.

4.4.10 Loading

It is essential that scaffolds are not loaded beyond their maximum design load. Materials should be distributed as evenly as possible with heavy items (such as piles of bricks) positioned adjacent to standard. Overloading of working platforms can result in the failure of the boards or a scaffold collapse.

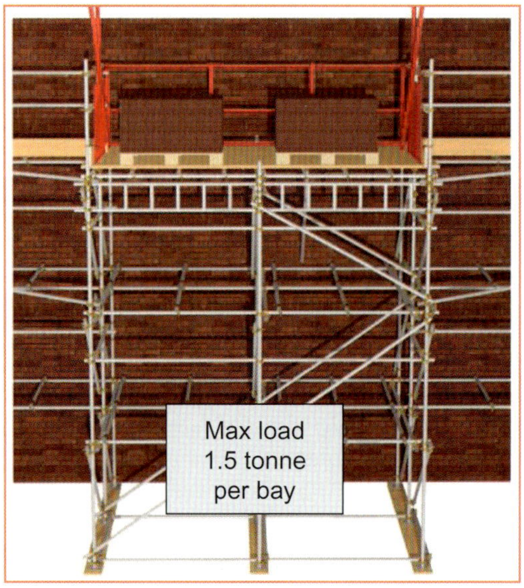

TG20 loading bay with safe load sign

BS EN 12811 identifies six scaffold load classes, from 0.75 kN/m^2 to 6 kN/m^2. TG20 provides standard configurations for load Classes 1-4 *(refer to the TG20 table Load classes and typical applications, and TG20 compliance sheet for the scaffold usage)*. Some system scaffolds may provide standard configurations for load Classes 5 and 6.

Regardless of how many lifts are boarded only one lift may be fully loaded with personnel and material (100%) and one lift loaded to 50%. If it is necessary to simultaneously load more than two lifts, then a bespoke design is required.

TG20 states a load rating of 0.75 kN/m^2 for inside boards.

Site managers should ensure that the loading and use of scaffolding is properly controlled to prevent overloading.

Where the loading and storage of materials will exceed the load class of the scaffolding, or it is to be loaded with mechanical handling equipment, then a specially strengthened section of the scaffold or a loading bay should be provided. Proprietary loading bays can be used in accordance with the manufacturer's instructions and TG20 provides compliance sheets for a compliant loading bay. Otherwise a bespoke design is required. The load rating and any special restrictions should be clearly displayed on the loading bay.

4.4.11 System scaffolding

- ☑ Manufactured to BS EN 12811 and BS EN 12810.
- ☑ There are various types of system scaffolding available and these must be used in accordance with the manufacturer's instructions.

Pressing type (such as Kwikstage)

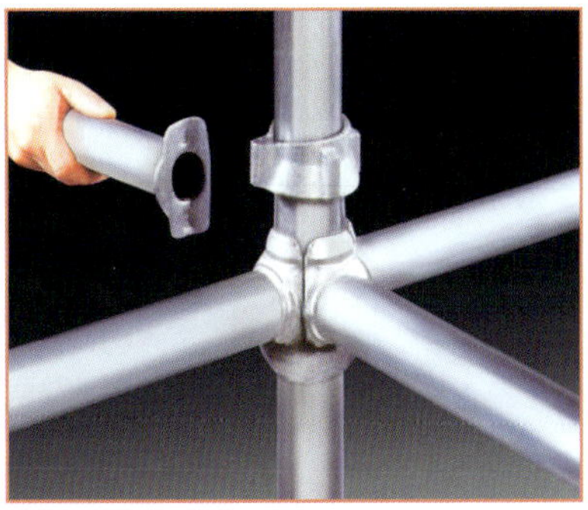

Cup type (such as Cuplok)

Rosette type (such as Layher)

All scaffolding material must be supplied in good condition and inspected before use. Scaffolding contractors should have systems in place to ensure scaffolding equipment is routinely inspected, serviced and, if necessary, repaired by a competent person.

4.4.12 Freestanding access scaffolds

TG20 includes compliant scaffolds designed to be used as freestanding structures, such as those listed below.

Typical TG20 freestanding independent scaffold with rakers

- ☑ Stationary freestanding towers.
- ☑ Chimneystack access scaffolding.
- ☑ Freestanding independent scaffolding (supported by rakers).
- ☑ Interior access birdcage scaffolding.

Freestanding access scaffolds or sections of scaffolds for modern methods of construction (such as timber-frame type structures) or demolition require calculations to be made for stability. These scaffolds would therefore be classed as special scaffolds and require bespoke design and calculations.

Engineers can utilise alternative methods of achieving stability (such as buttressing, kentledge (ballast or counterweights), guys and ground anchors). Returns around corners, access towers and loading bays can also be taken into account by engineers when calculating stability.

www.

For further information refer to the NASC guidance *Safe systems of work for scaffolding associated with timber-frame building construction* (SG28).

4.5 Methods of access

The **Work at Height Regulations** require employers to specify the use of existing structures as a means of access to height (for example, lifts or a permanent staircase) in preference to temporary measures (such as ladders).

Whilst ladders have been the commonly used means of access to scaffolds, the use of other, safer means of access (such as stair towers) should now be considered in preference. This would also aid timely evacuation in the event of an emergency (such as a fire).

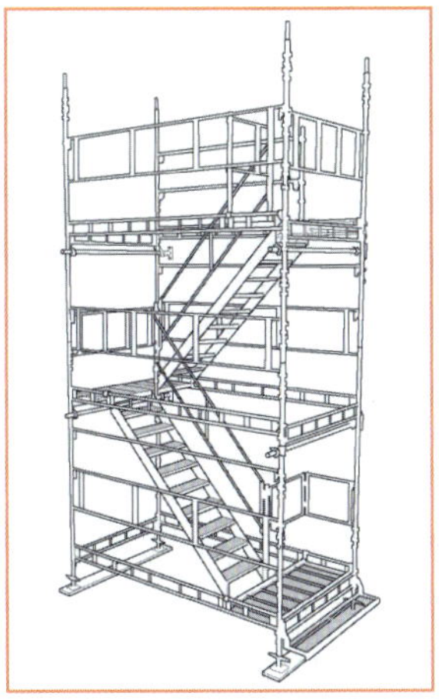

A typical site stairway

A typical ladder access tower with single lift ladders

BS EN 12811 recommends that where extensive work is carried out, stairways should be provided for access, and for taller scaffolds consideration should be given to the use of a passenger hoist.

Where passenger hoists are used, then additional non-mechanical access must also be provided in case of breakdown or emergencies.

NASC recommends the following hierarchy of access from TG20.

1. Staircases or lifts in permanent structures.
2. Mechanical hoists (for larger structures with additional emergency access).
3. Temporary stairways.
4. Ladder access towers with single lift ladders (to reduce the potential fall distance).
5. Ladder access bays with multiple lift ladders.
6. Internal ladder access with protected ladder traps.
7. External ladder using a safety gate.

D 04

For further information refer to the NASC Safety guidance note *Access and egress from scaffolds* (SG25) and TG20.

Straight ladders used for access to a scaffold must meet the following requirements.

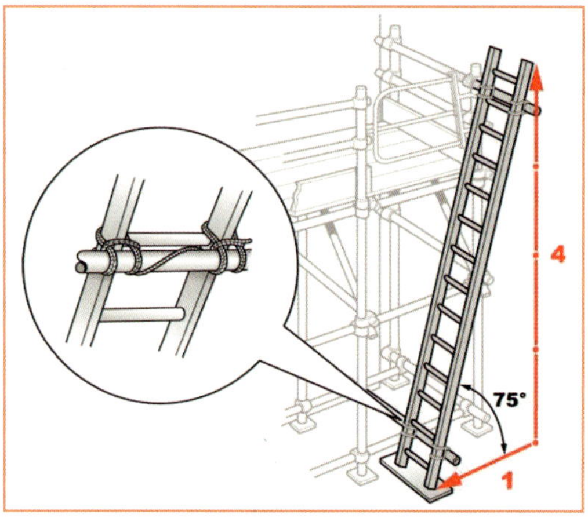

External access ladder and safety gate

- ☑ Be manufactured to BS EN 131/BS 1129.
- ☑ Not be defective in any way.
- ☑ Not be painted or treated in any way that might hide defects.
- ☑ Be placed on a firm footing, with each stile equally supported.
- ☑ Be so positioned that there is sufficient space at each rung to give an adequate foothold.
- ☑ Be positioned approximately at an angle of 75°, that is, one measure horizontal to four measures vertical.
- ☑ Be secured at the top using square lashings or a proprietary ladder clamp. For longer ladders, additional ladder supports (stays) can be used to prevent the ladder deflecting when used. The stay must not obstruct the rung of the ladder.
- ☑ Extend approximately one metre above the working platform, unless there is another adequate handhold.
- ☑ Be provided with suitable rest platforms if rising more than nine metres.
- ☑ Be the right way up (tie wires or bars positioned under the rungs).

Shorter ladders, which provide access to only one lift, are recommended to reduce the potential fall risk, although the Work at Height Regulations allows a maximum vertical height of nine metres between rest platforms.

Where scaffolds are designed with internal ladders, working platforms must be provided with access holes for each ladder. Such access holes should be at least 450 mm wide (across the platform) and not less than 600 mm in the other direction.

Typical ladder trapdoor

An alternative ladder trap protection

The access hole should be protected with a ladder trapdoor or similar (such as guard-rails and a gate).

Lateral gaps in guard-rails and toe-boards for access and egress must be kept to a minimum and protected with a ladder safety gate.

4.6 Inspection and handover

All scaffolds and working platforms (together with all other protective measures) are work equipment for the purposes of the Work at Height Regulations and so the inspection requirements of the regulations apply, which state:

> **... every employer shall ensure that where the safety of work equipment depends on how it is installed or assembled, it is not used after installation or assembly in any position unless it has been inspected in that position.**

This clearly applies to all access scaffolds, including mobile and static tower scaffolds.

The inspection must be carried out by a competent person. An employer may wish to have a commercial arrangement with a scaffolding contractor or independent consultant in order to carry out this function.

> **For further information about scaffold inspection qualifications refer to the CISRS scaffold inspection training scheme (SITS).**

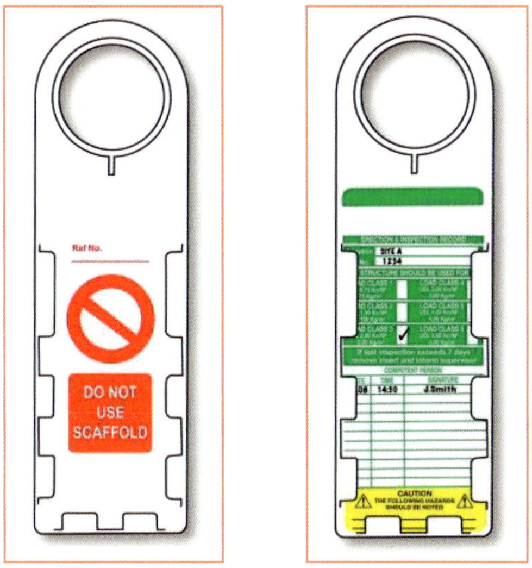

Typical scaffold tagging system

There is a further requirement in that every employer must ensure that work equipment exposed to conditions that may cause any deterioration liable to result in dangerous situations is inspected at suitable intervals, and also when any exceptional circumstances that are liable to jeopardise the safety of the work equipment have occurred.

In addition, employers must ensure that working platforms used for construction and from which a person could fall more than two metres are not used in any position unless they have been inspected in that position within the previous seven days.

It is common for proprietary inspection tags to be used to provide a status report for the scaffold. Where tags are used it is important that one is positioned at every access point to the scaffold.

4.6.1 Inspection of places of work at height

An additional requirement as regards inspection (or checking) is that every employer must ensure, so far as it is reasonably practicable, that every surface, parapet, permanent rail or other such fall protection measure of every place of work at height are checked before each use.

While there appears to be no requirement to record these checks, the prudent employer should do so to prove (for example, to the HSE or clients) that they have in fact been done.

4.6.2 Reports

Where an inspection has been carried out, a written report of the findings of the inspection must be made before the end of the working period.

The person who prepares the written report must provide a copy within 24 hours to the person on whose behalf the inspection was carried out. The report, or a copy of it, must be kept on the site where the inspection was carried out until the construction work is completed, and then kept at the company offices for three months.

Employers are free to design their own inspection report forms or purchase pads of them from commercial suppliers. In either case they must include the following information.

- ☑ The name and address of the person for whom the inspection was carried out.
- ☑ The location of the work equipment inspected.
- ☑ A description of the work equipment inspected.
- ☑ The date and time of the inspection.
- ☑ Details of any matter identified that could risk the health or safety of any person.
- ☑ Details of any action taken as a result of any matter identified above.
- ☑ Details of any further actions considered necessary.
- ☑ The name and position of the person making the report.

While it is not explicit in the regulations, where someone has carried out an inspection of a scaffold and believes that it is not safe to use or items require attention, they must inform the person for whom the inspection has been carried out that the scaffold is unsafe or remedial work is required. The scaffold or area in question must not then be used until it has been made safe.

The report must be completed within the shift the inspection was undertaken and issued to the person responsible for the scaffolding. The inspection report should be kept on site for a further period of three months thereafter.

An example of an inspection report form can be found in Section G: *Checklists and forms.*

4.6.3 Handover

After completion or following a modification to the scaffolding, a competent person must complete an inspection and report. It is good industry practice for scaffolding contractors to then complete a scaffold handover certificate and ensure that the client's representative receives a copy.

NASC provides a template certificate and guidance in *Handover of scaffold structures* (SG35) as a minimum.

Where a tagging system is used, an inspection system should be completed (for example, the green tag completed and inserted into the holder(s)) and at every access point of the scaffold. Some sites may require the report completed in the form of a site register.

Scaffolding contractors should include supporting documents (such as those listed below) with the handover certificate.

- ☑ TG20 compliance sheet(s).
- ☑ Bespoke design drawings and calculations.
- ☑ Anchor testing reports.

4.6.4 Incomplete scaffolding and danger areas

Where the erection of a scaffold has not been completed, physical measures must be taken to restrict access to the scaffold (for example, remove or board over the access ladder(s) and warn people of the fact that the scaffold is not safe to use).

Good example of a warning incorporated into a physical barrier

The method of warning is usually a 'Scaffold incomplete' sign at each point of access.

Warning and prohibition signs must conform to the requirements of the Health and Safety (Safety Signs and Signals) Regulations.

Any scaffold structure, or part of (for example, during alterations to a scaffold when part of the structure remains in use), and a workplace where scaffolding operations are being undertaken, where there exists a risk of a fall or a risk of a person being struck by a falling object, shall be defined as a danger area. Unauthorised access to danger areas should be restricted and communicated effectively to all concerned (for example, by guard-rails or other barriers and signs).

For further information refer to *Access and egress from scaffolds* (SG25).

4.7 Other considerations

4.7.1 Hoists with scaffolding

Special goods and personnel hoists are often used with scaffolding. Ideally mechanical hoists should be fixed to the permanent structure unless the scaffold has been specifically designed for the purpose. *(For further information refer to TG20.)*

NASC and the Construction Plant Association (CPA) have produced specific guidance for the use of hoists for transporting scaffolding materials during erection, alterations and dismantling. *(For further information refer to SG26.)*

Mechanical and non-mechanical winches are commonly used for both scaffolding operations and by the users of scaffolding (for example, gin wheels and ropes). *(For further guidance refer to NASC TG20 and SG9.)*

A selection of typical hoists and winches used with scaffolding

4.7.2 Protection of the public

Protection of the public and other persons against falling materials should be provided by the use of nets, brick guards, toe-boards, protective fans, and so on. The precautions to be adopted should be identified at the planning stage of the scaffold provision, including the risk assessment process.

www.

Guidance on protection of the public **(SG34) provides general advice for scaffolds erected in the public domain and TG20 includes compliant scaffolding features (such as pavement lifts up to 2.7 m and light-duty protection fans). Reference should also be made to the HSE guidance document *Protecting the public, your next move* (HSG151).**

TG20 light duty protection fan

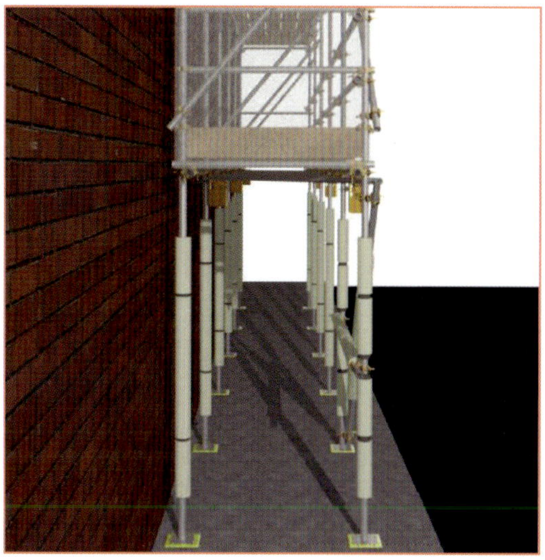

TG20 pavement lift

Local Authority permission will normally be required for scaffolds to be built on the pavement or footpaths. Scaffolds can cause particular problems to people with physical and visual disabilities, unless adequate steps are taken to reduce contact hazards with items such as tube ends and threads on fittings. This can usually be achieved by cladding the run of standards or binding the scaffold poles and fittings with suitable padding and/or brightly coloured bunting and tape (black and yellow are recommended for the partially sighted).

All joints should be wrapped to protect the public and other persons from sharp edges, and plastic protective cups should be placed in or over the ends of tubes.

It is not sufficient for employers to warn the public of the hazard just by placing safety signs on the scaffold, even if they meet the requirements of the Health and Safety (Safety Signs and Signals) Regulations. Employers must have acted to reduce the hazard as far as reasonably practicable.

To ensure the scaffold is not struck by vehicles, no part of it should be allowed to project into the roadway, unless appropriate measures are taken, such as traffic control or a road closure. The provision of lighting at night may also be necessary, as specified by the Local Authority.

Supplementary lights should be installed on the scaffold where it has been erected in a place to which the public has access (pedestrians or vehicles), unless the level of background lighting after dark is thought to be sufficient. Pavement gantries will require bespoke design and calculations.

4.7.3 Sheeting and netting

Sheeting, netting or hoarding should not be attached to scaffolding, unless the scaffold has been designed and calculated to resist the additional wind loading.

TG20 contains compliance sheets for scaffolds clad with brick guards, debris netting and solid sheeting.

Some proprietary scaffold sheeting includes sacrificial ties designed to break in tension at a certain load.

Planning for clad scaffolding needs to consider fire risk from sheeted scaffolding, particularly on occupied premises. Flame-resistant sheeting or netting should be specified and conform to the Loss Prevention Certification Board (LPCB) standard LPS1215 or equivalent.

4.7.4 Rubbish chutes

Rubbish chutes (also referred to as debris chutes) may be fixed to a TG20 compliant scaffold. However, the scaffold may need to be strengthened following advice from a scaffold designer. The chutes should be installed and inspected in accordance with the manufacturer's instructions.

Site managers should ensure that chutes are regularly checked for blockages as the increased load could affect the stability of the chute and the scaffolding.

www.

For further information refer to the *Erection, use and dismantling of temporary rubbish chutes on scaffolding* (TG3).

4.7.5 Temporary edge protection (scaffolding)

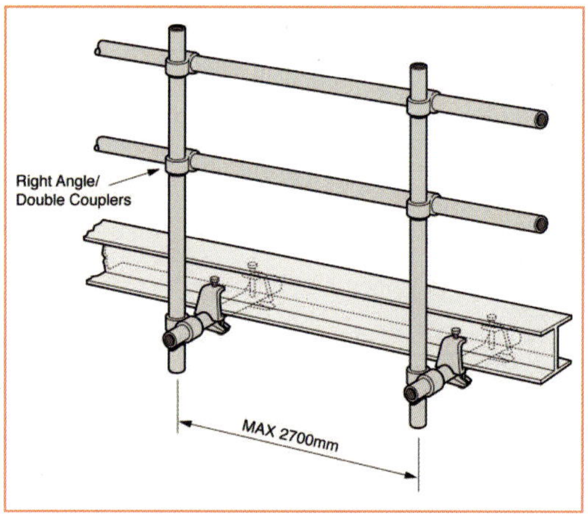

Example of temporary scaffolding edge protection

Temporary edge protection constructed from scaffolding should comply with *Temporary edge protection systems* (BS EN 13374).

www.

For further information refer to the HSE guidance *Health and safety in roof work* (HSG33) and NASC guidance *Temporary edge protection on open steelwork* (SG27).

4.7.6 Joints in ledgers and standards

For tube and fitting scaffolding joints in ledgers and standards should be staggered, as recommended in TG20.

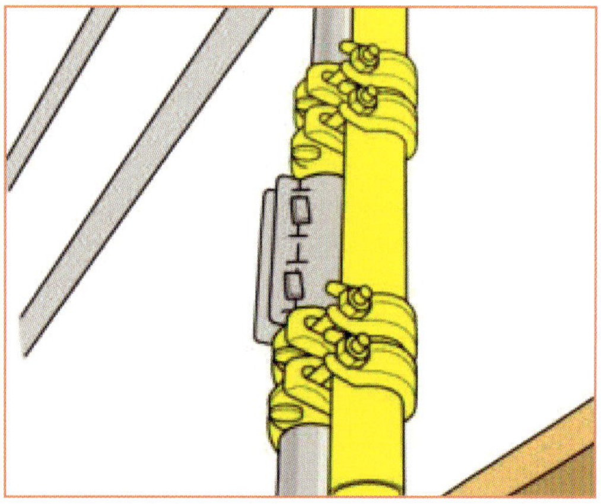

Example of a spliced joint

Adjacent standards should not have a joint in the same bay. If four joints fall in the same bay (for example, a table lift added) then one of the joints must be spliced with a short tube and load bearing parallel couplers (such as swivels or band and plate couplers).

Joints in ledgers in the same lift or adjacent lifts should be staggered. Where joints fall in the same lift one should be spliced *(as described above)*. Where joints in ledgers fall in adjacent lifts they may be permitted if the main guard-rail is continuous in that bay. Otherwise one joint should be spliced.

Guard-rails do not normally require joints to be staggered, unless specified in a TG20 compliance sheet or design, particularly in extreme wind conditions.

Appendix A – Putlog scaffold inspection guidance

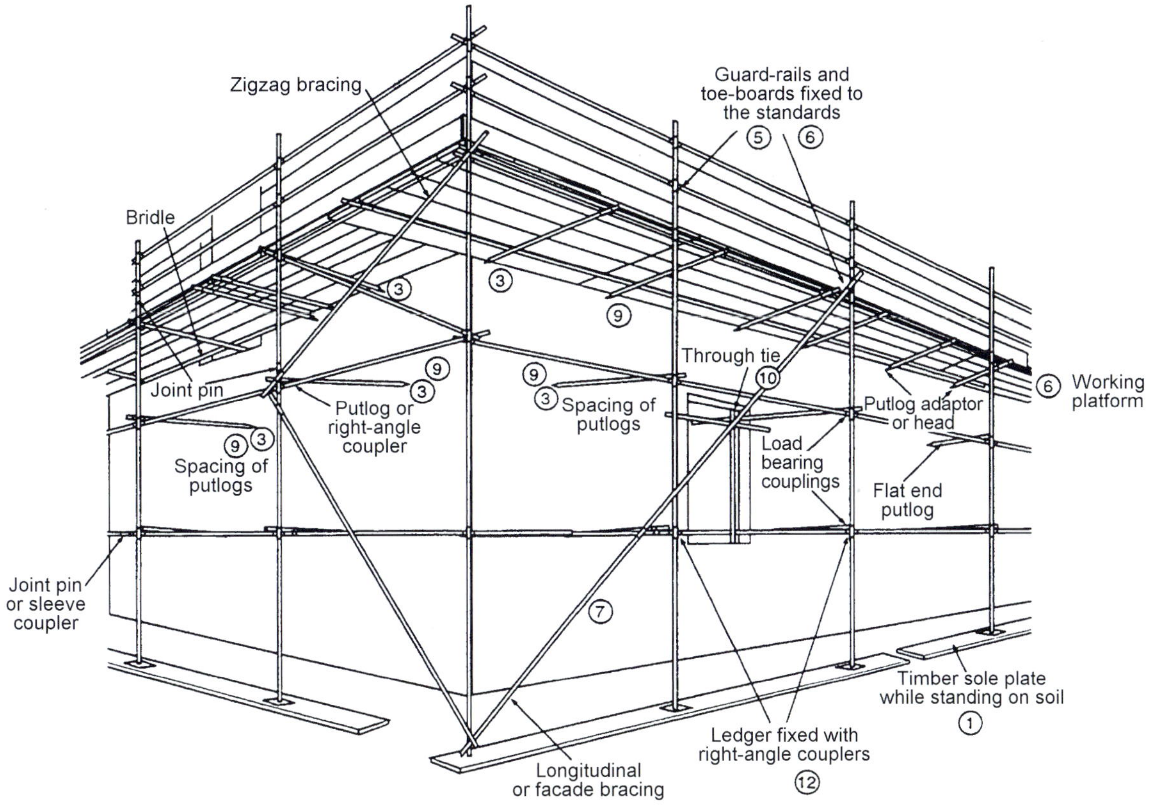

Components fitted during the erection of the scaffold to comply with the guidance given in NASC publication SG4 have been omitted for clarity.

Safety checklist	
Check from the ground	**Check from inside building or on the scaffold**
1. Base soundness; adequate spread of load; particularly as there is only one line of standards, avoidance of pavement lights, manhole covers, and so on; no nearby excavation	9. Spade end of putlog laid horizontally where possible, fully home (75 mm) in brickwork (bed joint)
2. Line of standards and ledgers. Standards vertical	10. Ties, particularly on lift below working platform or, in early stages, rakers on alternate standards. Special attention to 'through' ties on large flank ends without windows. Load-bearing couplers to be used
3. Spacing of putlogs	11. Platform loading (not overloaded)
4. Working platform. Check line and even support of boards; overhang; lapped boards and fillets	12. Security and correct use of all fittings (couplers), particularly on transoms and bracing
5. Guard-rails and toe-boards	13. Condition of tubes and fittings
6. Security of boards, toe-boards and guard-rails	14. Damage from falling material
7. Longitudinal bracing	15. Security of stacked materials
8. Means of access	

Appendix B – Independent tied scaffold inspection guidance

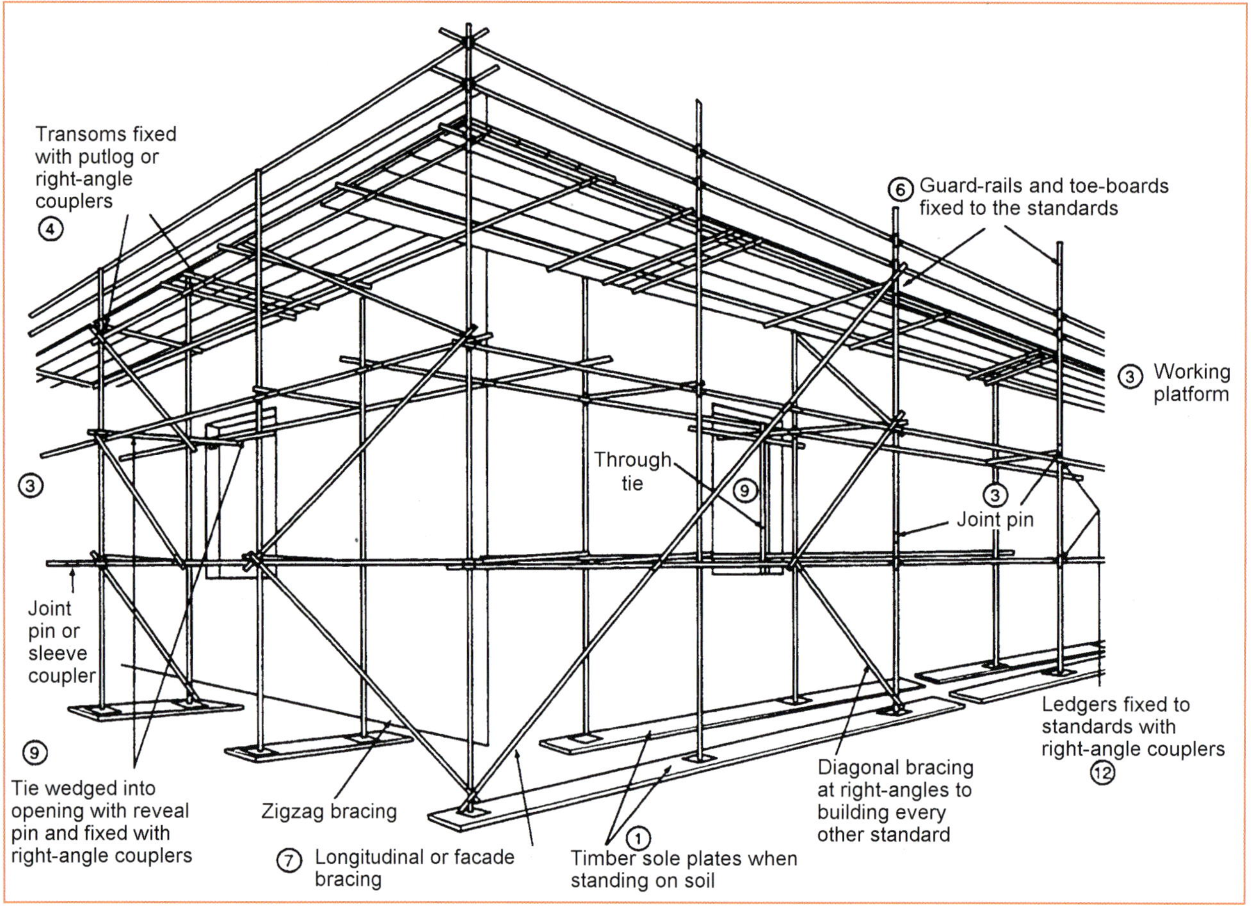

Components fitted during the erection of the scaffold to comply with the guidance given in NASC publication SG4 (latest version) have been omitted for clarity.

Safety checklist

Check from the ground	Check from the scaffold
1. Base soundness; adequate spread of load; avoidance of pavement lights, manhole covers, and so on; no nearby excavation	9. Ties, particularly on lift below working platform or, in early stages, rakers on alternate standards. Special attention to 'through' ties on large flank ends without windows. Load-bearing couplers to be used
2. Line of standards and ledgers; standards vertical	10. Special loadings by protective fans, wind sails, and so on; anchorage and spread of load
3. Staggering of joints (vertical and horizontal)	11. Security of boards, toe-boards and guard-rails
4. Spacing of transoms	12. Security and correct use of all fittings (couplers), particularly on transoms and bracing
5. Working platform. Check line and even support of boards; overhang; lapped boards and fillets	13. Condition of tubes and fittings
6. Security of guard-rails and toe-boards	14. Damage by loads swinging from cranes or by falling material
7. Longitudinal, ledger and plan bracing	15. Overloading
8. Means of access	16. Security of stacked materials

Appendix C – Birdcage scaffold inspection guidance

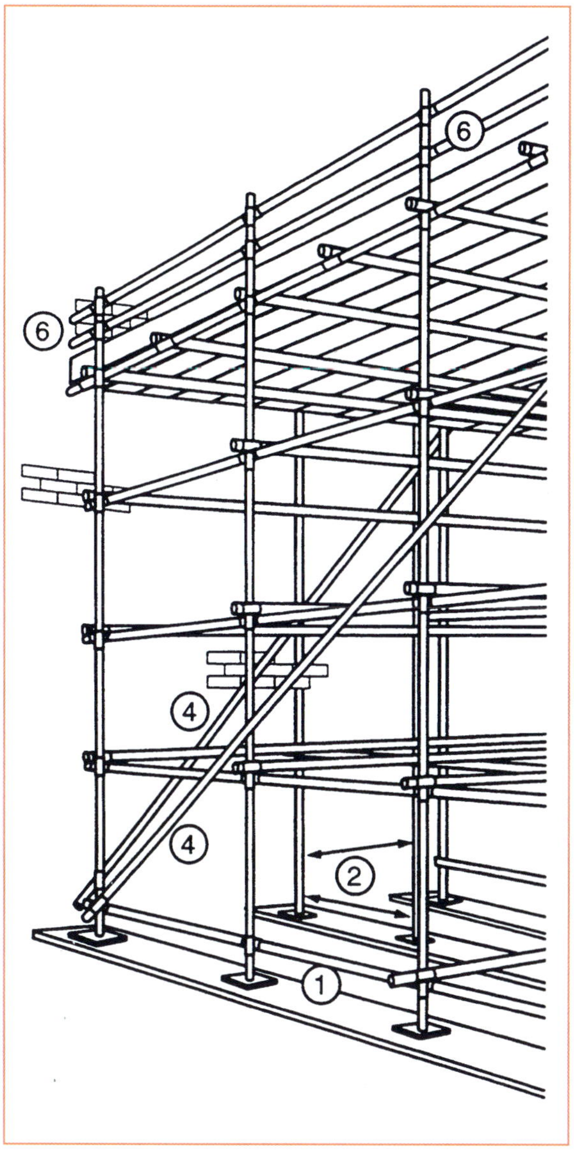

Components fitted during the erection of the scaffold to comply with the guidance given in NASC publication SG4 (latest version) have been omitted for clarity.

Safety checklist
1. Base
2. Line of standards and ledgers
3. Line and spacing of transoms
4. Diagonal bracing (in both directions)
5. Plan bracing
6. Security of boards, toe-boards and guard-rails. Maximum gap at wall
7. Security and correct use of couplers and fittings
8. Condition of tube and fittings
9. Even spread of load on platform
10. Means of access
11. Overloading
12. Security of stacked materials
With birdcage scaffolds, the floor of the building has to carry the full weight of the scaffold and its load. Sole plates are therefore necessary to help distribute the load as widely as possible – and they should always be set at right angles to the underlying floor beams or joists.

D 04

Appendix D – Unauthorised modifications to scaffolds

D
04

Introduction of safe structures

The consequences of any unauthorised alterations or modifications to scaffolds could result in a fatality or serious injury to contractors, the general public or yourself and may result in damage to adjacent property.

The practice of interfering or modifying of scaffolds by non-qualified scaffolding operatives is unacceptable under any circumstances and may lead to prosecution by the enforcing authorities. Scaffolds should only be modified by competent scaffolders who have been authorised to do so by the scaffold contractor. It is also unacceptable for the client and/or user to authorise alterations without prior consent from the scaffold contractor, as it may invalidate their insurance cover and could be an offence under Section 7 of the Health and Safety at Work Act 1974. Most contractors and principal contractors now enforce a zero tolerance policy in regards to unauthorised scaffold interference by their contractors, and work closely with the scaffolding contractor to ensure it is applied.

The most common types of scaffold interference are the removal of scaffold structural ties by other trades, the removal of handrails and toe-boards to allow materials to be loaded directly onto the working platforms and the undermining of the scaffold foundations by utility contractors.

Good planning and communication with all contractors will help prevent unauthorised scaffold modifications.

The guidance below will help the user in assuring that scaffold structures are, and remain, fit for purpose.

- ☑ All scaffolds shall be erected in accordance with statutory requirements and in accordance with the manufacturer's instructions when using system scaffolds. Wherever possible NASC-approved companies should be utilised.
- ☑ All tube and fitting and system scaffolding of any height shall be erected, modified and dismantled by a Construction Industry Scaffolders' Records Scheme (CISRS) qualified scaffolder or trainee under the supervision of a CISRS qualified scaffolder.
- ☑ All mobile tower scaffolds shall be erected by a competent person who is in the possession of a PASMA qualification or other recognised qualifications.
- ☑ All structures must be handed over by a competent person to the customer, in some cases a tag-type system is used at the ladder access points to clearly show the validity and suitability of the structure. It is a legal requirement within the Work at Height Regulations that every scaffold must be inspected:
  - before it is put into use
  - at seven-day intervals until it is dismantled
  - after bad or excessively wet weather or high winds or another event likely to have affected its strength or stability
  - after any substantial additions or other alterations
  - after unauthorised interference.
- ☑ A written report must be prepared by the competent person. A copy of the report should be kept on site and a further copy be retained for a period of three months from the completion of the work with the person on whose behalf the inspection was carried out. If a scaffold fails inspection this must be reported by the person carrying out the inspection, to the person responsible for the scaffolding, as soon as possible.

How to identify unauthorised modifications

The following information is not an exhaustive list but should assist you to recognise good practice before and whilst using scaffold structures.

Ground works around scaffold foundations

Removal of inside boards by other trades

Removal of guard-rails by other trades

(Photographs courtesy of Safety & Access Ltd.)

- ☑ Check that the foundations have not been disturbed or undermined and the standards are on base plates and sole boards (as necessary).
- ☑ Check that guard-rails are not missing and they are installed on every lift.
- ☑ Check that toe-boards have not been removed, or displaced.
- ☑ Check that any scaffold boards have not been removed, displaced or damaged (such as disc cutter marks).
- ☑ Check that transoms are suitably placed to support the boards and that the maximum support span identified on the board end plate has not been exceeded.
- ☑ Check that scaffold ties have not been removed.
- ☑ Check that any bracing is not missing.
- ☑ Check that any brickguards and/or netting, where fitted, are still in place.
- ☑ Check that the structure is not being overloaded.
- ☑ Check for any other signs of unauthorised interference. If found, report them to the scaffold contractor immediately.

Bricklayer tampering with the structure

Stop-end removed by other trades

Ladder removed by other trades

(Photographs courtesy of GKR Scaffolding Ltd.)

Action to be taken if concerned

If for any reason you identify that the structure has been interfered with, the first priority will be to ensure the safety of any contractors who may be working, or intending to work, on the structure. All users must vacate the structure by a safe means and access to the scaffold should be restricted until such time that it has been inspected and, if required, the components replaced by competent scaffolding operatives.

Case studies of when interference has taken place

Independent tied perimeter scaffold collapse

On Tuesday 11 April 2006, just after noon, an independent tied perimeter scaffold collapsed at a construction site in Milton Keynes. The collapse started on the west elevation, with a partial collapse of the north elevation. The scaffold collapse was contained within the site boundary. Three workers who were on the scaffold sustained multiple injuries. Sadly, one worker died three days later in hospital.

The Health and Safety Executive (HSE) issued a safety alert to the construction industry following this incident. The warning aimed to alert those working on similar projects to the importance of their arrangements to provide and maintain stable scaffolds. The HSE recommended that those arrangements are reviewed regularly.

HSE principal inspector Stephen Hartley said:

> **It is totally unacceptable for companies to disregard the safety of their workers. If the scaffolding had been designed, erected and managed properly, this incident would never have happened.**

Worker falls from unsafe scaffolding

A Tyneside construction company was fined after a worker suffered serious injuries following a fall from unsafe scaffolding. The company was prosecuted by the Health and Safety Executive (HSE) following the incident in the grounds of an old vicarage in County Durham on 1 May 2009.

The Magistrates' Court heard a worker was working on the windows of a new building when the scaffolding platform he was standing on became dislodged, causing him to fall more than four metres to the ground. The worker suffered several crushed vertebrae in his spine and a fractured left foot and was in hospital for two weeks following the incident.

The HSE investigation revealed that the company had failed to control alterations to the scaffolding, failed to conduct inspections of the scaffold at least every seven days, failed to identify and correct unsafe alterations and allowed workers to use unsafe scaffolding. The company pleaded guilty to breaching Section 2(1) of the Health and Safety at Work Act 1974.

After sentencing, the injured person said: 'I took it for granted the scaffolding I was working on was safe. If it had been checked properly the incident never would have happened and I wouldn't be left with the injuries I have to live with now.

I've had steel rods put in my spine, I'm in constant pain and it restricts my movement and makes walking really difficult. I'll probably never be able to do the job I did again.

I hope this prosecution helps make other employers realise the importance of ensuring scaffolding is safe so other workers don't have to suffer as I have'.

After the case, a HSE construction inspector said: 'This incident could and should have been prevented. The company failed in its legal duty to ensure the safety of its employees by failing to manage the scaffolding on site adequately.

As a result of these failures, the injured person has suffered serious injuries and is still living with the effects of those injuries more than a year and a half later.

Scaffolding is widely used as a temporary working platform or means of access and this incident clearly illustrates the absolute need to ensure that it is safe.

I'd like to stress to all companies and employees who use scaffolding that it should always be constructed to a recognised standard, any alterations should only be made by a competent person and it should be inspected by a competent person on handover and at least every seven days as work progresses'.

Note: *whilst every effort has been made to provide reliable and accurate information, we would welcome any corrections to information provided by the writer which may not be entirely accurate, therefore and for this reason, the NASC or indeed the writer, cannot accept responsibility for any misinformation posted.*

(The information within Appendix D has been reproduced with permission from NASC, publication SG36:12.)

05

Fall arrest and suspension equipment

Contents

Supporting information

G: Checklists and forms

GT 700 Toolbox talks

Overview

Where a risk assessment has identified that the risk of falls from height cannot be eliminated by the installation of working platforms with barriers, guard-rails or other similar measures, the use of fall-arrest equipment may then be the best option.

Safety nets or the use of other soft-landing systems are preferred to the use of safety harnesses and lines, as they provide a larger area and collective protection for persons working above them. They do not rely on individual workers wearing a safety harness and lanyard connected to a secure anchorage point.

5.1 Introduction

In situations where people and traffic pass below others working at height, in addition to exclusion zones (or danger areas), a safety net used in conjunction with a fine-mesh debris net will help to protect those below from falling objects and materials. It will also provide fall-arrest for the people working at height.

Where safety nets cannot be rigged for any reason, and it is not practical to use another form of soft-landing system, it may be necessary to resort to the use of a safety harness and lanyard.

In the first instance work/fall restraint should be considered (a technique used to prevent the worker from falling by positioning them so a fall cannot occur). If the worker is required to move around an area where they have the potential to fall then fall arrest should be used (a technique used to reduce the distance and consequences of a fall).

- ☑ It is imperative that operatives have been trained in the use and care of the equipment provided and that they wear it correctly.
- ☑ When operatives are utilising fall-arrest equipment, consideration must be given to the clear space beneath the work area required to allow the energy absorber within the lanyard to operate effectively. A 2 m lanyard anchored at foot level will require approximately 6.75 m of clear space beneath the anchorage point to prevent injury. This distance is made up of the 2 m lanyard, 1.75 m energy absorber maximum payout, approximately 2 m body height and a 1 m safety margin.
- ☑ A secure anchor point must be available.
- ☑ The person working at height must actually attach their personal fall protection equipment (PFPE) to a secure anchor point.

Whichever system is used for minimising injury from falling, whether it is safety nets, another soft-landing system or harness and lanyard, the system must be designed to provide a safe system of work, installed by competent persons and maintained, inspected, and adequately supervised to ensure it is used correctly.

For further information also refer to:

- ☑ **Chapter D01 Work at Height Regulations**
- ☑ **Chapter D03 Common access equipment**
- ☑ **Chapter D04 Scaffolding**
- ☑ **Chapter F05 Working over or near to water.**

In the first instance, where practicable, falls should be prevented by the use of collective control measures. These include the use of edge protection, parapets, scaffolding, temporary towers and mobile elevating work platforms (MEWPs) – all of which are preferable to the use of personal fall protection equipment.

5.2 Important points

- ☑ In situations where the prevention of falls from height cannot be guaranteed, it is essential that measures are put in place to ensure that any fall that does occur is arrested, without injury to the person who has suffered the fall.
- ☑ In many cases safety nets are the preferred method of arresting falls because:
  - they provide what is termed *collective fall protection*
  - if rigged immediately below the work area, they reduce the fall distance and recovery of the casualty should be executed as per the work at height rescue plan
  - they are a soft-landing system that should cause no injury to the person who has fallen.
- ☑ The condition of safety nets will deteriorate over time and so the requirement to carry out inspections to identify wear and tear will take on additional importance.
- ☑ Other forms of soft-landing systems (such as airbags or beanbags) also offer collective protection and may be appropriate in some circumstances. However, they will not limit fall distance and so closely rigged safety nets may be preferred.

- ☑ If fall protection is to be achieved using a safety harness and lanyard, the wearer must be trained in fitting and adjusting the harness and selecting the appropriate lanyard (such as fall restraint or fall arrest) and secure anchor point.
- ☑ Harness and lanyard offer personal fall-arrest protection only and therefore require a high degree of personal discipline to ensure they are used correctly.
- ☑ Some items used in a fall protection application (for example, retrieval devices) may need a regime of inspections and servicing in accordance with manufacturer's instructions and possibly thorough examinations under the Lifting Operations and Lifting Equipment Regulations (LOLER).
- ☑ It is imperative that any personal fall protection equipment is used only in the application for which it is intended. Inappropriate use can make some activities more hazardous and should be avoided at all costs.
- ☑ Personal suspension equipment (such as rope-access equipment and a boatswain's chair) must only be used by people who have been trained and are competent. BS 7985 gives practical advice and recommendations for good practice to those who use specialist rope access methods for work at height and those who commission rope access work. Rope access training can be achieved through the Industrial Rope Access Trade Association (IRATA).

www. **For further information refer to the HSE website.**

5.3 Safety nets

The use of nets has become widespread throughout the industry particularly on new build steel frame structures. They have revolutionised safety in roof work. Figures quoted by the trade association FASET (Fall arrest safety equipment training) suggest that upwards of 50 falls per year are arrested by nets, borne out of the fact that the fatal accident rate in industrial roofing has been massively reduced in recent years as the use of nets increases.

It is important to note that the use of nets does not eradicate risk entirely. It is vital that site managers appreciate that they have an important role in the safe provision of nets on their sites, and that this is best done by making sure that the net provider is following guidance in British Standards and that produced by the trade body for safety net installers (FASET).

Safety nets installed prior to roof works commencing

Nets are an area where complying with good practice means testing, inspection, record keeping and storage facilities are required to ensure that the net itself is fit for use. It is important that the end users appreciate that a safe net is not simply about whether the net erectors have a training record card. Systems should also be in place to ensure that the net itself has been checked and inspected.

There are a number of British Standards relating to safety nets. They should be manufactured to the requirements of BS EN 1263-1 and erected in accordance with BS EN 1263-2. This latter standard gives information on the installation and use of safety nets.

A further standard, BS 8411, contains construction-specific information and more importantly a list of duties for the parties usually involved in construction projects. This includes principal designers, designers, engineers, principal contractors, scaffold contractors and anyone having on-site responsibility for the integrity of safety net installations.

This standard specifies that anyone who is planning the installation of a safety net system should take the following points into account.

- ☑ Experience and competence of the net erectors.
- ☑ Sequence and type of work being carried out during installation and removal.
- ☑ Sequence of construction work to be carried out whilst the nets are in position.
- ☑ Provision of effective anchorages.
- ☑ Means of access for erecting and removal.
- ☑ Access for inspection, debris removal and temporary repair.
- ☑ Clearance distances below the net.
- ☑ Protection of anyone below.
- ☑ Recovery of anyone who has fallen into the net.

Modern safety nets are efficient at saving lives and preventing injury. They are an energy-absorbing system designed to minimise the consequences to the person who has fallen. Safety nets should be erected as close as possible to the working level to minimise the height of any fall that may occur. The area in which they are installed should be free from obstruction (such as plant or machinery) that may injure a casualty falling into the net.

There are two types of net manufacture.

- **Knotless**, which provide energy absorption by permanent plastic deformation (stretching) of the net material.
- **Knotted**, which is generally a heavier and older type of net, providing energy absorption by tightening at the knots and permanently deforming.

Safety nets are manufactured in square or diamond mesh, with two mesh sizes: 60 mm and 100 mm. The 100 mm is the normal mesh size used in the UK.

All safety nets should carry an identification label. This includes the date of manufacture, the net type, class and size, and reference to the BS EN 1263-1. It should also carry a unique serial number for record purposes and traceability.

Recent sector guidance has created a more rigorous regime for tagging nets. Any nets purchased after 1 January 2008 should have a tag showing their repair history and any net that is older than 12 months should have a tag showing that it has been tested within the last 12 months.

5.3.1 Fall heights

The positioning of a safety net system is critical to minimise the height of falls that may occur. Safety nets are designed for a maximum fall height of 6 m from the work position, which means that the maximum nominal fall height from the centre of gravity of a person is 7 m. It should be noted that for safety nets less than 35 m^2 in total area, or a side length less than 5 m, the maximum height an operative is allowed to work above a net is 2 m, as there is insufficient fabric area to absorb the energy of falls from a greater height. However, in accordance with the Working at Height Regulations any fall distance into a safety net must be as little as is reasonably practicable, as the greater the fall distance into a net the greater the likelihood of injury.

When nets are installed, the maximum amount of sag in the net should be no more than 10% of the bay width.

When a load or person falls into a correctly erected net, the net material will deform as it absorbs the energy from the fall. It is therefore critical to provide adequate clearance below the net, to allow the deformation to occur without the load or person striking the ground or another object within the netted area. Guidance on minimum clearance below nets is available from FASET and the manufacturer's data (for example, if a person were to fall 2 m into a net between 5 m and 9 m wide, the total deformation, including the erection sag, may be between 2.6 m and 3.5 m, depending on the width of net).

It is essential to check the manufacturer's specification to ensure that there is adequate clearance below the planned net position.

Where safety nets are rigged so that the fall distance is less than 6 m, the safety net must extend a minimum of 3 m beyond the leading edge where operatives are working. If the working area is inclined by more than 20° then there must always be 3 m minimum beyond the leading edge.

5.3.2 Competence

The way in which safety net systems are installed is critical. Not only must those installing the net system be trained and competent, so must the people who carry out the routine inspection of safety nets.

After rigging the nets must be inspected before use by a competent person and a handover certificate should be issued. The minimum competence to issue a handover certificate would be a safety net rigger who holds a blue, skilled worker Construction Skills Certification Scheme (CSCS) card, signifying that they have the appropriate experience and training. Consequently, anyone holding only an IRATA card plus a certificate of training would not be regarded as fully competent.

The CSCS safety net rigger card is the only evidence that an operative has undergone extensive training and assessment in the proficiency of fall-arrest safety equipment training and has achieved the required industry standard.

Always receive a handover certificate from the riggers for each section of netting as it is completed.

There are industry-agreed standards and qualifications for training in the rigging and inspection of safety nets. The training of inspectors is aimed at site management staff as well as professionals within the industry.

Information on netting training providers is available from FASET, the netting industry trade body.

5.3.3 FASET guidance

FASET's website contains the latest technical and safety information, guidance and bulletins for the selection, installation and use of safety nets. These are freely available on their website and should be consulted before selecting and installing nets (for example, understanding what the maximum numbers of workers above a safety net are, and how to attach safety nets to temporary edge protection).

Items included in the guidance are shown below.

1.	Why specify a FASET member?
2.	Safety net test records.
3.	The testing of safety nets for UV degradation.
4.	Safety net labels and record keeping.
5.	General arrangement for repairing both knotted and knotless safety nets.
6.	Repairs to a knotless safety net.
7.	Repairs to a knotted safety net.
8.	Tagging of safety net repairs.
9.	On-site safety net temporary repair.
10.	Maximum permissible gaps.
11.	Gathering and map; under-rolling.
12.	Joining safety nets together.
13.	Testing requirements for safety net attachment devices.
14.	Drilled fixings.
15.	Incorrect safety net support clamps – single Gravlock.
16.	Attaching safety nets to temporary edge protection.
17.	Number of workers above a safety net.
18.	Loading of safety nets.
19.	Safety netting – classification for temporary works.
20.	Ground conditions.
21.	Safety net handover and in-use inspections by a competent person.

FASET's *The selection of access methods to install and dismantle safety netting* can be freely downloaded from its website and site managers should familiarise themselves with it in order to manage and monitor the activities of the installation team.

5.3.3.1 FASET recommended hierarchy for work at height

There are four methods of access currently recommended for rigging and de-rigging safety nets, which should be considered in the following order.

1.	Rig/de-rig safety nets remotely (using remote attachment devices).
2.	Rig/de-rig using powered access (MEWPs).
3.	Rig/de-rig using ladders (recommended maximum height 4.5 m).
4.	Industrial climbing access techniques.

Rigging and de-rigging

FASET does not recommend the use of scaffold towers or hop ups for the rigging and de-rigging of safety nets under normal rigging conditions. There may be rare and isolated occasions for specific work where towers may be appropriate, having taken due regard of this document, and the hierarchy set out within it. Where such occasions arise, the rigging contractor must prepare a suitable specific risk assessment taking account of the rigging conditions and the additional control measures required. Towers must always be erected in accordance with the manufacturers'/suppliers' instructions by trained personnel.

5.3.4 Periodic testing

Safety nets are typically manufactured from polypropylene or nylon, which are materials that are adversely affected by ultra violet (UV) light. As such, safety nets must be tested to ascertain whether the safety net meets or exceeds the manufacturer's withdrawal from service level (minimum strength).

All safety nets that are in service must have been tested within the previous 12 months to ensure they meet or exceed this level. These tests typically include removal of a section of mesh and testing it to destruction, to ascertain its structural properties and to ensure the remainder of the net is in good condition.

Test results must be maintained electronically and should include detail relating to the date, serial number, test result and manufacturer. If this information is not available, the net cannot be considered safe for use.

Nets that have been tested and are safe for use must be tagged, to include the following details.

- ☑ Testing company's name.
- ☑ Date of the test.
- ☑ Confirmation that the test was passed.
- ☑ Date the next test is due.
- ☑ Any additional information.

For further information refer to FASET's *The testing of safety nets for UV degradation* (Bulletin no. 3).

5.3.5 Inspection

Safety nets are considered as being *work equipment* by the Work at Height Regulations and therefore, in addition to pre-use (handover) inspections, they should be inspected on a weekly basis by a competent person to ensure that they are still in a safe condition, fixed correctly and will provide the fall arrest capability if required.

Regular safety net inspections are vital

Inspections should be carried out more frequently if circumstances indicate that the integrity of the net system is in doubt.

A net should also be inspected after a person or substantial load has fallen into it, to determine whether it should remain in service or be replaced. In some cases, it may be necessary to seek specialist advice.

It is recommended that the findings of all inspections are recorded.

A safety net inspection sheet template is available from FASET upon request.

5.3.6 Care of nets

Care should be taken to reduce to a minimum unnecessary wear and mechanical damage likely to weaken the net. Materials must not be stacked on it, and deliberate jumping into it or dropping of objects onto it must be prohibited, as permanent deformation may occur.

The following sources of damage or wear should be avoided as far as possible.

- ☑ Dragging the net over rough surfaces.
- ☑ Contact between the net and sharp edges.
- ☑ An accumulation of debris in the net.
- ☑ Any sparks from hot work, welding, grinding, burning operations, hot gases from blowlamps, or hot ash from chimneys or furnaces.
- ☑ Chemical attack.
- ☑ Any form of radiation.

Special care should be exercised and precautions taken to prevent the net and any supporting framework from being struck by loads on moving vehicles or by the vehicles themselves.

The net manufacturer should be consulted when there is any doubt about the suitability of nets for use in hazardous conditions, after any known contamination or when deformation has occurred.

If overhead power lines are present in the vicinity of an area where safety nets are required, they should not be installed (nor should any access to height be permitted) until such time that the DNO has been contacted and it has been established that it is safe to do so.

5.3.7 Maintenance

Nets must always be thoroughly inspected after use and before being returned to storage to identify any damage and any required repairs.

If contaminated by acids or alkalis, nets should be thoroughly washed, preferably by hosing, and allowed to dry naturally away from heat.

If areas of damage are found, or chemical damage is suspected, contact the manufacturer to obtain a list of competent people able to repair or clean the nets.

5.3.8 Storage

- ☑ Nets should be stored away from heat, chemicals and out of direct light.
- ☑ Nets should be stored in dry conditions.
- ☑ Nets should be stored away from rodents to minimise damage.
- ☑ Wet nets should be dried naturally.
- ☑ Storage areas should be well ventilated.
- ☑ Nets should be turned periodically to allow air circulation.
- ☑ If stacked, nets should be packed up clear of the ground.
- ☑ Nets should be segregated into three distinguishable categories (for example, nets that are safe for use, nets that are awaiting repair and nets that are beyond economical repair).

5.3.9 Rescue from a net system

Where the net is erected as close as possible below the work area, many of the situations where persons enter a net will be minor, with a self-rescue being possible.

On other occasions, a person may fall a considerable height into a net. They may fall onto materials lying in the net, or strike their head or body on, for example, structural steelwork during the fall.

When such accidents occur, extreme care must be taken during the rescue of the person lying injured in the net. Due to the stretching nature of the net, it is possible that any rescuer entering it could inadvertently and unavoidably cause further injury to the victim.

It is therefore essential that companies using safety net systems have, as part of their risk assessment process, emergency procedures written for:

- ☑ treating first aid needs whilst the injured person is in the net
- ☑ emergency recovery from a rigged net system (an additional two people may enter the net in an emergency situation)
- ☑ gaining access to height to execute a prompt recovery of the casualty.

It must be recognised that procedures for the above must be robust and, where additional equipment is required (for example, MEWPs), this should be instantly available in the work area and suitable for the circumstances. Therefore, rescue must always be pre-planned and must consider the work activities and the changing site environment.

5.4 Other soft-landing systems

Soft-landing systems can provide an effective alternative to safety nets in some circumstances. They are essentially bags that are packed with polystyrene chippings or another energy-absorbing material, which serve to both cushion a fall and reduce the distance of that fall (by the depth of the bag).

The bags are linked together with plastic snap clips to completely fill the area over which protection is required. They can also be used on the first or subsequent floors while trusses are being installed or in the roof space when fixing bracings.

An alternative system that may be considered in appropriate circumstances is the use of air-filled bags. Similar to the above, bags of varying sizes may be clipped together to completely fill the area over which fall-arrest protection is required. Airbags require an air compressor running all the time that fall arrest is required, to maintain the pressure in the airbag system. These devices work on the principle of a controlled rate of constant inflation and leakage so that the airbags will absorb the energy of someone falling onto them without bouncing.

Whilst soft-landing systems do not prevent falls, they can be effective in eliminating injuries arising from low level falls. However, care should be taken when selecting the particular system for use as maximum fall heights vary from product to product.

5.5 Personal fall prevention equipment

- ☑ All PFPE must be manufactured to the relevant British and European Standards.
- ☑ PFPE must only be selected if safer options cannot be justified.
- ☑ The use of PFPE must be justified by a risk assessment. (Methods of rescue must be considered.)
- ☑ All training must be carried out in accordance with BS 8454.
- ☑ All operatives using PFPE must be trained in the use and inspection of PFPE. Training must also include specialist equipment required for rescue.
- ☑ All PFPE must be subject to a before use inspection by the operative, which must be included in the user training.
- ☑ Contractors must demonstrate records of formal thorough inspections at a suitable frequency recommended by HSE guidance INDG367.
- ☑ Inspections must be carried out by a competent person who has received specific inspection training.
- ☑ PFPE must be formally inspected by a competent person at the following minimum frequencies.
  - Every six months for normal use.
  - Every three months for arduous conditions, environments or occupations.
  - Interim inspections, as determined through risk assessment.
  - Installed systems (horizontal and vertical lines), as per the manufacturer's recommendations.
- ☑ PFPE must be identified by its unique serial number or other means.
- ☑ Any PFPE found to be defective or damaged must be removed from service immediately.

If fall prevention measures (for example, working platforms, barriers or guard-rails) or collective fall-arrest measures (such as safety nets or other soft-landing systems) are not practical, an alternative safe system of work must be employed. This safe system may require the use of safety harnesses and lanyards but, as with any item of PPE, it should be considered only as a last resort. Whereas safety nets and other soft-landing systems are collective measures (in other words, they automatically provide protection for more than one person), safety harness systems only protect the user.

PFPE can be broadly grouped into the following four categories.

- ☑ Fall-restraint systems.
- ☑ Work positioning systems.
- ☑ Rope access systems.
- ☑ Fall-arrest systems.

Fall-restraint system

Work positioning system

Rope access system
(Image supplied by PETZL)

Fall-arrest system

5.5.1 Selection of equipment

It is important to recognise that few safety harnesses serve multiple purposes and they are very often provided for use in a particular application. Examples include harnesses that arrest falls, harnesses that restrict movement of the individual to prevent access to the leading edge and harnesses that are used to facilitate the rescue of an individual from a dangerous situation (such as a confined space or vessel).

Care must be taken when planning to use a safety harness and lanyard, as anchor points and fall distances are critical considerations. Consequently, individuals planning work of this nature should have a high degree of training and competence and the work activity will need to be very closely supervised.

The type and nature of the safety harness to be used must be provided only after having given consideration to the individual that will be using it, the work activity to be carried out and other factors that may impact on the effectiveness of the equipment (for example, the ability of a lanyard to resist abrasions from a sharp or abrasive edge in a fall, known as a running edge.

In addition to different types of harness, there are also several types of lanyard, with each being intended for a particular purpose. Some of these are shown below.

5.5.1.1 Fall-arrest lanyards

Fall-arrest lanyards incorporate an energy-absorbing feature to reduce the shock loading on the body of the wearer.

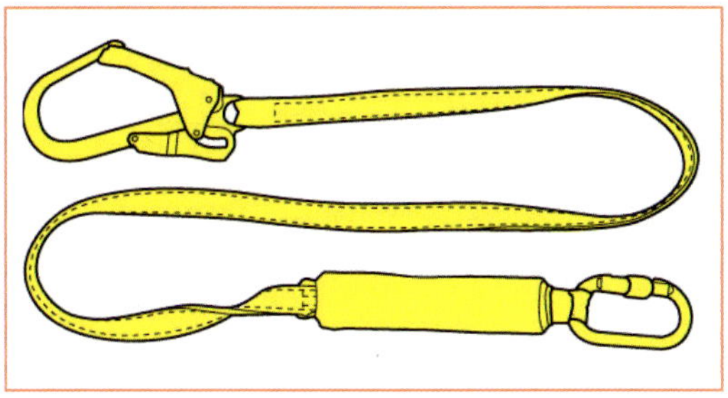

Fall-arrest lanyard

5.5.1.2 Twin tailed lanyards

Twin tailed lanyards are a type of fall-arrest lanyard. They allow greater mobility at height by enabling the repositioning of one tail at a time so that the user is constantly attached to an anchor point.

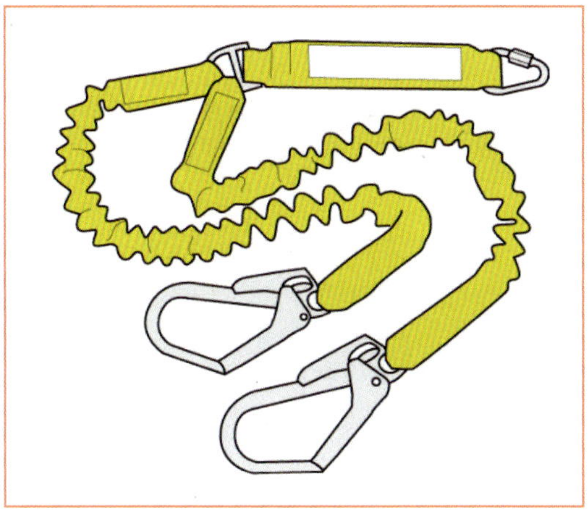

Twin tailed lanyard

Users of this type of lanyard should note that if used incorrectly they can pose additional risks to safety. If only one tail is clipped to a secure anchorage and the second tail is not located correctly, then during a fall the second tail could loop over a fixed object and arrest the fall before the energy-absorber has deployed, which may cause severe personal injury.

The second tail must never be clipped back on to the user's harness, unless it is fitted with purpose fitted (sacrificial) parking points that will break away from the harness if the second tail comes under tension. Alternatively, the second tail can be either left to hang free or be simultaneously clipped to the same secure anchorage.

5.5.1.3 Restraint lanyards

Restraint lanyards are used as a means of limiting the range of movement of the wearer in order to stop them falling from an exposed edge. For example, when allowing maintenance to be carried out on a gutter on the edge of a roof, the worker can reach the gutter but the lanyard is not long enough to allow the worker to physically lose contact with the structure, thus preventing a fall from the roof.

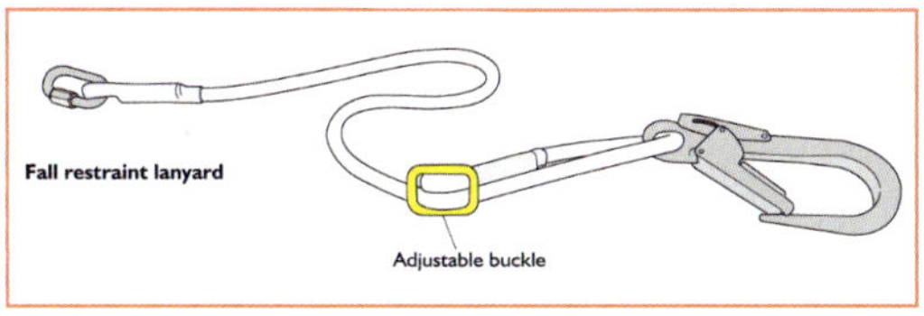

Restraint lanyard

These lanyards are not designed to arrest falls and have no energy-absorbing feature. Sometimes two of these may be worn at the same time, with each lanyard fixed to a clip on either side of the harness (EN 358) to make the harness what is termed a *work positioning harness*.

Irrespective of the type of lanyard used, they are only effective if the free end is securely anchored to a suitable anchorage point.

5.5.2 Training

Any training should cover the selection, fitting, adjustment, maintenance and use of PFPE and explain the choice and use of suitable anchorage points. Employees should not be permitted to use the equipment before adequate instruction has been given and they have been judged to be competent in its use.

5.5.3 Selecting the anchor point

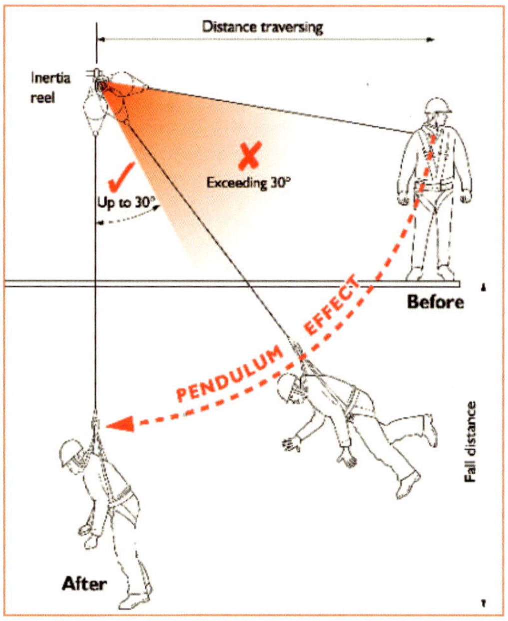

Pendulum effect

When working in fall arrest, in order to limit the drop, the anchorage points should always be as high as possible above the person and as near to vertical as possible in order to avoid the pendulum effect (the casualty swinging from the point of work to the point of attachment).

Anchor points must be capable of withstanding the anticipated shock loading *(refer to BS 7883 and other industry guidance)*.

Consideration should also be given to how persons would be rescued following an arrested fall, particularly when work is from high structures.

Some harness manufacturers also produce rescue systems that enable a single rescuer to raise a suspended person back to the working platform or safely lower them to ground level.

5.5.4 Arrester devices

These devices operate with a similar mechanism to the seat belts used in cars and snap to the clocked position as a result of sudden movement.

Most inertia reel-type arresters are only designed to safely arrest someone who is working in and has fallen from a position that is almost directly vertical to the anchor point. As with lanyards, these devices will not counter the pendulum effect or swing fall.

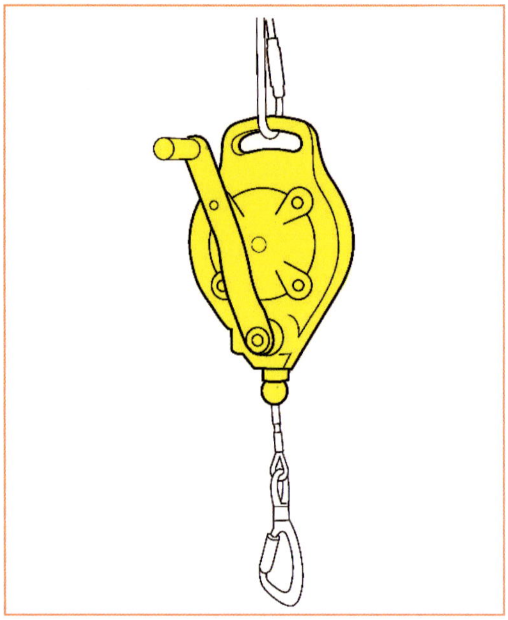

Typical arrester device

Most equipment of this nature is not tested for over the edge type falls in which the retractable lanyard is pulled tight across the edge of a surface (for example, a roof sheet or floor slab) by the weight of the fallen person. In these circumstances, the abrasive action of webbing being pulled taut over an adjacent surface can have catastrophic effects in terms of the device's ability to successfully protect against falls.

If the proposed work method involves the equipment trailing over a running edge, it is unlikely to be a suitable method of work and advice must be taken from the manufacturer to ensure that the equipment is suitable for use in this application.

Other types of fall arrester are available, such as a traveller on a pre-tensioned vertical cable. There are also proprietary systems where the lanyard is attached to a traveller that moves along a pre-positioned and tensioned horizontal or vertical steel cable. These systems can improve movement around corners and past obstacles without the need to unclip.

Advice should be sought on the best type to be used for the job to be done. Refer to the manufacturer for information for inspection and maintenance of fall-arrest devices. Where the client provides this equipment, as is common in many cases, care still needs to be taken that it has been inspected and checked as required and that the users understand how it works.

5.5.5 Shock absorbers

If a person wearing a harness and lanyard falls, there is a considerable shock loading to the body impact force and, the greater the fall distance, the greater the force that is applied.

The maximum distance a person can fall will depend on the height of their anchor point and length of lanyard. A higher anchor point essentially means the fall distance is reduced. In a worst-case scenario, with a 2 m lanyard (the maximum permitted length under EN 354) anchored at foot level, the area of clear space beneath the person required is 6.75 m, made up from the following.

- ☑ 2 m lanyard length.
- ☑ 1.75 m energy absorber extension.
- ☑ 2 m body height.
- ☑ 1 m safety.

Shock absorbers in the form of tearaway stitching, stretch springs or a deforming metal strip are built into fall-arrest lanyards as a means of reducing the shock loading.

Once a lanyard has been used to arrest a fall and the energy-absorber has been deployed, it must be discarded.

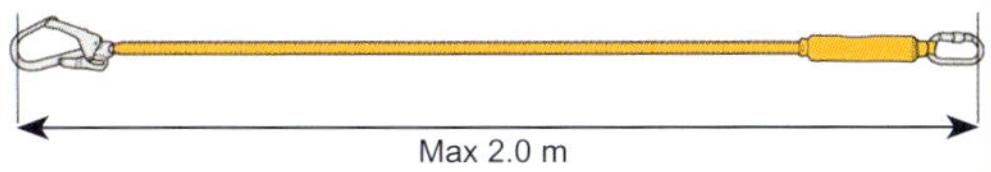

A shock absorbing lanyard

5.5.6 Markings on fall protection equipment

Fall protection equipment must be clearly and indelibly marked or permanently labelled with the following.

- British or European Standard to which it conforms. (This is in addition to the standard CE marking.)
- Name, trademark or other means of identification of the manufacturer.
- Year in which the fall protection equipment was manufactured (a maximum working life of 5-10 years, depending on the manufacturer).
- Type of fall protection equipment.
- Manufacturer's serial number.
- Company serial number, or other recognition system, for recording maintenance and inspections.

The Work at Height Safety Association (WAHSA) has produced leaflets and information on use and positioning of fall-arrest equipment for those working at height.

Main performance standards

- *Code of Practice for selection, use and maintenance of personal fall protection systems and equipment for use in the workplace* (BS 8437).
- *Code of Practice for delivery of training and education for work at height and rescue* (BS 8454).
- *Code of Practice for the design, selection, installation, use and maintenance of anchor devices conforming to BS EN 795* (BS 7883).
- *Code of Practice for the use of rope access methods for industrial purposes* (BS 7985).
- *Inspecting fall-arrest equipment made from webbing or rope* (HSE guidance INDG367).
- WAHSA Technical guidance notes.
- IRATA International Code of Practice.
- *Preventing falls in scaffolding* (SC4).

For further information refer to the HSE website.

5.5.7 Storage

While not being worn, equipment should be stored in a cool, dry place and not be subjected to direct sunlight. The use of purpose-designed cabinets, which allow ventilation, is recommended. If fall protection equipment becomes wet it should be dried thoroughly by natural means.

The equipment should not be subjected to unnecessary strain or pressure and must be kept free from contact with sharp implements, corrosives and other possible causes of damage. Manufacturer's guidance is the best resource for checking usage, storage and maintenance requirements.

5.5.8 Inspection

Reduction of a lanyard's strength

Research carried out for the HSE involving synthetic fibre webbing lanyards confirmed potential causes of degradation.

A 1 mm cut in the edge of a lanyard was shown to result in up to a 40% loss of strength, depending on the make of lanyard being used for the test. Most users do not appreciate the possible loss of strength as they assume that there is a proportional strength-to-width relationship; so in their eyes a 1 mm nick on a 25 mm flat sling is not really significant.

A further study investigated the resistance of the webbing material (used to make harnesses and lanyards) to abrasion by various types of surface, including concrete and angle iron. The findings of this study revealed that severe abrasion of the material, and a significant reduction in its strength, occurred after a small number of cycles of abrading the material across concrete. Abrasion across angle iron also degraded the material but at a significantly slower rate.

The wearer must make a visual inspection of safety equipment before use. The equipment should be examined by a competent person at least once every six months and the results recorded. Many contractors have a weekly inspection regime because of the rigorous conditions of use.

Harnesses and lanyards should be examined by a competent person after a fall or other circumstances in which the equipment has been deployed, before it is reissued for use. Any equipment found to be damaged should be removed from service immediately.

Safety belts, harnesses and lanyards should be taken out of use if found to be damaged or defective.

Under most circumstances, knots in lanyards would be considered a significant problem. Typically, a knot is presumed to reduce the strength of a lanyard by 50%.

Particular attention during inspection should be directed to the points below.

- **Webbing and leather.** Examine for cuts, cracks, tears or abrasions, stretching and distortion, damage due to deterioration, contact with heat, acids or other corrosives and rot.
- **Snap hooks.** Examine for damaged or distorted hooks, faulty springs, strained jaws, hairline cracks and corrosion.
- **Buckles.** Carefully examine the shoulders of buckles; inspect for open or distorted rollers, undue wear, hairline cracks and corrosion.
- **Stitching.** Examine for broken, cut or worn threads, open seams and failed or loose stitching.
- **Lanyards and ropes.** Examine for damage or signs of wear, cuts, abrasions, flat spots, knots, permanent kinks and, for kernmatle ropes (the variety often used in climbing and abseiling activities), check for visible signs of the inner core.
- **Unauthorised modifications.** Examine equipment for homemade attachments, repairs or adaptations. Impress on the wearers that their lives could depend on the continued efficiency and durability of their safety equipment and that, by frequent personal inspections, the possibility of equipment failure will be reduced to a minimum.

For webbing lanyards, specific attention should be given to the following.

- Cuts of 1 mm or more to the edge of the lanyard (for example, as a result of being choke-hitched around steelwork).
- Surface abrasions to surface or edges and damaged stitching.
- Knots in the lanyard.
- Results of chemical attack.
- Damaged or deformed fittings.
- Partially deployed energy-absorbers.

For full details refer to the HSE publication INDG367 and the safety nets checklist in Section G: *Checklists and forms.*

5.5.9 Records

An inspection and maintenance record should be kept for each harness and lanyard. This should be used to document the life cycle of the equipment. It is imperative that each piece of equipment should be marked with an individual serial number for identification purposes. If the unique serial number is no longer visible, the item should be withdrawn from service and replaced.

5.5.10 Dead weight anchor devices (mobile man anchors)

The use of dead weight anchors in accordance with European and British Standards BS EN 795 and BS 7883 (Class E) has become an acceptable means of providing a safe fall protection system on flat roof surfaces, particularly where it is not possible to penetrate the roof surface, and they can sometimes be used in both fall restraint and fall-arrest applications, but are more commonly associated with fall restraint.

It should be noted that a recent change to BS EN 795 now requires these devices to be tested for capability to arrest falls due to the foreseeability of misuse, even for use in a restraint application. (Note that BS EN 795 applies only to single-user systems. Where multiple-user systems are required, CEN TS 16415 will apply.)

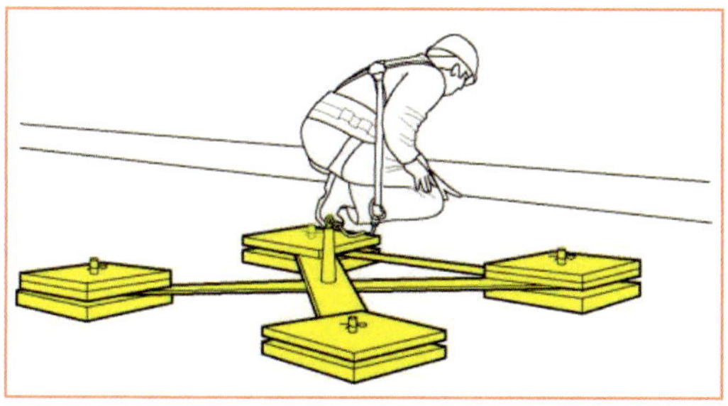

Typical man anchor system

As with all other systems, deadweight anchors do have their limitations, as detailed below.

- ☑ Location distances from the edge of the surface they offer protection against.
- ☑ Their safe use is impacted by the presence of water.
- ☑ They can be cumbersome to install.
- ☑ They are less suitable for heavier people (due to loading limitations).
- ☑ They are often unsuitable for use on surfaces with a slope in excess of five degrees.

As with other items of fall protection equipment, deadweight anchor devices should be used only after thorough consideration of the task and reference to manufacturer's guidance has been made.

D
05

5.5.11 Suspension risk (syncope or fainting)

The term *suspension trauma* is one that has developed as parlance amongst many who work in the fall protection and construction industries, but which HSE research (RR708) suggests is inappropriate because orthostasis, motionless vertical suspension is responsible, as opposed to physical injury as had become widely believed. For this reason, the terms *suspension syncope* or *fainting* are preferred.

Previous guidance has recommended that rescued casualties should be placed into a sitting position, as opposed to the more common recovery position suggested by most medical guidance. However, the HSE's research document states: 'there is no evidence to support assertions that post rescue this position is physiologically superior or even equivalent to the horizontal position' and consequently the traditional lying down recovery position is recommended.

In all situations, when a worker has fallen and their fall has been arrested by fall protection equipment, the individual should be retrieved as quickly as possible to prevent the onset of fainting. In many cases, the casualty may be able to assist either fully (self-rescue) or partially. When rescued, the casualty should be referred to a medical practitioner for professional medical assessment, even if it seems there have been no harmful effects caused by the fall.

Casualties who are conscious and uninjured and are suspended by fall protection equipment are able to slow the onset of suspension syncope by moving their legs, by positioning their body in a horizontal or slight leg-high position or, in the presence of the appropriate equipment, using a proprietary suspension loop that will enable the casualty to stand up whilst suspended.

Research suggests that if rescue is effected within 10 minutes, most people will not experience symptoms of pre-syncope (dizziness) or syncope (fainting).

5.5.12 Harness fall recovery with specialist equipment

Many of the companies who manufacture and supply fall protection equipment also produce kits that are specifically designed to facilitate the rescue of those suspended at height.

Depending upon the design of the equipment, sometimes a single person is able to attach the rescue system to the D-ring of the fallen person's harness and either lower them to ground level or raise them back up on to the working platform in a controlled manner.

This type of rescue equipment is classified as lifting equipment under LOLER and therefore carries all of the training, inspection and maintenance obligations that this brings.

5.6 Rope access (abseiling)

Rope access is often seen as a cost effective access solution for certain work at height activities. However, due to the risk involved and high levels of skills and control required, it should only be selected after all other forms of collective protection have been considered. It is generally suitable for inspection, cleaning and maintenance work, but is only used for construction activities in exceptional circumstances. An example might be the rigging of safety nets where it is not reasonably practicable to do it by using other means of access (such as a MEWP or another form of working platform).

General requirements for rope access are listed below.

- ☑ All personnel involved in rope access operations must be trained and assessed in accordance with the IRATA training scheme.
- ☑ Each working party (crew) must have at least one Level 3 technician who is responsible for the direct planning and supervision of the work.
- ☑ The team leader shall prepare an access permit before beginning rope access work. The access permit should include all salient aspects of the work to be undertaken, including detail of other workers involved, equipment to be used, associated hazards, PPE requirements, rescue arrangements and safety arrangements (safety line and back-up line), and so on.

- All work must be carried out in accordance with the following.
  - The *Code of Practice for the use of rope access methods for industrial purposes* (BS 7985).
  - *Personal equipment for protection against falls. Rope access systems. Fundamental principles for a system of work* (ISO 22846 Part 1).
  - The *Code of Practice. Personal equipment for protection against falls. Rope access systems* (ISO 22846 Part 2).

The trade association that governs the rope access industry is the Industrial Rope Access Trade Association (IRATA).

A second group of specialists (steeplejacks) commonly use rope access. Steeplejacking is work at height and therefore the requirements of the Work at Height Regulations apply, as they would to any other activity.

The trade associations for the steeplejack industry are the Association of Technical Lightning and Access Specialists (ATLAS) and the Steeplejack and Lightning Protection Training Group.

5.7 Boatswain's chairs

Boatswain's (or bosun's) chairs should only be used where the work is of a relatively short duration and where no other means of access or working (such as a suspended scaffold) is practicable.

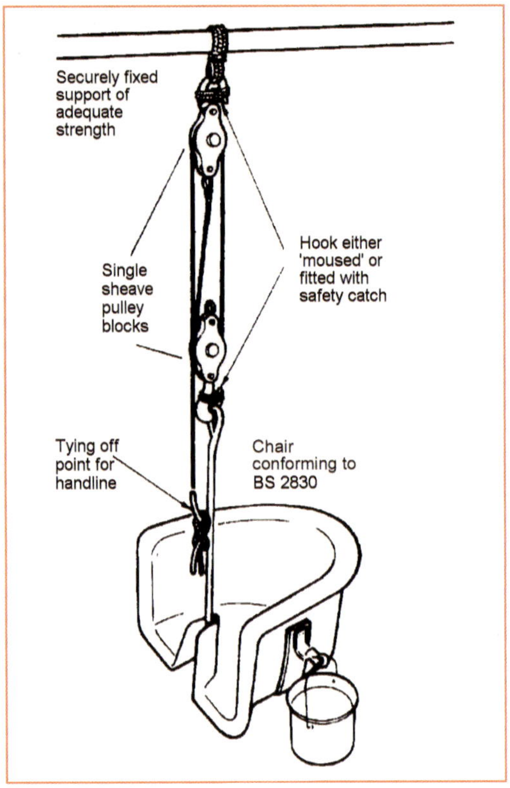

Boatswain's chair

A person in a boatswain's chair is extremely vulnerable. They are suspended high above the ground and, if anything goes wrong, the chances are that they are beyond rapid or immediate help. The risk assessment should cover rescue procedures should an emergency occur.

The installation and use of a boatswain's chair must be supervised by an experienced and competent person. Only properly trained and competent operatives should be permitted to use them. The regulations must be strictly observed.

The traditional non-British Standard boatswain's chair is still used by specialist trades (such as steeplejacks and lightning conductor engineers). Operatives need to be fully trained and competent before being permitted to use and work from it.

Where possible, consideration should be given to the provision of a second safety line connected to a harness being worn by the operative. In this way, should there be a problem with the boatswain's chair, this safe system of working will prevent a fall. It may not always be possible and if this is the case, then the reason for this should be recorded as part of the work at height risk assessment.

(An independently anchored safety line and safety harness are not shown in the diagram.)

5.7.1 Rigging

In the construction industry, a boatswain's chair should always be rigged with a pair of single sheave pulley blocks, having a safe working load of at least 225 kg. Outriggers and other supports must be strong enough, and be securely fastened down. Where weights are used, a safety factor of four is required.

A boatswain's chair is classified as a roped access system under the Work at Height Regulations. Therefore, the system should be rigged with a separately anchored safety line complete with an automatic locking device attached to the user of the seat that prevents or limits a fall should the primary suspension system fail.

5.7.2 Chair

A boatswain's chair should meet the following requirements.

- ☑ Comply with BS 2830 (a certificate of compliance should be available from the manufacturer).
- ☑ Be of a recommended size:
  - between 450 mm and 610 mm wide
  - not less than 225 mm deep
  - have a back not less than 250 mm high.
- ☑ If the chair has a single central leg or suspension member, this should be without sharp bends and be securely fixed to the seat as far back as practicable, so that the user sits with one leg at either side.
- ☑ Be provided with a safety harness to prevent the occupant falling out.
- ☑ The back and the suspension member should be placed so that no-one can fall out.
- ☑ The suspension point must be at least 500 mm above the seat, with provisions for suspension (no part should be able to become detached).
- ☑ Be made for a safe working load of 115 kg (a proof test of 150 kg is recommended).

5.7.3 Protection of the public

When the risk assessment identifies that work from a boatswain's chair will take place above areas where people may be present, adequate protection must be installed to prevent them being injured from falling equipment or materials. This is reinforced by the requirement for the creation and management of danger areas under the Work at Height Regulations.

5.7.4 Lifting equipment

All ropes and chains used should be thoroughly examined before their first use for any sign of chafing or wear, and then every six months. They must be securely attached to the chair and to the anchor. Swivel connections should be used to prevent spinning.

Fall ropes should not be less than 18 mm in diameter. They should be tied off correctly in the working position. The rope must not be removed from the cleat while the chair is in use. A controlled descent is achieved by removing the locking-hitch from the rope in the tied-off position and easing it around the cleat.

All lifting equipment and ancillary equipment must conform to LOLER.

5.7.5 Hooks

Hooks should be moused, C-shaped or fitted with a spring-loaded device to prevent the displacement of the load.

D 05

5.8 Cradles

Permanently installed cradle system for future building maintenance used during construction operations

- ☑ All proprietary cradle systems must conform to *Safety requirements on suspended access equipment. Design calculations, stability criteria, construction. Tests.* (BS EN 1808)
- ☑ Temporary suspended cradles and scaffolds must conform to the *Code of Practice for temporarily installed suspended scaffolds and access equipment* (BS 5974).
- ☑ The design, inspection, testing and use of suspended cradles must be in accordance with the Specialist Access Engineering and Maintenance Association (SAEMA) guidance.
- ☑ Installers of proprietary cradle systems must be trained in accordance with the manufacturer's instructions.
- ☑ Users of suspended cradles must use PFPE and be attached to a designated anchor point within the cradle or line system.
- ☑ The use of permanently installed cradle systems for access during construction, designed for future maintenance use, may be a practical option. However, consideration should be given to the nature of use and advice should be sought from the manufacturer.

www.

For further information refer to the Specialist Access Equipment and Maintenance Association (SAEMA) website.

Appendix A – Inspection of webbing harnesses and lanyards

The Health and Safety Executive and other key industry stakeholders (including the British Safety Industry Federation, the Height Safety Group and the Working at Height Safety Association) recommend that a three-tier inspection regime (pre-use, detailed inspections and interim inspections) is implemented where webbing harnesses and lanyards are in use. The regime should be drawn up by a competent person and include the following information.

- ☑ The equipment to be inspected (including unique identification references).
- ☑ The frequency and type of inspection (pre-use checks, detailed inspection and, where appropriate, interim inspection).
- ☑ Designated competent persons to carry out the inspections.
- ☑ Action to be taken on finding defective equipment.
- ☑ Means of recording the inspections.
- ☑ Training of users.
- ☑ Means of monitoring the inspection regime to verify inspections are carried out accordingly.

All persons who carry out any inspection must have the independence and impartiality to make objective decisions, and sufficient authority to discard defective equipment.

In the unlikely event of a fall, a webbing harness and lanyard that are worn or damaged may not take the impact and stress of a person arresting, and fail. A harness, lanyard and secure anchor point are the last resort to a person falling – their sole purpose is to save lives.

The importance of pre-use checks and regular inspections cannot be overemphasised.

Inspection regime

Harnesses and lanyards should be subjected to the following checks and inspections.

Pre-use checks

These are visual and tactile inspections, carried out by slowly passing the lanyard through the hands to detect small cuts in the edges, softening or hardening of the fibres and traces of contaminants. The inspection should only take a few minutes and should be carried out by the user prior to each period of use. These inspections do not need to be recorded.

Detailed inspections

These are more formal and in-depth inspections carried out at least every six months and three months for frequently used lanyards, particularly where these are used in demanding conditions (such as demolition scaffolding and steel erection). They are normally carried out by a designated individual who is also responsible for recording the results and implementing the required action.

Interim inspections

These are in-depth, formal inspections, carried out when it is suspected that a lanyard has deteriorated and an inspection is needed before the next scheduled detailed inspection. Results of these inspections must also be recorded.

Examples of damaged equipment - the user should check for signs of tears, damage and wear

For a safety belts, harnesses and lanyards checklist refer to Section G: *Checklists and forms*.

Appendix B – Fall arrest safety equipment training (FASET) top ten dos and don'ts for safety net use

FASET top ten dos and don'ts for safety net use
Dos
☑ Ensure you use competent safety net rigging companies with relevant experience (such as FASET member companies).
☑ Ensure you use competent safety net riggers (those with a safety net rigger CSCS card).
☑ Ensure that methods of access for work at height have been properly assessed, and the safest method that is reasonably practicable has been chosen.
☑ Carry out a formal inspection if nets are in place for more than seven days, or subjected to extreme weather conditions. A visual user inspection should be carried out prior to working above the safety nets.
☑ Ensure that all materials are secure before lifting/craning above a safety net.
☑ Ensure that a handover certificate is completed prior to allowing works above a safety net.
☑ Ensure that nets are struck prior to any hot works being carried out above.
☑ Report any damage to a safety net.
☑ Ensure all falls into a safety net are reported to site management and call FASET. Ensure the supervision of the loaded nets removal from service.
☑ Ensure that the safety nets used conform to BS EN 1263 1:2002 and are rigged in accordance with BS EN 1263 2:2002.
Don'ts
☒ Allow the use of nets unless there is evidence of an appropriate inspection and maintenance regime and UV testing within the last 12 months.
☒ Allow the use of nets unless a competent person has verified there is sufficient clearance distance (rule of thumb: no less than three metres).
☒ Allow work above nets without evidence that any repairs have been carried out by a competent person authorised by the manufacturer.
☒ Allow work above nets which don't have serial numbers or labels.
☒ Allow workers to use the nets as a means of access or working platform.
☒ Attach nets to any structure without first confirming it has the capacity to deal with a minimum 6 kN loading at a 45° angle.
☒ Allow gaps >100 mm unless exceptional circumstances dictate otherwise (in these cases not >225 mm).
☒ Tamper with or adjust any nets and attachment points.
☒ Allow work above net systems that have been damaged or loaded.
☒ Allow work above the net if it is positioned >2 m from the working level.

D
05

06
Frame erection

Contents

Supporting information

G: Checklists and forms

Overview

The erection of structures can be both difficult and dangerous. The principal hazard and cause of injury is falls from height, while either working from, or gaining access to, working positions. Other hazards include structural instability during erection, lifting operations and moving plant.

Reading this chapter will not give you the competence to erect structures. It will, however, inform you of the common hazards and how, through practical measures, the risks arising from those hazards can be effectively controlled, enabling the work to be carried out safely.

6.1 Introduction

The building and construction industry as a whole has an unacceptably high accident rate, and workers involved in handling and erecting steelwork are in the group that suffers one of the highest fatality and serious injury rates within the industry.

The majority of fatal accidents are as a result of falls from height. In addition, many serious accidents occur due to workers being struck by falling materials.

According to the British Constructional Steelwork Association (BCSA), the increased use of mobile elevating work platforms (MEWPs) in recent years has reduced the need to put operatives onto the steelwork, which has resulted in a significant reduction of fall-arrest accidents reported to the Health and Safety Executive (HSE).

www. **For further information on BCSA refer to their website.**

6.2 Important points

- ☑ The majority of jobs that involve erecting steelwork will also involve working at height, and exposure to the associated potential hazards.
- ☑ A schedule of erection should be in place to ensure the safe erection and stability of the structure until it is complete.
- ☑ All steel erection must be the subject of a risk assessment and carried out in accordance with a method statement.
- ☑ Ideally, the erection of steelwork will be carried out in such a way that those doing the job are on a stable working platform at all times, be that a scaffold or a mobile elevating work platform (MEWP). Operatives having to go onto the steelwork should be a last resort.
- ☑ Designers should consider fitting steelwork with proprietary edge protection before it is lifted into place at height as a collective fall prevention measure.
- ☑ Ground conditions must be suitable to take the weight of MEWPs, cranes and their loads.
- ☑ Designers have the potential to ensure that the erection of steelwork can be carried out safely (for example, designing-in lifting eye attachment points, or specifying ground-level fabrication).
- ☑ The erection of steelwork will usually involve extended crane operations, the use of MEWPs in and around the new structure, lorry movements, steel laydown areas and possibly a lorry-park, all of which must be planned for when the site is first set up.
- ☑ All lifting operations, including the use of cranes and MEWPs, must be carried out by, and under the control of, competent persons.
- ☑ The presence of overhead power cables and the possible need to manually align steelwork components for connection are other potential hazards associated with the erection of steelwork.

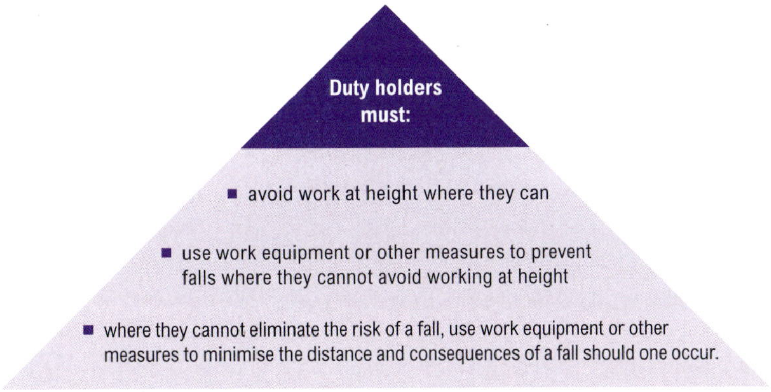

Falls from height are the biggest cause of fatal accidents at work within the UK.

For additional information and resources regarding work at height refer to the HSE website.

6.3 Design and planning

Important items that should receive attention during design and planning include the following.

6.3.1 Structural stability

The structure must be stable at all times, from when the first piece of steelwork is put into position until it is completed.

Temporary supports (such as bracing, guys or stays) must be used during the erection of any structure that may be unstable or liable to collapse before it is completed. Additionally, where any work is carried out that is likely to adversely affect the foundations or stability of any existing building or structure (or one under construction), all practicable precautions (such as shoring) must be taken.

6.3.2 Temporary structures

Any temporary structure must be of good construction, adequate strength and stability, made of sound materials, free from obvious defects and be properly maintained.

For further information refer to Chapter C04 Temporary works.

6.3.3 Safe means of assembly or making connections

Assembly of steelwork components or making connections should be planned so that erectors can do as much of the work as possible at ground level.

Where erectors have to work at a height, provision must be made for safe means of access to the connecting points and any other working places. Ideally, work will be carried out from MEWPs operating on a suitable floor surface. However, where this is not possible, design consideration should be given to the following points.

- Ensuring there is adequate working space and a suitable work platform for a crane.
- Connections between steelwork components that are simple to make off site, ground-level assembly or fabrication to reduce work at height.
- The provision of fixed work platforms and ladders.
- The provision of anchorage points for safety nets and fall prevention and arrest devices.

6.3.4 Steelwork components

The size, weight and shape of individual steelwork components will influence safe handling and erecting. The designer should therefore consider the following.

- ☑ Marking components as an aid to identification (also to prevent costly mistakes).
- ☑ Optimising the length of structural members in an attempt to reduce the number of connections at height.
- ☑ Calculating the weights of components to assist in the estimation of safe crane capacities and the location of cranes.
- ☑ Identifying the positions where components should be lifted.
- ☑ Indicating centres of gravity where these are not readily evident.

6.3.5 Method statements

The amount of detail required in a method statement will depend on how big or complex the job is. However, method statements should be written for even small steel erection jobs. It is clear evidence that attention has been given to design and planning aspects, as well as being a plan to ensure that the project is completed without risks to health and safety.

A typical method statement should include the following information.

- ☑ Details of how the project will be managed and health and safety risks eliminated, avoided or reduced.
- ☑ Details about the site, including any hazardous features (such as overhead electric power lines) and what effect these will have on the project.
- ☑ Details of plant requirements (such as cranes, MEWPs and other lifting equipment) and the competencies required to operate them.
- ☑ Arrangements for the safe receipt, off-loading, storage and handling of steelwork components on site.
- ☑ Details on where and how steelwork will be assembled prior to erection.
- ☑ The sequential method of erecting the structure and how stability will be ensured at all times.
- ☑ How work, such as slinging, lifting, unslinging and the initial and final connecting of steelwork components, will be carried out safely.
- ☑ The safety precaution to prevent falls from height (for example, arranging for as much assembling as possible to be done at ground level, minimising the number of connections to be made at a height).
- ☑ The means of providing safe access and a safe place of work by methods such as mobile towers, temporary platforms and walkways.
- ☑ Details of the means of communication during lifting operations.
- ☑ Any requirement for safety nets, safety harnesses and fall-arrest devices (provisions for design features should be specified, for example, attachment points for ladders, safety nets and fall-arrest devices).
- ☑ How people will be protected from falling objects (for example, use of screens, fans and debris nets, installation of barriers and warning notices at ground level).
- ☑ A contingency plan for dealing with any problems that may arise.
- ☑ The expected level of competence of the people undertaking the work.

For further information refer to Chapter A05 Risk assessments and method statements.

6.4 Site considerations

Potentially hazardous site conditions should be identified. Some typical examples include the following items.

6.4.1 Overhead electric cables

If there are any overhead power lines near the proposed erection site, the local electricity company should be consulted. Either the power lines should be made dead, temporarily rerouted or other suitable precautions taken to prevent any close approach to, or contact with, live overhead lines.

No work should take place within:

- ☑ **9 m of overhead power lines on wood or concrete poles**
- ☑ **15 m of overhead power lines on steel towers.**

D 06

For further information on the regulations and for additional resources refer to the HSE website.

6.4.2 Other contractors and their work

Certain work or processes on, or adjacent to, the site may have the potential to adversely affect the health and safety of workers on site. For example, noxious gases, vapours or dusts may be given off from chimneys, stacks, tank vents and ventilation ducts. These may not cause a problem at ground level but may affect steelwork erectors working at height.

6.4.3 Managing the safe erection of steelwork

Following a detailed risk assessment of the work activity, the next step in ensuring safe working practices in erection is the preparation of a method statement. This important document should detail the proposed erection scheme and should form part of the health and safety plan for the project.

6.4.4 Site access and egress

The contractor, or principal contractor on a project involving more than one contractor, should check that all of the vehicles associated with the erection or dismantling of steelwork can access and egress the site safely. It is envisaged that the vehicles will mainly be cranes and delivery lorries (delivering steel and MEWPs).

A safe location for lorries to park must be identified and communicated to the steelwork contractor if their lorries may have to wait to be admitted to the site to be unloaded. This area must not be immediately outside the site or on any access road, if doing so would create an unacceptable obstruction or other hazards for passing traffic or pedestrians. On larger sites space should be allocated as a dedicated lorry or trailer park.

On sites where there is simply not space to park large vehicles, appropriate arrangements (such as a road or lane closure) must be made for delivery lorries (and possibly the mobile crane) to be parked on the public highway adjacent to the site boundary for the off-loading of steel.

Where there is a loading or unloading bay for only a single lorry, a strict schedule of delivery times must be written, communicated to the steel delivery contractors and adhered to. In this instance it is highly advisable to identify a lorry holding area, to which lorries that miss their slot can be sent pending the allocation of another unloading slot.

Every effort should be made to avoid the need for vehicles to reverse, particularly out of the site gate and back on to a public road. Where this is not possible, suitable precautions must be taken (for example, the use of one or more signallers or an alternative traffic-control system).

Where it is considered unsafe for vehicles and pedestrians to use the same site entrance, one or more separate pedestrian entrances must be provided, clearly indicated and kept free of obstruction.

6.4.5 Housekeeping

Construction sites must, so far as is reasonably practicable, be kept in good order and a reasonable state of cleanliness.

Platforms, gangways, floors and other places must not be obstructed by loose materials.

Projecting nails or similar sharp objects in timber or other materials must be removed or knocked down to prevent injury.

Materials must be stacked safely.

For posters that can be used to prevent slip and trip hazards refer to the HSE website.

6.4.6 Site features that require attention

- ☑ Lack of space for the handling and storage of steelwork.
- ☑ Restricted (crane) oversailing rights.
- ☑ Restricted area(s) for vehicle movements.
- ☑ Low resistance to ground-bearing pressures.
- ☑ Poor access onto the site.
- ☑ Any buildings close to the site that may affect the erection process.
- ☑ Any rights of access that may bring members of the public close to the erection site.
- ☑ Ground contamination from previous use of the land.

6.4.7 Lighting

The following areas must be adequately and suitably lit.

- Every working place.
- Access to working places.
- Where lifting operations are in progress.
- All dangerous openings.

6.4.8 Protection from falling material

At any place where people work, steps must be taken to prevent them from being struck by any falling material or article.

Scaffold components, tools and other objects must not be thrown or tipped down from a height where they are liable to cause injury, but should be properly lowered.

6.4.9 Lifting and slinging

Competent people must be used to operate lifting equipment and give signals in line with either BS 7121 or the Health and Safety (Safety Signs and Signals) Regulations.

All critical lifts, including tandem lifts, should be carefully planned and supervised and, where appropriate, a lifting plan should be developed for more complex operations.

Appropriate precautions must be taken to ensure the stability of lifting appliances when used on soft, uneven or sloping ground. These could include measures such as ground levelling, use of mats or hard standing.

The load must not exceed the safe working load of the lifting appliance (allowance should be made for the weight of lifting slings, beams, and so on).

Any load that approaches the safe working load of a crane should be carefully raised a short distance and the operation stopped to check safety and stability before continuing.

If more than one lifting appliance is used to raise or lower a load, a competent person must supervise the operation, which must be arranged so that no lifting appliance is loaded above its safe working load or is made unstable.

Suitable packing should be used to prevent the edges of the load from damaging the slings.

Loads should be lifted and lowered slowly to avoid any shock loading. The use of hand lines, fixed near the ends of the load, will help to prevent the load spinning when being lifted or lowered.

Loads should be lowered onto timber battens to protect slings and enable them to be removed easily.

For further information refer to:

- **Chapter C07 Lifting operations**
- **Chapter C08 Lifting equipment**
- **The Lifting Operations and Lifting Equipment Regulations**
- ***Code of Practice for safe use of cranes* (BS 7121).**

For further information and for additional resources refer to the HSE website.

6.4.10 Off-loading, stacking and storage of steelwork

A safe means of access and a safe workplace must be provided when off-loading components from delivery lorries. Two examples of recently developed safety systems are listed below.

This example of unloading reinforcement shows the use of a fall-arrest unloading device and pre-slung loads

- Tensioned steel wire running the length of the lorry trailer, at above the head-height of anyone standing on the trailer. Each slinger wears a safety harness and a restraint lanyard, the free end of which is clipped to the tension steel wire. In the event of a trip or stumble, the slinger is prevented from falling from the trailer.
- A 'U' shaped inflatable airbag or a beanbag that fits around the back and sides of the trailer to act as a soft-landing system, should anyone fall off the trailer.

Many accidents have occurred during the off-loading of lorries when the load-securing mechanism was released. This is because the load was either not stable when loaded or because it moved and became unstable during the journey.

The stability of the load on the lorry, or in the stack, must be ensured at all times. Suitable timber wedges or packing pieces can be used as an aid to stability.

Precautions should be taken to prevent slingers being struck by the load. For example, taking up a safe position off the lorry before the load is lifted.

The stack must be constructed so that components can be removed without risk of someone being trapped or struck.

There may be an advantage in using a suitable transportable storage rack (stillage) for smaller components.

Anyone not directly involved in the off-loading activity should not be allowed into the area.

Pedestrians and vehicles should be kept apart where practicable.

The HSE leaflet *Safe unloading of steel stock* offers practical advice to everyone involved in the delivery and unloading of steel stock.

6.4.11 Traffic routes and vehicles

Prior to, and during, steel erection, deliveries of steel on articulated lorries will be a feature of many jobs. In the context of this chapter, these regulations place a legal duty on the person in charge of the site to ensure the following.

- That pedestrians and vehicles can move safely and without risks to health, so far as is reasonably practicable.
- There are sufficient traffic routes, all of which must be suitable for the vehicles using them.
- There is sufficient segregation between pedestrians and moving vehicles but where this is not reasonably practicable:
  - other means of protection are provided
  - a means of warning pedestrians of the approach of vehicles, where the pedestrians would otherwise be at risk, is provided.
- That (vehicle) loading bays have one exit for the exclusive use of pedestrians.
- Appropriate signs are erected in the interests of health and safety.
- Steps are taken to prevent the unintentional movement of any vehicle.
- Each vehicle must be operated in a safe manner with its load arranged safely.
- Every vehicle is fitted with means of warning persons who may be at risk when the vehicle is moving.

6.5 Safe working

The safe system of work must also ensure the operative's safety:

- whilst getting up to the place of work and down again
- during the period of time at high level before the operative is able to clip on.

If access has to be made inside a structural steel box section or any configuration of steelwork where ventilation is poor, it should be treated as a confined space and appropriate precautions taken. The atmosphere should be tested by a competent person, before entry is made, to ensure that there is sufficient oxygen present. Continuous monitoring for oxygen deficiency is strongly recommended.

Tests for flammable or toxic gases or vapours and oxygen enrichment should be carried out as appropriate, depending on the proposed work activity. (For example, oxypropane cutting or burning may lead to a build up of toxic gases or toxic metal fumes, or there may be a leakage of propane or oxygen.)

For further information refer to Chapter D09 Confined spaces.

6.5.1 Stability of structures

Steel erection, by its very definition, involves creating structures, which these regulations require to be stable at all times. In particular:

- all practicable steps must be taken to ensure that no person is put at risk by the collapse of any structure that may become unstable or weakened
- structures must not be loaded to an extent that they become unsafe
- any temporary means of supporting a permanent structure must be:
  - designed and maintained to withstand any stresses and strains that are put on it
  - only used for the purpose for which it was designed, installed and maintained
  - not overloaded so as to render it unsafe.

6.5.2 Safe means of access and safe place of work

To comply with the Work at Height Regulations, consideration must be given to reducing the need to work at height, for example by:

- ☑ doing as much of the connecting work as possible at ground level or from erected floor decks, as the work progresses
- ☑ using a releasing device so that lifting gear can be released remotely
- ☑ ensuring that, wherever possible, inspection and testing is carried out at low level.

When people must work at height, consideration should be given to the following requirements.

- ☑ Installing permanent or temporary handrails, stairways, ladders, walkways and floor decking, so that these can be used by erectors as the work progresses.
- ☑ Providing hard standings or floor slabs so that mobile access platforms can be used.
- ☑ Providing temporary access and working platforms, including scaffolds, lightweight staging and purpose-built platforms with safe means of access.
- ☑ Working from MEWPs.

Whilst the increased use of MEWPs has brought about safer working at height, it has also created the need to ensure that MEWP operators are adequately trained and competent, and that ground conditions on the site are properly surveyed and prepared to enable the safe use of such heavy plant without risk of sinking or overturning.

Steel erection in progress using a mobile crane, two MEWPs and edge protection being attached to steelwork at ground level before being lifted into position

Traditionally, scaffolding was the main form of edge protection and could only be installed, modified or removed by trained scaffolders, after the steelwork was in place. However, the development of various types of system edge protection has provided opportunities for pre-installing edge protection before work at height commences. The use of such systems can also eliminate the need for successive trades to install their own edge protection and then remove it when leaving site, only for it to be replaced by the next trade's edge protection. The elimination of such duplication has obvious safety benefits.

It may be appropriate in some circumstances to use other means of access to height, such as the use of roped access techniques, which must be carried out by trained and competent persons. Alternatively, access may be achieved by using a man-riding basket suspended from a crane.

There may be occasions when it is necessary to use fall arrest rather than fall-prevention measures, with safety nets or other soft-landing systems being the preferred method of fall arrest. BCSA has stated that the increased use of safety nets has had a significant beneficial effect on the steel construction industry's accident rate.

For further information refer to Chapter D02 Safe working at height, and Chapter D05 Fall arrest and suspension equipment.

6.5.3 Edge protection

Consideration should be given to how edge protection for the following work will be provided. One option is to use proprietary edge protection, which can be fitted directly to the steelwork at ground level and lifted with the steelwork into position. This can save time, or reduce the risk for installing edge protection at height.

6.5.4 Beam straddling

There may be occasions where the work cannot be done from a MEWP or other platform and erectors may have to work from the steel. This is known as beam straddling. This form of access is only permissible for specific short-duration jobs where the beam is of I-beam section.

A full body harness with a twin-tailed lanyard system may be used. However, users must ensure that this system is used correctly and that the second leg is not attached to the user's harness, as this may interfere with the operation of the energy absorber.

Consideration must be made as to suitable anchor points to which the harness lanyard can be attached. The erector can sit astride the flange with the sole and heel of each foot resting on the bottom flange and both hands able to grasp either side of the top flange.

Alternatively, proprietary beam-gliding devices are available to improve mobility.

The risk assessment must consider how anyone carrying out this practice is going to be rescued following a fall.

The use of a safety harness or lanyard requires a minimum clearance below the high-level place of work to allow the lanyard to function properly in arresting a fall. Expert advice should be sought.

For further information on safe working at height refer to Chapter D01 Work at Height Regulations.

6.5.5 The weather

A regular weather forecast should be obtained by the manager in charge of the erection programme. Erection should not take place where weather conditions impose an adverse effect, for example, from ice, frost, snow, strong winds, rain, dew and poor visibility (such as fog, mist or glare).

If erection work is stopped, measures should be taken to ensure that the structure remains stable.

After a stoppage due to the weather, stability of the structure should be checked before work is allowed to restart.

07 Excavations

Contents

Supporting information

G: Checklists and forms

GT 700 Toolbox talks

Overview

This chapter gives some practical guidance on factors to be considered when planning excavations, the setting up of the work and safe working within them. This will include the elements to consider, such as soil composition, depth, support structures and emergency evacuation.

Good planning and correct preparation for excavations are essential, as every year people are killed or seriously injured by collapses and falling materials while working in excavations.

7.1 Introduction

Most construction work will involve a form of excavation, for foundations, sewers or drainage. These will vary in depth but are always a high risk activity as they can be affected by diverse factors (such as rainwater, hot weather, adjoining structures, ground conditions and vibration).

Many accidents occur when the excavation appears in good condition, with its sides clean and self-supporting, and with no obvious hazards.

Some excavations may need to be classed as confined spaces, and will therefore need additional precautions.

Neither the shallowness of an excavation nor the appearance of the ground should be taken as indicators of safety. Accident reports suggest that far too often such assumptions are made incorrectly.

An unsafe excavation

The HSE inspector served a prohibition notice for this excavation, which was 1.9 m deep and unsupported.

The contractor was fined £10,000 and the HSE was awarded £8,000 costs. In addition the supervisor was fined £1,000 and the HSE was awarded £800 costs.

The method of excavation must be specific to local conditions and may need to be different to an excavation nearby. Workers will often have to improvise and use their knowledge and skills to overcome unforeseen obstructions and different ground conditions. It is important that supervisors and their workers are trained and competent to ensure excavation work is completed in a safe way.

7.2 Important points

You need to complete a **risk assessment** for any works that are to be undertaken, and this must be done by a competent person.

This risk assessment must take into consideration the potential for the sides to collapse, that someone may be injured and the possible need for a support structure.

Try to ensure the risk assessment seeks to eliminate or reduce the risk at source (such as using trenchless techniques and having the sides battered or stepped).

D 07

Risk, from the following hazards, must also be taken into consideration.

- Collapse of the sides.
- Underground services.
- Contaminated ground.
- Fall of persons, materials, plant or equipment into the excavation.
- Confined spaces – poisonous/explosive atmospheres or lack of oxygen.
- Flooding.
- Overhead services.
- Moving plant – injury to persons.
- Lifting operations.
- Undermining adjacent structures or services.
- Surcharging the excavation, meaning applying pressure to the sides (for example, planning vehicle routes or material storage areas too close to the excavation).

For details on safety awareness for working around excavations refer to Appendix A.

Control measures described in the risk assessment should include the following.

- Protection of person(s) installing the support system.
- Safe exposure, and if necessary, support of underground services.
- Safe access and egress from the excavation.
- Adequate ventilation of the workspace.
- Arrangements to dewater the trench if necessary.
- Inspections of the excavation by a competent person.
- Consideration for the stability of adjacent structures or land.
- Arranging for guarding and lighting where necessary.

A cubic metre of soil can weigh over a tonne.

A collapse captured while taking site record photos

The excavation was 1.8 m deep and the collapse took less than two seconds. The method was to dig and pour with no-one entering. Due to heavy rain, this method was abandoned and trench support installed. The section that broke away weighed about one tonne and it can be seen how easily a serious accident could happen.

Information on preventing accidents in excavations can be found on the HSE website.

7.3 Excavation support

There will always be water present during excavations, even if only moisture in the soil, and this is an additional hazard to be considered, as shown in the illustration below.

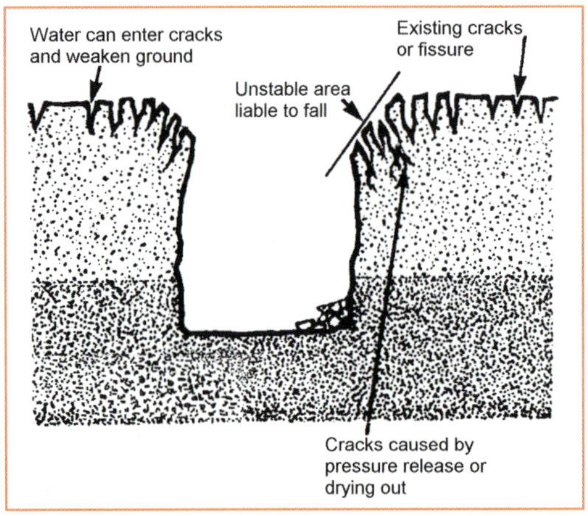

Firm or stiff clay-type ground

Soils that are akin to fine sand flow easily; however, those like stiff clay stick together better.

Do not rely on any soil, whatever its structure, to support its own weight. If it cannot be battered or stepped, then alternative support will be essential.

Loose and fractured rock will also need support.

Before commencing any excavation work consider what temporary support is required, and whether any equipment or special precautions are needed.

Clients must provide information to contractors before work begins. This should include relevant information on ground conditions, underground structures or water courses and the location of existing services.

This information should be used during the planning and preparation for excavation work. It will allow the contractor to choose the most suitable method to support the excavation.

Prevent collapse – shore, step or batter back. Don't assume the ground will stand unsupported.

7.3.1 Trenchless techniques

Persons planning construction work should also be aware of alternative techniques that may be able to eliminate totally or partially the need for excavations.

Examples of the trenchless techniques include boring, directional drilling and pipe jacking – some will need excavation pits at each end to launch and retrieve equipment.

7.3.2 Battering or stepping excavations

Battering or stepping excavations will depend on the nature of the soil, and could be a mix of materials. Consideration will need to be given to the water content, and the increase or decrease of this while the excavation is open. A small percentage increase in water content can reduce the stability of the excavation sides.

The diagram *(below left)* is an example of typical safe slope angles and should be used for guidance purposes only. If there is any doubt regarding soil conditions, the site engineer or the shoring provider should be consulted.

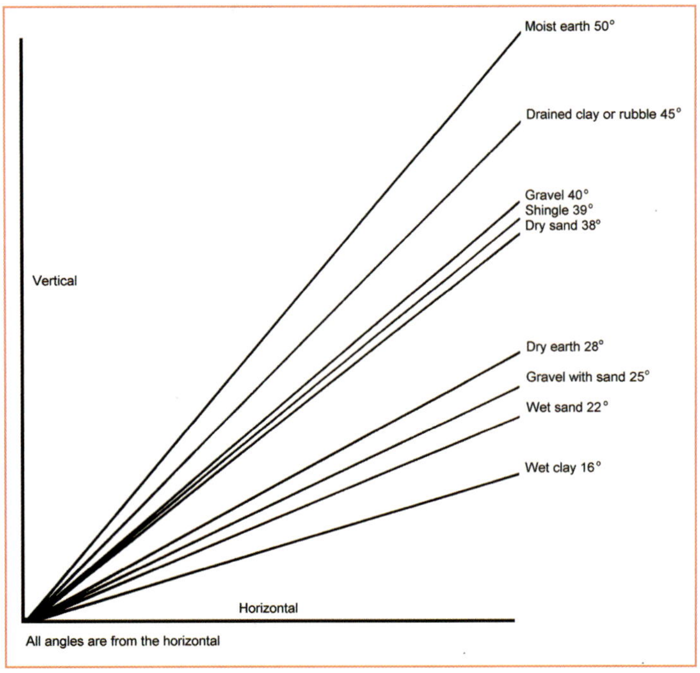

Typical safe slope angles. The vertical distance should not exceed 1.2 m

Stepped excavation – but showing Chapter 8-type barriers, which should not be used for edge protection
(Image supplied by Barconn Ltd/Paramount Health and Safety)

Examples of stepped excavations

7.3.3 Trench supports

The type of support will depend on the following.

- ☑ The type of excavation.
- ☑ The nature of the ground.
- ☑ Groundwater conditions.
- ☑ Surcharge of sides of excavation.

Depending on the risk assessment the excavation may need to be supported.

A survey should be carried out for all but shallow trenches, to determine the type of soil and other ground conditions; this will then show what support will be required. This survey must be carried out by a competent person.

A specialist engineer will be required for large or complex excavations.

Materials for support must be available before excavation work is started, and be of good quality and well maintained; they must also be fixed securely.

All erection, dismantling and alteration of any support must be under the supervision of a competent person.

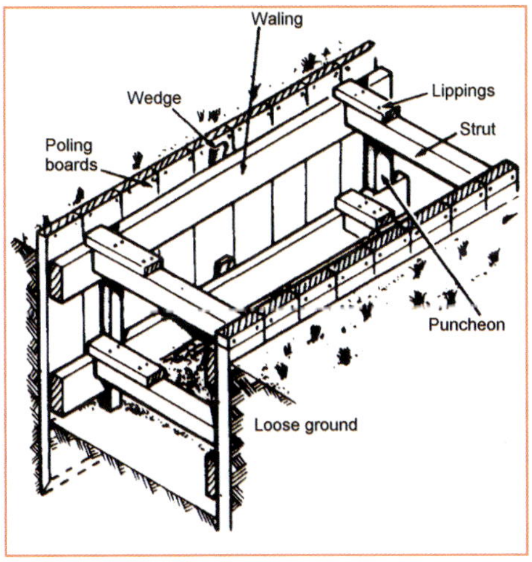

Close-boarded excavation

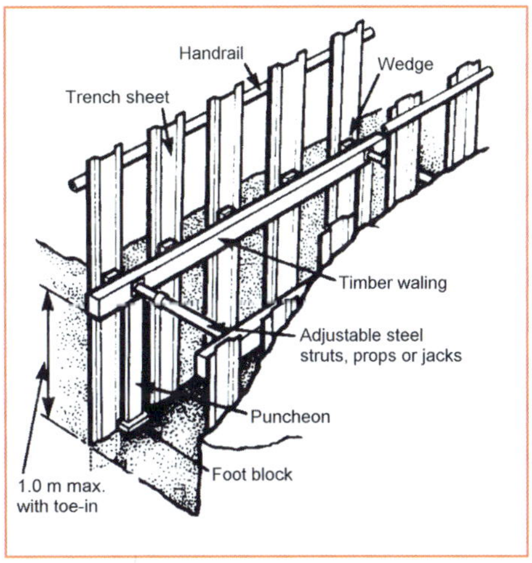

Open sheeting using steel sheets and jacks

7.3.3.1 Types of support systems

Timber shuttering, steel trench and adjustable props should be used; the props can be mechanical or hydraulic.

A temporary framework of support of a protective box/cage type may be required to protect workers. This can be moved forward as timbering progresses.

www.

The Construction Plant-hire Association has produced guidance on management of shoring in excavations, aimed at anyone involved in the planning, management, design and supervision of excavation works.

D 07

Safe working in a deep excavation using trench boxes and a tied ladder. The boxes extend one metre above the excavation to form edge protection

Proprietary support systems are available and include the following.

- **Shields,** which are two vertical plates braced permanently apart, intended as temporary localised protection for workers and they can be dragged along as work progresses.
- **Trench boxes,** which are modular and are lowered in, and form a permanent support for the trench sides; they can be extended in height and width.
- **Plate lining systems** have metal plates that slide into position between vertical soldier posts at preset intervals; the posts counteract stress from trench sides.

You need to be aware that any of these support systems can cause problems when underground services cross the line of the trench being excavated.

The use of a hydraulic waling frame is better used in this case, as spaces can be left between the metals sheets once they are in position.

Hydraulic frames are ideal when excavating pits and manholes as they can be extended in both length and width.

D
07

7.3.4 Inspection and maintenance of support systems

Excavations must be closely monitored when they are first opened and sides are unsupported. The CDM Regulations state that practicable steps must be taken to prevent danger to any person, including the provision of supports and battering to ensure that no excavation or part of it collapses, the walls of any excavation do not dislodge or fall and that no person is buried or trapped in an excavation by materials that are dislodged or by falls. All excavations must be inspected by a competent person at the start of the shift, after any event that may have affected the strength or stability of the excavation, or if material unintentionally falls or is dislodged. No work should be undertaken until the inspection has taken place and the excavation is safe. *(For further information refer to 7.5 Inspections and reports.)*

Little movements of 6-12 mm are usually the only sign of weakening in cohesive soils – be aware of them, as they can pass unnoticed but they mean something is wrong.

Movement can be seen from slight distortion in the timbering, bowing of poling boards and walings, or signs of local crushing.

The ground can also dry out and shrink, which loosens timbering. Timber can be displaced by the ground absorbing additional moisture.

- Avoid damage to struts or walings when moving loads into or out of the excavation.
- Check timber regularly – it can dry out, shrink or rot.
- In bad weather spoil heaps can slump and loose boulders or masonry can fall into the excavation.
- A guideline is that the distance from the edge of the trench and the bottom of the spoil heap must not be less than the depth of the excavation.
- Do not allow heavy vehicles near the edge of an excavation unless the support work has been designed to permit it.
- Take care not to affect the stability of any neighbouring structure or features.
- Take into account the Party Wall Act and any permissions or restrictions.
- Take precautions to protect workers (and others) before and during excavation works.

An unsupported excavation

This excavation was only about 650 mm deep and it was left unsupported overnight. There was heavy rain during the evening and the team returned to find this collapse and the existing cast iron gas main at risk.

7.4 Excavation safety

7.4.1 Access

There must be safe means of getting into and out of an excavation (access and egress).

Safe access into a deep excavation, together with all-round secure edge protection

If the workers use ladders then these must be fit-for-purpose and strong enough. They must be on a firm, level base, secured to prevent slipping, and, if no handhold is available, extended to at least one metre (five rungs) above the top of the excavation.

Climbing in or out using walings, underground services or struts must be prohibited. This must be specifically covered in the safe system of work and/or method statement.

7.4.2 Guarding excavations

Suitable steps must be taken to prevent any person, vehicle, plant or equipment, or any accumulation of earth or other materials, from falling into an excavation.

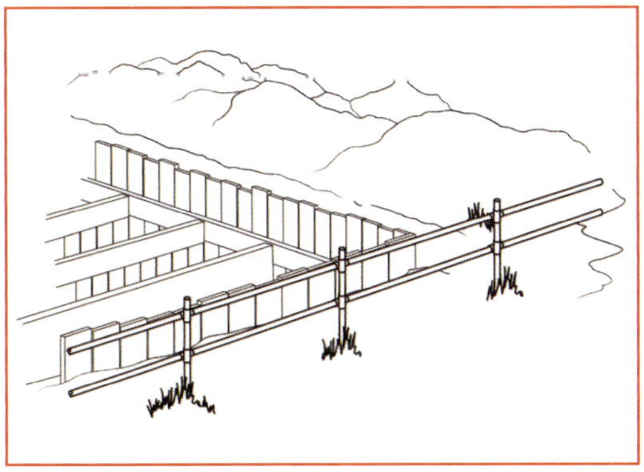

- Physical barriers (not pin-and-rope or rolls of orange plastic mesh) should be used to keep materials, plant and equipment away from the edges.
- When barriers are removed, they should be replaced as soon as possible.
- Edges of an excavation should be lit during darkness, particularly if close to public road and spaces.
- If excavation work is carried out on the highway, Local Authority approval is required and appropriate signing and guarding complying with the *Traffic signs manual*, Chapter 8, and the *Code of Practice for safety at street works and road works* must be utilised.
- Ensure adequate hazard warning lighting is used when it is dark or during foggy conditions.

If plastic, Chapter 8-type barriers are used, they must be installed to be robust enough to stop a person if they fell or leant against them. This is particularly important if they are being used to protect the public.

For further information on guarding excavations refer to Chapter F01 Street works and road works.

D 07

7.4.3 Vehicles and plant

Plan your traffic routes so that no vehicles or plant go near excavations, other than those that need to be in that area.

Be aware of surcharging when heavy items of construction plant are near to an excavation. Where this cannot be avoided, it must be considered in the design of the support system that will be installed.

Stop blocks must be used if vehicles are required to tip into an excavation. Ensure these are placed far enough away to avoid the edge of the excavation being damaged.

Use a signaller to give directions to the vehicle driver/plant operator.

Stop blocks should be used, where appropriate

Safe segregation of excavation work and plant

For further guidance refer to the HSE publication *The safe use of vehicles on construction sites* (HSG144), which can be downloaded free from its website.

For further information refer to Chapter C06 Mobile plant and vehicles.

7.4.4 Site lighting

There must be suitable and sufficient lighting at every workplace, the approaches to it and on traffic routes.

You must pay particular attention to ensuring there is adequate lighting for access points, openings and lifting operations.

7.4.5 Ventilation

Excavations must be kept clear of suffocating, toxic or explosive gases. Gases can seep through the soil and accumulate in the bottom of the excavation.

Gases that are heavier than air (such as plant exhaust emissions) can leak or roll into an excavation and displace the air, which can lead to asphyxiation.

Leakage of propane and butane from liquefied petroleum gas (LPG) cylinders is potentially very dangerous; the gases will sink to the lowest point and form an explosive concentration that cannot disperse naturally.

The excavation will need to be checked and continuously monitored for the presence of gases and purged before entry by workers if these are found.

For further information on ventilation refer to Chapter B07 Control of substances hazardous to health.

7.4.6 Confined spaces

If an excavation is classified as a confined space, tests for toxic gas or oxygen depletion must be carried out before work starts and continuously as work progresses.

It is also recommended that the work should be subject to the issue of a permit to work certificate.

You must ensure that every workplace or approach is safe and without risks to health. There must be a sufficient supply of purified air. The most common method of ventilation is to blow clean air into the excavation in sufficient volume to dissipate any gas and provide adequate breathable air.

e.g. Safe systems in practice

Deep manhole excavation with good access and edge protection

Deep manhole excavation with good access and edge protection

Protected shallow excavation

Drag boxes with guard-rail attachments and ladder access

Remote controlled trench compactor avoiding the need to enter the excavation

Designated bucket changing area

Fencing along utility trench

For further information refer to Chapter D09 Confined spaces.

7.4.7 Underground cables and services

Before any excavation works take place, you must ensure underground services (such as gas, electricity, water and telecommunications) have been identified.

Many injuries each year are caused by accidental contact with underground services.

You must have controls in place to reduce the risk of injury from underground cables or other underground services.

For further information refer to Chapter D08 Underground and overhead services.

7.5 Inspections and reports

An inspection of an excavation must be carried out by a competent person at the following intervals.

- At the start of each shift during which work is to be carried out.
- After an event that is likely to have affected the stability of the structure.
- After the accidental fall or dislodgement of any material.

The competent person must be satisfied that work can be carried out safely and a report, containing the following information, must be prepared.

- Name and address of the person on whose behalf the inspection was carried out.
- Location of the work being inspected.
- Description of the place of work, or part of that place of work inspection, including plant and equipment or materials.
- Date and time of the inspection.
- Details of any matter identified that could give risk to the health and safety of any person.
- Details of any action taken as a result of any matter identified.
- Details of any further actions considered necessary.
- Name and position of the person making the report.

The report must be written before the end of the shift during which it was completed and a copy provided within 24 hours to the person on whose behalf it was undertaken.

A copy of the report must be kept on site until the work is completed and for three months from the date of completion.

You do not need to do more than one written report in any period of seven days. However, it is advisable that a daily record of inspection is kept (for example, in the site diary).

There is no statutory form for inspections and it can be kept electronically. However, you must be able to produce a hard copy for an HSE inspector, if so requested.

Details of what the report on a cofferdam, caisson or excavation should contain can be found in Regulation 24 of the CDM Regulations.

D
07

For an example of an inspection report refer to Section G: *Checklists and forms*.

7.6 Excavators used as cranes

Excavators are mobile work equipment and are therefore subject to the requirements and provisions of the Provision and Use of Work Equipment Regulations (PUWER) and the Lifting Operations and Lifting Equipment Regulations (LOLER) when being used for lifting operations.

Note: *at the time of going to print LOLER is under review – refer to the companion website for updates.*

Excavators and backhoes are principally designed for earth moving operations and not designed for all types of lifting operations as a main function. The planning for a lifting operation using excavators should primarily consider whether these types of machine are suitable for the undertaking of the required lifting activity. As a lifting operation, it is subject to suitable and sufficient planning by a competent person, including a risk assessment and a safe system of work, that takes into account the capabilities of the excavator for the selected task.

The risk assessment and method statement should take into account that when an excavator is in the object handling mode (being used as a crane), it will be necessary for the slinger to approach the machine to attach or detach the lifting accessories. They will then be within a hazardous area (the slewing arc of the boom and dipper) and be at risk of being struck by the load, bucket or excavator arm. Excavator operators and slingers must be made aware of these dangers; effective communication and constant vigilance are essential.

When the slinger is within the slewing arc of the machine's boom to attach or remove lifting accessories, the operating controls of the machine must be isolated.

The weight of the bucket (if still fitted), plus the quick hitch coupler must be added to the weight of the load to establish if the machine will be working within its safe working load. Unless required, the bucket should be removed to improve the excavator operator's visibility. If a quick hitch coupler is fitted, the operator must ensure that the link is facing downwards (operating ram extended) so that any part of the lifting accessory will not foul the coupler, allowing the accessory to hang free at all times.

The risk assessment must also address the following.

- The need for the lifting operation to be ideally segregated from other work activities taking place in the vicinity, particularly where it is necessary for the machine to travel with a suspended load.
- Ground conditions, particularly where an excavator will carry out the lifting operation, which should be on level, firm terrain. Where a pick and carry operation is required, the intended travel route must be checked (for both tracked and wheeled types) so that there are no voids, it is clear of trenches and is on firm, level ground.

A rated object handling capacity table must be available in the cab. If the rated lifting capacity for an excavator (or the backhoe of a backhoe-loader) is greater than 1 tonne (or the overturning moment is greater than 40,000 Nm), the machine must be fitted with the following.

- A boom lowering control device on the raising boom cylinder(s) (a safety check valve), which meets the requirements of BS 6912-1.
- An acoustic or visual warning device, which indicates to the operator when the object handling capacity or corresponding load movement is reached.

Where the upper structure of a 360 excavator needs to slew, the machine's lifting capacity is reduced when slewing away from the front or rear of the tracks or axles. This is because the track or wheel width is less than the track length or wheel base.

Chains or slings for lifting must not be placed around or on the teeth of the bucket. Accessories for lifting may only be attached to a purpose-made point on the machine.

Where the risk assessment shows that there is a significant risk of overloading or overturning of the excavator, the fitment of a rated capacity indicator may be required.

www.

For further guidance refer to the CPA guidance *Lifting operations in construction when using excavators.*

For further detailed guidance refer to Chapter C08 Lifting equipment.

Appendix A – Safety awareness around excavators

This information covers basic safety rules that should be followed by the operator, bankspersons, vehicle marshal and others working around both tracked and wheeled excavators to reduce the risk of injury and allow everyone to go home safely. Plant and plant movements are a significant risk for everyone on site, not just those working directly around the excavator.

From 2007-12 there were 29 fatalities in construction where someone was struck by a moving vehicle.

People working around excavators are at high risk of sustaining serious injuries, possibly leading to specified injuries or death, and some less serious injuries (such as crushing of feet), if the work is not managed safely. In confined work areas or where more than one piece of plant is in use, near misses involving collisions and plant damage are also highly likely.

Technical advances in machinery (such as remote operated cut-off switch) and familiarisation periods for new machines coming on to site, help to reduce incidents and accidents.

Communication and risk assessment

Before beginning any activity, a pre-task briefing should be carried out to ensure everyone involved is familiar with the task, is aware of any risks and the control measures required. Any interface between different tasks can also be discussed to co-ordinate activities.

A risk assessment of the task should reflect the hierarchy of risk control to eliminate, reduce, isolate, control and provide PPE in order to manage the risks associated with working near to an excavator.

- ☑ Does the workforce need to be working around the excavator?
- ☑ Where personnel are close to plant, are exclusion zones in place and are the required safety critical items fitted to the excavator fully functional?
- ☑ Are adequate vehicle plant marshals (VPM) required for a safe system of work?
- ☑ Is everyone wearing appropriate high-visibility clothing, which is in good order?

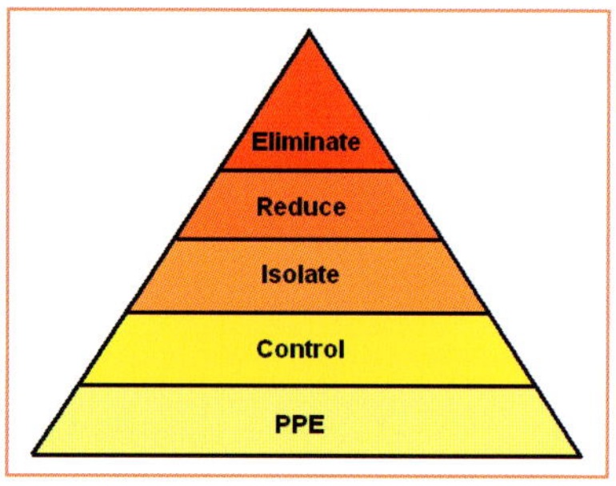

Safety zones

When working around an excavator it is important to be aware of the operator's limited all-round vision and the safety zones for the machine. Where a risk assessment has identified the need for a competent VPM to manage the excavator movements then all instructions by the VPM must be followed. A VPM is responsible for managing the movement of people and vehicles safely around the excavator.

A bankspersons carries out a separate role and supervises the specific activity that the excavator is carrying out (for example, excavating a trench).

Before entering the radius of the excavator, wait in an area of safety and acknowledge the machine operator or, where provided, VPM. The VPM will then instruct the excavator to stop and, when this has been done, the operator to power down the engine, apply the dead man's lever and turn the engine off. Once the operator has acknowledged you, if you wish to approach, it is then safe to approach the excavator.

Approach the excavator cabin in the operator's clear line of sight.

Safety zones of an excavator

You should only approach the excavator cabin in the operator's clear line of sight. Approaching the excavator from any other angle should be avoided *(Zone 1 in the illustration on the following page)*. Where this is not possible (such as when an excavator is working near to a pedestrian route) the machine operator or VPM must acknowledge your need to approach and the correct shut-off procedure followed, as described above, before personnel enter the exclusion zone.

The machine operator should only restart the machine once the VPM has confirmed that it is safe to do so.

Pedestrians often still approach an excavator from the operator's blind side, assuming the operator is unlikely to move or that they can be seen by the operator. It is important that all personnel on site are aware of the visibility available in excavators. This can be done by allowing non-excavator operators to sit in the cab in controlled conditions. Stickers on the machine can be used as a reminder.

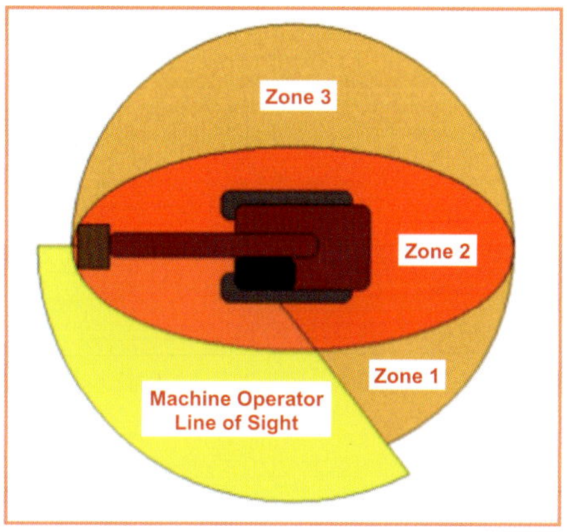

e.g.

Danger! You are approaching on my blind side. I cannot see you.

It should not be necessary to enter the area directly around the machine or underneath the boom *(Zone 2 in the illustration)*. Any tasks where this is unavoidable should be individually considered and have a site and task specific safe system of work put in place. These activities may include the following.

- ☑ Drainage.
- ☑ Archaeology.
- ☑ Piling.
- ☑ Earth moving.
- ☑ Bearing tests.
- ☑ Lifting operations.
- ☑ Plant maintenance.

Always gain permission from the VPM or bankperson before entering an excavator's working area.

Safety zones

Using the safety zones guidance spot what is wrong in the example below?

- ☒ Supervisor and workforce are on the blind side of the plant operator.
- ☒ No exclusion zone visible if operatives are to be excluded from works area.
- ☒ No visible control of excavator. No eye contact with operator, no VPM present.
- ☒ No-one taking the decision to work safely or not at all.

D 07

08
Underground and overhead services

Contents

Supporting information

G: Checklists and forms

GT 700 Toolbox talks

Overview

This chapter provides practical guidance on factors to be considered when preparing to work with, or near to, underground and overhead services.

On the majority of occasions a licensed utility company will carry out this type of work. However, existing services, whether known or unknown, remain a risk on nearly all projects.

Always bear in mind that drawings are not always accurate. Therefore positions may not be correct and there may even be some services that have not been charted.

This chapter also includes practical guidance for dealing with the hazards and the subsequent risks of working, or coming into contact, with overhead power lines.

8.1 Introduction

Underground services are, to a great extent, out of sight and out of mind until, perhaps, there is a fault or another reason to excavate. Every year people are injured and some killed due to accidental contact with underground services, such as electricity cables and gas pipes.

Coming into contact with overhead services also includes the lines serving the railway network.

In every case, the damage and injury could have been avoided if the proper procedures had been followed. The statistic of 70,000 instances of damage and 400 injuries per year as a result of coming into contact with electricity overhead and underground cables show that there is considerable room for improvement.

For further information refer to Chapter F02 Trackside safety.

This chapter makes reference to plant or equipment (for example, cranes and scaffold poles) that may come into contact with overhead power lines (OHPLs).

The health and safety construction phase plan will provide information about hazards specific to a site, and must include locations and types of underground and overhead services that can be found in the area.

8.2 Important points

- PLAN the work.
- LOCATE the underground services.
- DIG using a safe method of work.

8.2.1 Underground services

- Before doing anything yourself, check with the utility providers for existing services in the area that you are planning to work in.
- Ensure existing service routes are clearly marked on your plans.
- Use paint, tape or markers to identify existing services. Do not use metal spikes, which might penetrate a cable or pipe.
- Changes in colour of the surface material (sometimes known as tracks) may indicate where a service trench can be found.
- Absence of marker posts is not evidence that there are no underground services.
- Damage to gas pipes can cause leaks, which can result in fire and/or explosion.
- The most common injury is from contact with electrical cables. These often carry high voltages and can result in death and/or major burns.

Remember the exact position of a service will only be known once the service is uncovered.

8.2.2 Overhead services

- Where work cannot be avoided you must consult the local electricity supplier or distribution network operator (DNO) for advice before any work begins.
- A safe system of work must be planned and implemented for all overhead electrical works.
- Ensure power lines are dead, or suitable precautions taken.
- Contact with overhead power lines can burn, give an electric shock or **kill**.
- Injury can also occur when a person or object gets too close to a line and a flashover occurs.
- Establish a safe zone under or around the overhead power lines. Ensure no materials or machinery are stored nearby.
- Voltages lower than 230 volts can kill people.

8.3 Underground services

8.3.1 Risks and costs of damage

The most common injury is from contact with electrical cables. These often carry high voltages and on many occasions death and/or major burns have resulted.

Damage to gas pipes can cause leaks, which can result in fire and/or explosions. This can happen even when their location is known (such as contact by excavator bucket).

Damage to water and telephone cables is often less evident but still potentially serious and can affect, for example, places dependent on those services (such as hospitals and persons requiring the emergency services).

If plant damages a fibre optic cable, for example, this could result in a long section needing to be replaced, costing thousands of pounds.

- **In the event of a gas leak, suspected gas leak or any other emergency relating to gas, immediately phone the gas emergency services.**
- **In the event of an electrical emergency phone CableSafe.**
- **The HSE guidance document *Avoiding danger from underground services* (HSG47) can be downloaded from its website.**

8.3.2 Types of underground services

The most commonly encountered underground services are gas, water, electricity and telecommunications; but drains and sewers will also need to be located as they are also underground services.

There are other services that may not be known about or detected other than through investigation before digging or excavation is started; these include cable television, hydraulics, private telecommunications and street lighting cables.

In some cases, depending on the location, it may be necessary to investigate for petroleum and fuel oils (large bore, deep pipelines linking major installations).

If work in the vicinity of gas transmission pipelines is being considered, the local gas company will be able to provide details of suitable procedures.

For further information on types of underground services refer to Chapter C03 Electrical safety and Chapter F01 Street works and road works.

8.3.3 Colour coding of underground services

There is national agreement between the utility groups for colour coding of services.

Full information can be obtained from NJUG guidelines on the *Positioning and colour coding of underground utilities apparatus.*

You will, however, need to bear in mind that large numbers of pipes and services have been laid over the last 100 years, in a mixture of materials and colours.

Recommended colour coding for underground utility apparatus		
Pipe or cable	**Colour**	**Service(s)**
Black PVC	Black	Electricity, water, oil, fuel pipelines and telecoms
Blue PVC	Blue	Water
Grey PVC	Grey	Water and telecoms
Red PVC	Red	Electricity
Natural PV	Natural	Telecoms
Yellow PVC	Yellow	Gas

Note: *all plastic, polythene and polyvinylchloride pipes are shown above as PVC.*

(The information in the table below is for guidance purposes only.)

Pipe or cable material used by the different services	
Pipe or cable	**Service(s)**
Cast iron	Gas and water
Steel	Gas and water
Braided steel	Electricity
Yellow steel	Gas
Copper	Water
Lead or lead covered	Electricity and water
Asbestos	Water
Hessian wrapped	Electricity

D 08

Considerations when identifying underground services

- The coal authority has laid some yellow PVC electric cable.
- Black PVC must always be assumed to be live electricity until proved otherwise.
- All cast iron and steel must be assumed to be carrying gas until proved otherwise.
- Ducts may contain any one of the services, irrespective of type or colour of the duct.

8.3.4 Checking for underground services

Before carrying out any work, check with all public and private utilities for existence of services in the area that work is planned for and ensure these routes are clearly marked on the plans.

The local electricity or gas company will give advice by telephone. BT operates a similar type of service and those wishing to make such enquiries should phone and select the option 'dial before you dig'.

Be careful when reading plans; reference points may have been moved, surfaces regraded, services moved without authority and not all connections may be shown.

Shallow service

On old brownfield sites there may be abandoned services and underground metallic items (such as tram lines and cast iron pipes); these can distort survey results.

Once routes have been identified, mark them with paint, tape or markers but **not** metal spikes, which might penetrate a cable or pipe.

Remember that the exact position will only be known when the underground service is uncovered.

Changes in colour of the surface material (sometimes known as tracks) may indicate where a service trench can be found. Absence of markers posts is not evidence that there are no underground services.

Working with underground services

Types of marker posts commonly found to indicate the location of underground services

Never assume that services have been installed at the recommended depth – they are often shallower.

Never assume that a located service is the only one; there may be others adjacent to, above or underneath it.

Beware of services encased in concrete bases or structures, or in the concrete backing to kerbs.

Beware of services rising over obstructions, culverts, bridges, and so on. They are often much shallower in these locations.

The presence of the following items indicates that underground services exist.

- ☑ Lamp posts.
- ☑ Illuminated traffic signs.
- ☑ Telephone boxes.
- ☑ Concrete or steel manhole covers.
- ☑ Hydrant and valve pit covers.

An electricity cable was damaged by the floor saw used to cut the road prior to excavating a new service trench. Although a cable avoidance tool (CAT) survey had located the cable, it was discovered that it was directly under the asphalt sub-base, which was 270 mm thick.

8.3.5 Using cable and pipe locators

Be aware that the CAT and generator should be used together, to provide the full picture. Equipment should be regularly serviced, at intervals not exceeding 12 months.

Recent developments in technology include depth read-outs.

A CAT will find most electricity cables whilst power is flowing through them, but it may not work in the following situations.

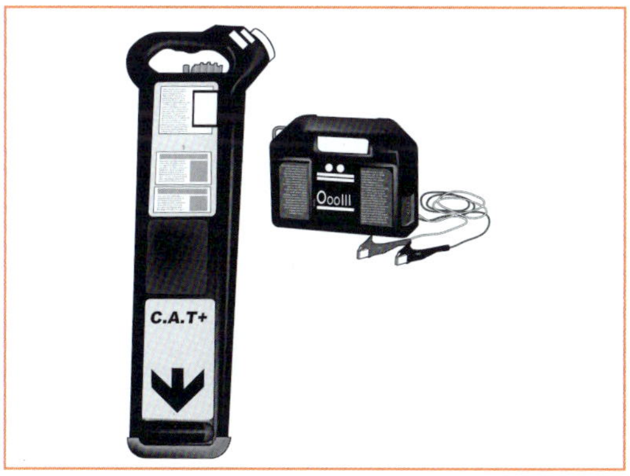

- ☑ If the cable has been disconnected.
- ☑ When the loading on a three-phase supply is evenly distributed.
- ☑ If the current is so small it is beyond the detection capability of the tool.
- ☑ If no current is flowing as the device is inactive (such as street lighting in the daytime).

Radio frequency can be used to detect electricity cables that have not been found by power detection, but its limitations can be geographical and it can also pick up other metal objects.

The **transmitter and receiver** (inductive or conductive) method is good when there is no current in services being sought.

Conventional cable locators will not find plastic pipes.

A **generator** (genny), when attached to an exposed part of a pipe or cable, will provide a signal for a CAT to track; it is important to continue to use the locator as the excavation progresses.

Metal detectors can detect hidden flat metal covers, joint boxes, and so on, but can miss cables or pipes. The deeper these objects are buried, the less chance of detection.

Ground penetrating radar is a portable hand transmitter that can sweep the area of land where there are thought to be underground services. The transmitter will display variations in the materials below the surface and can show where land has been disturbed.

An operative properly trained in the use of radar equipment can detect the majority of underground services and this result should then be compared with existing plans.

Information on all cables and pipes detected should be recorded and passed to the principal designer for inclusion in the client's health and safety file. Ensure that co-ordinates, lines and levels of newly installed services are included.

8.4 Digging

8.4.1 Permit to work and permit to dig

Where necessary, a formal permit to work system should be employed.

For a copy of a sample permit to dig refer to Section G: *Checklists and forms*.

This will show precautions to be taken, what has been done and what is required. The permit to work also enables the person in charge to check that all the conditions have been met before work commences.

Some sites operate a system where a copy of the permit to dig is held by the worker in an armband. This allows site management and supervisors to monitor that excavation work is being undertaken under a permit.

Permit in armband

8.4.2 Digging methods

Depending upon the potential hazards, it may be necessary to use a permit to work system before commencing any digging. On some sites a specific permit to dig system is used prior to breaking the ground.

Deep excavation with sheet piling

Hand digging near live services

Trial holes should be dug by hand to establish the exact location and depth of service; do not assume the service runs a direct line or same depth between two trial holes.

Do not use power tools or excavators within 500 mm of services. Hand digging must be adopted using insulated tools (such as spades or shovels). Excavate alongside the service rather than directly above it. Final exposure of the service by horizontal digging is recommended, as the force applied to hand tools can be controlled more effectively.

Power tools can be used to break paved surfaces but be careful to avoid over-penetration as services near buildings may have been laid shallowly.

Do not use power tools directly over an indicated line of a cable unless it has been made dead or steps have been taken to avoid damage.

The sides of an excavation must be suitable to allow services to pass through. Services may need to be supported in these surroundings.

Never assume that a service is dead – always treat it as live until confirmed otherwise.

Before and during excavation

- Check with all utilities and landowners before starting work.
- Assume the presence of services when digging, even if nothing is shown on plans.
- Use detection devices and keep a close watch for signs of underground services (such as marker tape or tiles).
- Although there are recommended minimum depths for all services, they may be closer to the surface than normal, especially in the vicinity of works, structures or other services.
- Markers (such as plastic tape, tiles, slabs or battens) may have been displaced and will not necessarily indicate the exact location of the underground service.
- Some electric cables and water pipes look alike, as do some gas pipes and water pipes. Ensure each pipe is properly identified before starting work on them.
- Services could be easily damaged by a fork or a pickaxe forced into the ground, but careful use of insulated spades and shovels enables services to be safely uncovered.
- Depending upon the risk assessment, those that are likely to encounter live services on a regular basis should wear flame resistant clothing, gloves and light eye protection.
- Carefully lever out rocks, stones and boulders.
- Over-penetration of the ground or surface with hand-held power tools is a common cause of accidents.
- If an excavator or digger is being used near any service, take extra care to prevent accidental damage. Where possible, no-one should be near the digger bucket while it is digging.
- Ensure the excavator operator and others excavating are informed of the presence of suspected services.
- If the service is embedded in concrete or paving material, the owner should de-energise it, otherwise make it safe or approve a safe system of work before it is broken out.
- Always assume closed, capped, sealed, loose or pot-ended services are live or charged, not dead or abandoned, until proved otherwise.
- Follow the guidelines and advice issued by the electricity, gas, water and telecommunication industries.
- Where possible, carry out the final exposure of underground services in a way that prevents any damage (such as using a compressed air lance).

For further information refer to Chapter D07 Excavations.

8.4.3 Piling and drilling

A safe system of work must be devised and implemented before any piling or drilling takes place.

If it is possible that there are services nearby, their position must be exposed by hand digging first.

For further information refer to *Safety on piling sites* (GE708).

8.4.4 Exposure and protection

If a service in a trench is exposed, protect it with wood or other suitable materials.

Services crossing trenches need support to avoid stress. Seek advice from the relevant utility company, if necessary.

Never use services crossing in a trench as footholds, anchorage or climbing points.

D 08

Information on working adjacent to underground pipelines and the location of underground pipelines around the UK can be found on the Linewatch and Linesearch websites.

8.4.5 Backfilling

When backfilling a trench **do not** dump hard core, surplus concrete, rock, rubble and flint onto a service pipe or cable, as it may damage it.

Use suitable material and ensure it is compacted with care to avoid shocking the service pipe or cable.

Warning tape should then be placed above the service at approximately 300 mm.

If gas service pipes have been exposed, advice on backfilling should be obtained from the local gas company.

8.4.6 Emergency works

Emergency works often mean there is no time to contact the utility companies. However, this work can be carried out safely if:

- the area is marked out carefully
- detectors are used correctly
- trial holes are dug by hand
- the practice of safe digging is followed.

8.4.7 Working in the roadway

Only licensed utility companies may carry out work in the footway, carriageway or any verge. When working in the roadway, ensure compliance with the New Roads and Street Works Act.

For further information refer to Chapter F01 Street works and road works.

D
08

8.5 Damage to underground services

Damage to underground services **must** be reported to the owner and/or occupier immediately. When such damage causes an emergency situation, call the **police**, **fire** and/or **ambulance** services as necessary.

8.5.1 Gas

For gas emergencies phone the gas emergency services.

If a gas leak is suspected, contact the police, fire brigade and gas supply company immediately. If there is a dangerous situation and the emergency services have not arrived, try to evacuate the immediate area including, if necessary, the occupants of nearby properties to an upwind position. As far as possible, prevent anyone from smoking and keep traffic clear of the area.

If the gas escape catches fire, do not attempt to extinguish the flames.

The normal minimum depth of cover for gas mains operating in the low and medium pressure ranges is:

- 600 mm in footways or verges
- 750 mm in carriageways.

These figures may vary since each gas company can have its own standards.

8.5.2 Electricity

For electricity emergencies phone CableSafe.

Avoid contact with any damaged cable or apparatus. When operating a machine do not attempt to disentangle any equipment. If at all possible, jump clear of the machine, ensuring that contact is not made with the vehicle and ground at the same time.

If this is not possible, stay exactly where you are. As far as possible, do not touch any metallic part of the vehicle and shout for help. If possible, inform the electricity company or ask someone else to do so. Keep people away.

The depth at which electricity cables or ducts are usually installed in the ground is decided by the need to avoid undue interference or damage.

Depending on the type of cable and the power that it may be carrying, the depth of cover may vary from 450–900 mm.

However, existing services can be found at any depth. It is not uncommon for them to have as little as 50 mm cover.

In all cases where the depth of cover is likely to increase or decrease, the service owner must be consulted.

8.5.3 Other services

Leave a damaged service well alone and inform the owner.

Some cables are automatically re-energised by the local sub-station after a short time following the supply tripping out due to damage. Do not assume that a damaged cable will remain dead.

8.6 Overhead services

Every year people are killed or seriously injured when they come into contact with overhead electricity power lines.

Incidents occur when working activities are not properly planned and result in contact with power lines (for example, contact with tipping trailers, cranes and scaffolding tubes and ladders).

If there is contact with a power line, or even if a piece of equipment gets too close to it, the electricity can be conducted to earth, which can cause fire, an explosion and shock or burns to anyone touching the machine or equipment.

Overhead lines can be difficult to spot, particularly in foggy or dull conditions. Often, people just fail to look up.

Electricity supplies above 33,000 volts are usually routed overhead. Supplies below this voltage may be either overhead or underground.

There is a legal minimum height above ground level for overhead power lines that varies according to voltage carried. These heights are shown below.

- 400 kV — 7.3 m.
- 275 kV — 7.0 m.
- 132 kV — 6.7 m.
- 33 kV-low voltage — 5.2 m except for roads where the minimum is 5.8 m.

The law requires that work may only be carried out in close proximity to live overhead lines when there is no alternative, and only when the risks are acceptable and can be properly controlled.

Where work cannot be avoided consult the local electricity company before any work is started and a safe system of work must be planned and implemented.

The regulations need power lines to be **dead** or suitable precautions taken to prevent danger before any work takes place.

There may be other suppliers who have to be notified (such as Local Authorities, National Grid and other electricity companies). Where necessary, wait for the supplier to isolate or re-route to enable the work to take place.

Take practical steps to prevent danger from any live cable or apparatus. This should include the placing of substantial and highly visible barriers. A barrier is only required one side if access is only required from one side, but if the line crosses the site, barriers will need to be placed on both sides.

If there is a danger to people with scaffold poles or other conducting objects then the barriers should exclude people and mobile plant.

8.6.1 Working near but not underneath overhead services

Where there will be no work or passage of machinery or equipment under the power lines, ground level barriers can be erected to establish a safety zone. This area should not be used to store materials or machinery.

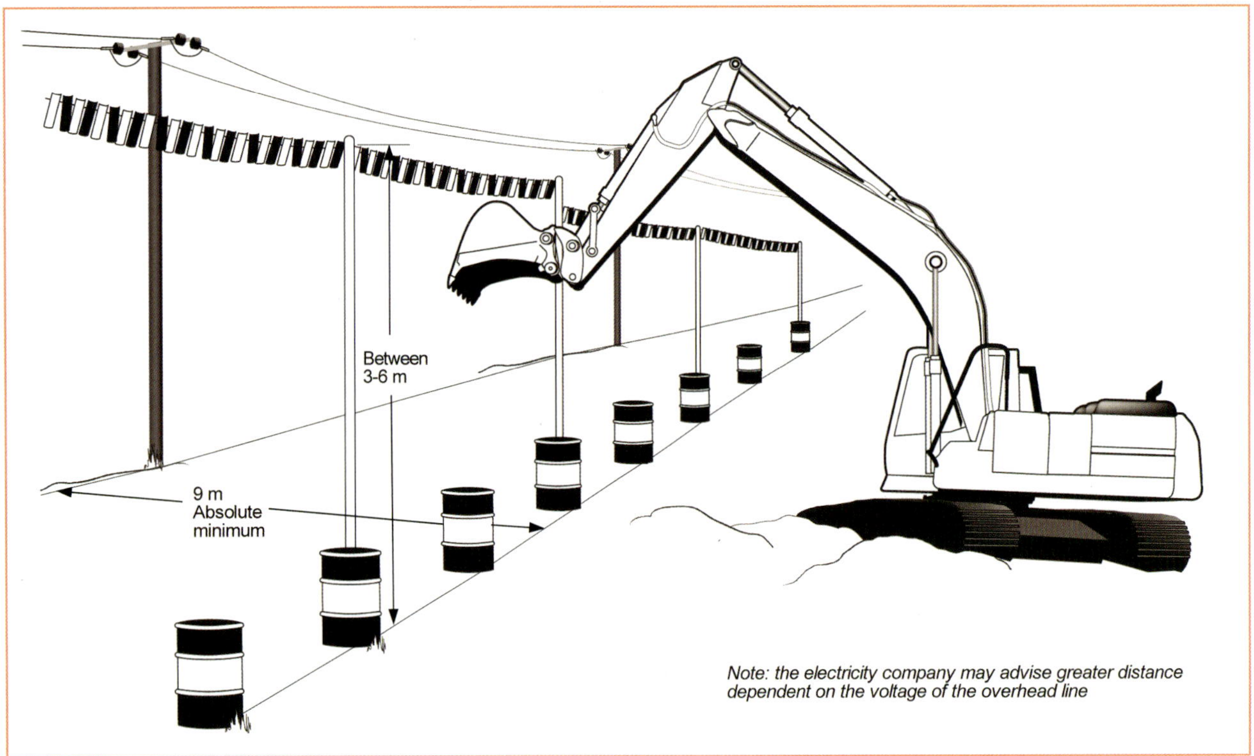

Example of a safety zone

8.6.2 Isolating the area containing the overhead services

Any ground-level barriers could consist of the following.

- ☑ A stout post and rail fence.
- ☑ A tension wire fence, earthed at both ends, with flags on the wire (the fence is earthed in consultation with the electricity company).
- ☑ Large steel drums (for example 200 litre oil drums) filled with rubble or concrete, and placed at frequent intervals.
- ☑ An earth bank, not less than one metre high and marked by posts to stop vehicles.
- ☑ Substantial timber baulks to act as wheel stops.

Ensure that post and oil drums are made as distinctive as possible by being painted with red and white stripes. Red and white flags or hazard bunting can be used on wire fences.

Ensure all work is carried out under the direct supervision of a responsible supervisor (someone who is familiar with all the hazards that need to be taken into consideration). Ensure that any barriers can be seen at night. This could be achieved by using white or fluorescent paint or attaching reflective strips.

The safety zone should extend 6 m horizontally from the nearest wire on either side of the overhead line. It may be possible to reduce the safety zone but an assessment would need to be undertaken to ensure that there is no possibility of encroachment into the safe clearance distances stated in the risk assessment.

It must be assumed that all overhead lines and cables are live unless advised otherwise by the electricity company.

8.6.3 Safe working when passing underneath overhead services

Ensure that everyone working on site is aware that no work should take place:

- ☑ until the electricity company is consulted for advice
- ☑ within 9 m of overhead power lines on wood or concrete poles
- ☑ within 15 m of overhead power lines on steel towers.

All personnel must be aware that the distances above are measured horizontally at ground level, from directly below the outermost conduction.

It is essential that ongoing liaison is maintained between the contractor and the electricity company.

If the overhead lines have not been diverted or made dead, ensure all practicable steps been taken to provide adequate barriers to comply with the regulations.

Ensure arrangements have been made for the passage of tall plant at specific times where overhead power lines have been made dead.

Electricity carried by overhead cables, which are generally uninsulated:

- ☑ will flow though any metal object that comes into contact with them (such as a metal ladder, a scaffold pole or a raised excavator bucket)
- ☑ may jump through the air (arc) to anything nearby that will conduct electricity.

Working on or near live conductors

Regulation 14 of the Electricity at Work Regulations for work on or near live conductors states:

- ☑ no person shall be engaged in any work activity on or so near any live conductor (other than one suitably covered with insulating material so as to prevent danger) that danger may arise unless:
  - it is unreasonable in all circumstances for it to be dead
  - it is reasonable in all circumstances for work on or near it while it is live
  - suitable precautions (including where necessary the provision of suitable protective equipment) are taken to prevent injury.

If plant needs to pass under the overhead lines then the danger must be reduced. This can be done by restricting the access way to the minimum possible width.

The following precautions are also recommended.

- ☑ Keep the number of access passageways to a minimum.
- ☑ Fence the services to define its route and erect goal posts at each end.
- ☑ Construct the goal posts from non-conducting material and highlight them.
- ☑ Maintain barriers and goal posts.
- ☑ Give warning notices on either side of the passageway.
- ☑ Give information to drivers on clearance height and instructing them to lower jibs, tipper bodies, and so on, and to keep below this height whilst crossing.
- ☑ If lighting is needed, place at ground level and project upwards towards the conductors. It may also be necessary to illuminate the notices and cross bar at night.
- ☑ Place additional notices on the approaches to the crossing (approximately 30 m prior to the approach).
- ☑ Ensure the access route's surface is kept level, firm and well maintained to prevent undue tilting or bouncing of equipment whilst moving under the power lines.

For further information refer to the HSE guidance note GS6.

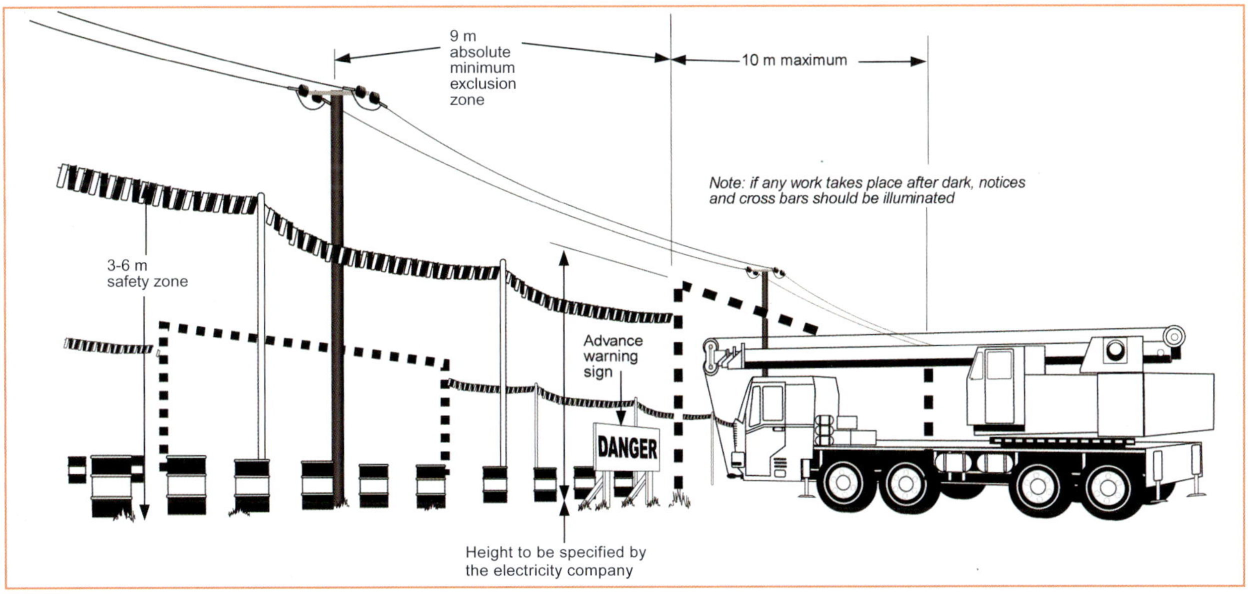

Example of a passageway through barriers

D 08

Requirements for safe passageway through barriers

- ☑ The safety zone should extend 6 m horizontally from the nearest wire on either side. It may be necessary to increase this width depending on advice from the line owner or to allow for moving parts of the machinery encroaching into the safety zone.
- ☑ Where a crane is operating in the area, an additional high level indication should be erected. A line of coloured bunting 3-6 m above the ground and over the barrier is suitable.
- ☑ Manage the risks if work will be carried out within a 10 m distance, measured at ground level horizontally from below the nearest wire.

8.6.4 Working underneath overhead services

Risks will be increased, either by the existence of buildings where work needs to be undertaken on or in it, or where buildings are being erected under overhead power lines.

A risk assessment must identify any situations that could lead to danger from the overhead lines. If there is no risk of accidental contact or safe clearance distances being breached then no further precautionary measures are required. If the services cannot be made dead or diverted then the following precautions are strongly recommended.

- ☑ Consult the owner of the line as to how the work should be done.
- ☑ Appoint a competent supervisor to oversee the work and ensure it is carried out safely.
- ☑ Avoid any equipment that can reach the overhead services or is near enough to cause a flashover (such as scaffold poles and ladders).
- ☑ Ensure that workers understand the risks and are provided with instructions for risk prevention measures and supervision is provided.
- ☑ If overhead power lines cannot be switched off for the duration of the works reference should be made to the Energy Networks Association (ENA) Publication *Look up! A guide to the safe use of mechanical plant in the vicinity of electricity overhead lines*. This advises establishing exclusion zones around the line and any other equipment that may be fitted to the pole or pylon. No part of plant, piece of equipment or hand tools should be able to go into these areas, but allowances should be made for unexpected movements (for example, wind conditions).

Electricity can kill. The correct information, instruction, training and supervision can help to keep workers, and others coming into contact with them, alive.

Worker receives fatal electric shock from overhead power line

A trainee scaffolder received a fatal electric shock whilst handling a 6.4 m long scaffold tube that came into contact with an 11,000 volt overhead power line. No site specific risk assessment had been carried out, only generic ones at the office.

The company employing the worker was prosecuted under the Health and Safety at Work Act, Section 2(1), and fined.

The company should have:

- ☑ closely supervised the trainee until he was able to demonstrate competence in a wide range of work situations
- ☑ undertaken a risk assessment for that site and informed all workers of the outcome
- ☑ taken action to reduce the risks from contact with overhead power lines (for example, requesting that the electricity distributor made the overhead power line dead during the work).

09
Confined spaces

Contents

Supporting information

G: Checklists and forms

GT 700 Toolbox talks

Overview

Every entry into a confined space is potentially hazardous. Accidents in confined spaces are a major source of deaths at work, killing several people each year in a wide range of industries.

Some confined spaces are easy to identify (such as closed tanks, vessels and sewers). Others are less obvious but may be equally dangerous, including basement-level boiler rooms or toilets, as well as open-topped tanks, vats, silos or other structures that become confined spaces during their manufacture.

9.1 Introduction

A confined space is a place which is substantially enclosed (though not always entirely), and where serious injury can occur from hazardous substances or conditions (such as lack of oxygen) within that space or nearby.

Accidents in confined spaces are caused by a combination of factors arising from a lack of awareness, inadequate supervision and a lack of training. The situation is often made worse by heroic but ill-conceived rescue attempts, founded on insufficient planning and knowledge, which may lead to multiple fatalities. It is essential, therefore, to be able to identify confined spaces and the hazards associated with entering and working in them.

Within confined spaces a *specified risk* can mean a risk of any of the following.

- Serious injury to any person at work, arising from a fire or explosion.
- The loss of consciousness of any person at work arising from an increase in body temperature.
- The loss of consciousness or asphyxiation of any person at work arising from gas, fumes, vapour or the lack of oxygen.
- Drowning of any person at work arising from an increase in the level of liquid.
- Asphyxiation of any person at work arising from a free-flowing solid or the inability to reach a respirable environment due to entrapment by a free flowing solid.

Some places may become a confined space only occasionally, perhaps due to the type of work to be undertaken (such as a room during paint spraying). A confined space may not necessarily be enclosed on all sides; some confined spaces (such as vats, silos or deep excavations) may have open tops. Places not usually considered to be confined spaces may become confined spaces because of a change in the condition inside or a change in the degree of enclosure or confinement.

Care must be taken when entering a confined space

The expression *confined space* means any place, including any chamber, tank, vat, silo, pit, trench, pipe, sewer, flue, well or other similar space in which, by virtue of its enclosed nature, there arises a reasonably foreseeable specified risk. Application of the Confined Spaces Regulations in any of these places will depend on the presence of a reasonably foreseeable risk of serious injury from a hazardous substance or condition within the space or nearby.

Below are some examples of confined spaces that may be encountered during construction work.

- Cellars or an inadequately ventilated basement room.
- Boilers, boiler flues or chimneys.
- Manholes, sewers, drains or excavations.
- Ceiling voids or ducts.
- Caissons or cofferdams.
- Loft spaces or plant rooms.
- Any room or enclosed space with poor ventilation, as these can become a confined space (for example, painting a room or power floating in a large hanger using petrol-powered equipment).

There are many more examples of confined spaces and the hazards will vary with the location, the type of work being carried out, and the equipment or substances used.

9.2 Important points

- Working in confined spaces has the potential to be very hazardous unless the appropriate controls are put in place.
- Many people have died as a result of work in confined spaces not being adequately planned, organised or safely carried out; many of them were would-be rescuers.
- Ideally carry out the work without anyone having to enter a confined space.
- Confined spaces are not just sewers and ducts; under the regulations many other work areas could also be classified as confined spaces.

- ☑ A risk assessment must be carried out for all work in a confined space.
- ☑ Where the findings of the risk assessment reveal significant risks to health or safety, it will normally result in a method statement being written.
- ☑ Any plan of the work must consider the method of rescuing the people in the confined space should the situation become unsafe.
- ☑ Entry to a confined space should be controlled by a permit to work and, where considered necessary, a separate permit to enter.
- ☑ Any training may need to be specific for the type of confined space – a sewer entry course may not be appropriate for someone who has to work in a hot roof space. Training should extend not only to those entering confined spaces but also to managers, supervisors, emergency personnel, and so on.
- ☑ The use of respiratory protective equipment (RPE) is common in confined space work and users must be face-fit tested and trained in its use, general care and maintenance.
- ☑ Unplanned or poorly planned work in confined spaces has the potential to kill – reading and understanding this chapter is not a substitute for adequate training and experience.

Take great care identifying what is and what could be a confined space. Many confined space accidents occur in work areas that have simply not been identified as potential confined spaces.

9.3 Dangers in confined spaces

9.3.1 Oxygen deprivation and suffocation

The air that we breathe contains around 21% oxygen and, at that level, people can work without difficulty. A falling level of oxygen will create an increasingly serious situation if breathing apparatus is not worn. Generally, the following symptoms are experienced at the corresponding level of oxygen depletion.

Oxygen depletion	Symptoms
19%	Tiredness (normal acceptable minimum level for working).
17%	Judgement (decision making) is affected.
12%	Respiration is affected and fatigue experienced.
10%	Light-headedness and increasing breathing difficulties.
8%	Nausea and possible collapse.
6%	Respiration stops and death follows within minutes.

Oxygen deprivation may be the result of any of the following.

- ☑ The displacement of oxygen by gas leaking in from elsewhere, or the deliberate introduction of purge gas (for example, nitrogen or argon).
- ☑ The displacement of oxygen by a naturally occurring gas (such as methane).
- ☑ Oxidisation, rusting or bacterial growth using up the oxygen in air.
- ☑ Oxygen being consumed by people working and breathing, or by any process of combustion.
- ☑ Welding and other hot works.
- ☑ The prior discharge of a fire extinguisher containing carbon dioxide or other asphyxiating gas.

9.3.2 Hazards of excess oxygen

An oxygen-enriched atmosphere is, in itself, a major hazard. Organic materials (such as oil and wood) become highly combustible, and ordinary materials (such as paper and clothing) will burn with exceptional ferocity.

An increase of only 4% oxygen is sufficient to create a hazard and this may occur inadvertently. In oxyacetylene and oxypropane processes, sometimes not all of the oxygen supplied to a cutting torch is consumed. Some may be released, increasing the atmospheric oxygen above the normal 21%.

The oxygen enrichment of the atmosphere in a confined space also results from the practice of using oxygen to sweeten or enrich the atmosphere when it has become oppressive, stale, hot, fume-filled or otherwise unpleasant. This is a very dangerous practice and must be prohibited.

Another way in which the atmosphere may become oxygen-enriched is through leakage from torches or hoses during meal breaks or overnight. For this reason, they should be removed at each breaktime. The deliberate kinking or nipping of an oxygen hose while changing a torch does not usually cut off the supply completely and can result in the release of substantial quantities of oxygen.

If excess oxygen is discovered, the space must be quickly evacuated and ventilated until normal levels of oxygen are regained.

9.3.3 Toxic atmospheres

However much oxygen is present in the atmosphere, if there is also a toxic gas present in sufficient quantity it will create a hazard.

Below are some of the many toxic gases that may be encountered.

- ☑ Hydrogen sulphide, usually from sewage or decaying vegetation.
- ☑ Carbon monoxide, from internal combustion engines, or any incomplete combustion, especially of liquefied petroleum gases (LPG).
- ☑ Carbon dioxide, from any fermentation, or being naturally evolved in soil and rocks, or coming from the combustion of LPG.
- ☑ Fumes and vapours, from chemicals such as ammonia, chlorine, sodium, and from petrol and solvents.

Whenever a toxic gas (or any gas, fume or vapour that may be hazardous to health) is thought to be (or known to be) present, then an assessment of the risk to health must be made under the provisions of the Control of Substances Hazardous to Health (COSHH) Regulations and the appropriate control measures must be put into place to eliminate the hazard or control the risks.

Petrol and diesel engines create carbon monoxide, which is an extremely toxic gas.

Liquid petroleum gas-powered engines create an excess of carbon dioxide, which is a suffocating hazard. The use of any form of internal combustion engine within a confined space must be prohibited, unless a specifically dedicated exhaust extraction system is operative.

9.3.4 Flammable atmospheres

Some gases and vapours need to only be present in very small quantities to create a hazard. A few of the major sources of explosive and flammable hazards are shown below.

- ☑ Petrol or liquefied petroleum gas, propane, butane and acetylene. These are explosive in the range of 2% upwards in air. The hazard is normally created by a spillage or leakage.
- ☑ Methane and hydrogen sulphide, which are naturally evolved from sewage or decaying organic matter. These are explosive in the range of 4% upwards in air.
- ☑ Solvents, acetone, toluene, white spirit, alcohol, benzene, thinners, and so on. These are explosive in the range of 2% upwards in air. The hazard generally results from process plants and/or spillage.
- ☑ Hydrogen and other gases evolved from processes such as battery charging.

In an explosive or flammable atmosphere, a toxic or suffocating hazard may also exist.

9.3.5 Hostile environments

Apart from the hazards dealt with above, other dangers may arise from the use of electrical and mechanical equipment, from chemicals, process gases and liquids, dust, paint fumes, welding and cutting fumes.

Depending upon the work activity, any space can become a confined space, including lofts, lifts or inspection pits, service risers and unventilated rooms, even if they are large spaces

Extremes of excess heat and cold can have adverse effects and may be intensified in a confined space. Consideration must be given to the timing of what would otherwise be considered standard work. During hot weather, roof spaces and other types of confined spaces may reach temperatures that will lead to a dangerous increase in body temperature.

If work cannot be planned to avoid this (for example, by starting early) then physical measures (such as cooling and reducing the time spent working in the confined space) must be introduced following an assessment by a competent person.

Further dangers exist in the sheer difficulty of getting into or out of, and working in, a confined space. The potential hazards of an inrush of water, gas or sludge due to a failure of walls or barriers, or leakage from valves, flanges or blanks, must all be considered at the risk assessment stage.

9.4 Confined Spaces Regulations

These require employers to plan work so that entry to confined spaces is avoided so far as is reasonably practicable (for example, by doing the work from outside). They also require a safe system of work to be developed and implemented if entry to a confined space is unavoidable, and adequate emergency arrangements, which will also safeguard rescuers, to be put in place before work starts.

Duties to comply with the regulations are placed on:

- employers in respect of work carried out by their own employees and work carried out by any person (for example, a contractor) insofar as work is, to any extent, under the employer's control
- the self-employed in respect of work carried out by any other person insofar as work is, to any extent, under the control of the self-employed person.

The main duty under Regulation 4 is a complete prohibition of any person entering a confined space to carry out any work for any purpose whatsoever, where it is reasonably practicable to carry out the work by any other means.

If entry into a confined space is necessary then a risk assessment by a competent person, under the **Management of Health and Safety at Work Regulations**, is required. The outcome of the risk assessment will then provide the basis for the development of a full and effective safe system of work, including rescue arrangements.

These regulations are supported and explained by an Approved Code of Practice (ACoP) and guidance notes. The competent person responsible for carrying out the risk assessment, or otherwise planning work in a confined space, should be familiar with the principles outlined in the document.

For the definition of reasonably practicable refer to Chapter A01 Health and safety law.

The complete regulations and the ACoP and guidance notes can be viewed online.

9.5 Information, instruction and training

The information, instruction and training given to employees must enable them to carry out work safely and without risks to their health. The extent of training needed will vary according to circumstances and the type of space being entered.

Any entry into a confined space requiring the use of breathing apparatus would require a full breathing apparatus and rescue course. However, training to enter a bund around a large diesel tank where the risks are less significant (such as fumes and possible drowning in diesel) would not require such an intensive course, and indeed adopting the use of breathing apparatus in this instance may be entirely inappropriate.

Using protective equipment within a confined space

Training should involve demonstrations and practical exercises. It is important that trainees are familiar with both equipment and procedures before working for the first time in confined spaces.

Practical refresher training should be organised and available. The frequency with which refresher training is provided will depend upon how long it is since the type of work was last done, or if there have been changes to methods of work, safety procedures or equipment.

The training needs for confined space working should be considered for each of the four categories of employee.

- Supervisors.
- Employees entering confined spaces.
- People employed as attendants outside of confined spaces.
- Rescue teams.

Some of the roles identified may be carried out by the same person.

Prior to working in a confined space, there is currently no legal requirement to have obtained a specific standard of training. However, there has been discussion between the utility companies, who are the clients for much of the sewer-entry work, with regard to recognising each other's training standards.

No person should enter a confined space unless they are trained and competent to do so safely (Regulation 4).

Tunnelling offers more specific challenges and the Pipe Jacking Association and the British Tunnelling Society websites should be consulted for the latest updates on training standards.

9.6 Safe working

If you cannot avoid entry into a confined space a safe system of work should be implemented. This can be achieved by the use of a permit to work system, in which each step is planned and all foreseeable hazards are taken into account. Such a system, backed up by adequate rescue facilities, should enable work to be carried out safely.

At the planning stage it will be necessary for the following information to be determined.

- Whether an entry into the confined space is required, or whether an alternative method of doing the work exists.
- If an entry is necessary, whether it can be carried out without the use of breathing apparatus.
- Whether the entry must be made with the use of breathing apparatus.

In respect of the final point, it should be emphasised that entry into a confined space using breathing apparatus should not be made routinely or undertaken as a matter of convenience, where the use of isolation and mechanical or forced ventilation would achieve a safe atmosphere.

If it is decided that the work can be done without anyone entering the confined space, provided that a safe system of work exists and the confined space has been isolated from potential sources of hazard, the work can proceed. It is important to avoid systems or plant being re-energised while work is proceeding and everyone involved should be advised accordingly.

Once it has been decided that people must enter a confined space, a preliminary meeting should be held with all concerned, and effective lines of authority and communication established in order to minimise any risk of subsequent misunderstanding.

The exact routine to be followed will vary, depending on the type of confined space to be entered. The provisions and precautions required for entry into a large, empty surface water tank will obviously be different from those needed for entry into a narrow service duct containing pipes and valves, but the fundamental principle of a safe system of work applies to these and other cases. The risk assessment, as mentioned previously, will have identified many of the above points and should be used as the basis for developing the safe system of work.

It is stressed that all personal protective equipment (PPE) in general, and RPE in particular, must have been specified by a competent person who is clearly aware of all of the circumstances surrounding its use.

If the fire and rescue service forms a part of the rescue plan, they must be given a warning that a confined space entry is to be made. This will give them the opportunity to assess the risks to their own staff and identify any equipment they might need.

9.6.1 Supervision

Supervisors should be given responsibility to ensure that the necessary precautions are taken to check safety at each stage. They will also need to remain present when the work is underway.

9.6.2 Isolation

The confined space must be isolated from all possible external sources of danger to persons entering it. It is good practice to use **positive isolations** for confined space entries – this means complete separation of the plant/equipment to be worked on from other parts of the system. If this is not possible then isolation should generally be proved.

A full permit to work system should be used to record the location and types of isolation, and the hazards being guarded against.

Electrical isolation must never rely on a switch or fuse. The switch gear or fuse holder must be locked off and a warning notice applied. *(For further information refer to 9.6.15 Permits.)*

Mechanical isolation of pipework should not rely on a single valve or on a non-return valve; these may leak and create a hazard. Whenever possible, a section of pipe should be removed or a blank or spade should be put into a flange between the valve and the confined space and a warning notice displayed.

Isolation from mechanical and electrical equipment will often include locking off the switch and formally securing the key in accordance with a permit to work, until it is no longer necessary to control access. Lock-and-tag systems can be useful here, where each operator has their own lock and key giving self-assurance of the inactivated mechanism or system. Check there is no stored energy of any kind left in the system that could activate the equipment inadvertently.

Paddles, stirrers or agitators, whether electrically or mechanically operated, should be physically disconnected by the removal of an operating arm, and a warning notice displayed.

9.6.3 Cleaning

There is a variety of methods of cleaning the inside of confined spaces to remove hazardous solids, liquids or gases. Cold water washing, hot water washing and steaming will remove many contaminants, while solvents or neutralising agents may be necessary for others. If hot water or steam is used, with or without a solvent, care must be taken to ensure that adequate ventilation exists for steam pressure and that condensation does not build up to unacceptable levels.

If steam is used or water is boiled in a confined space, account must be taken of the vacuum that can be created on cooling.

When steam or solvents are used, these may create a toxic, suffocating or flammable hazard. Even though a space has been well cleaned, it must not be entered until it has been monitored.

Great care must be taken if encountering any sludge or heavy deposits that may release toxic gases if disturbed.

9.6.4 Purging and ventilation

Air purging and ventilation can be carried out by removing covers, opening inspection doors, or similar, and allowing ordinary air circulation, or by the introduction of compressed air via an air line. However, higher rates of air exchange can be achieved by the use of air movers, induction fans or extractor fans.

It is especially important that when an inert gas (such as nitrogen) has been used to purge or render inert a flammable atmosphere, the inert gas itself is properly purged with air.

When air purging is taking place, the flow of air should be of a sufficient volume and velocity to ensure that no pockets or layers of gas remain undisturbed. This also needs to be constantly monitored.

9.6.5 Atmospheric monitoring

Depending on the circumstances, as a result of the assessment made under the COSHH Regulations, or the risk assessment made under the Management of Health and Safety at Work Regulations, continuous atmospheric monitoring may well be necessary when any work is to be done that would expose employees to any substance hazardous to health.

Before an entry is made into such a confined space, tests must be carried out to establish the levels of oxygen, toxic gas or flammable gas in the atmosphere.

The external atmosphere around the opening should be monitored first, and if the results are satisfactory, internal monitoring should be carried out by lowering a gas monitor into the confined space before it is occupied.

If entry into the confined space is necessary to carry out the tests, breathing apparatus or other RPE must be worn.

Suitably trained and competent personnel may use simple, reliable instruments to measure oxygen and flammable gas levels.

The accuracy of the instruments must be assured by periodic calibration.

A satisfactory oxygen content must not in itself be relied on to indicate safety since flammable, explosive or toxic gas may exist alongside oxygen and need only be present in minute quantities to create a serious hazard.

The tests applied should take account of what the space is known to have contained, including any inert gas used to purge a flammable atmosphere, which may itself produce toxic hazards or the risk of asphyxiation. Account must also be taken of hazards arising from other sources (such as materials used for cleaning). Methane, hydrogen sulphide and carbon dioxide can all evolve naturally due to the decomposition of organic matter or, in some cases, by the effect of rainwater percolating through certain types of ground. It is necessary to test the atmosphere of a confined space at both high and low level as well as in any corners where pockets of gas may exist.

Instances have occurred of carbon dioxide displacing oxygen at lower levels while a normal oxygen level continues to exist at higher levels of the same confined space.

The sense of smell must never be relied upon to detect gases. Some are odourless, and hydrogen sulphide, in particular, can paralyse the sense of smell to such an extent that even fatally high concentrations of the gas cannot be detected. In any case, the sense of smell varies from person to person and deteriorates with age.

9.6.6 Monitoring and testing equipment

Providing that the specific contaminant is known, tests can be carried out by competent persons using the individual detector tubes available for the detection of specific toxic and asphyxiant flammable or explosive fumes or gases.

The tubes have a wide range of tolerance, so readings close to an occupational exposure limit should not be acted upon until the test has been repeated and the manufacturer's standard of accuracy applied.

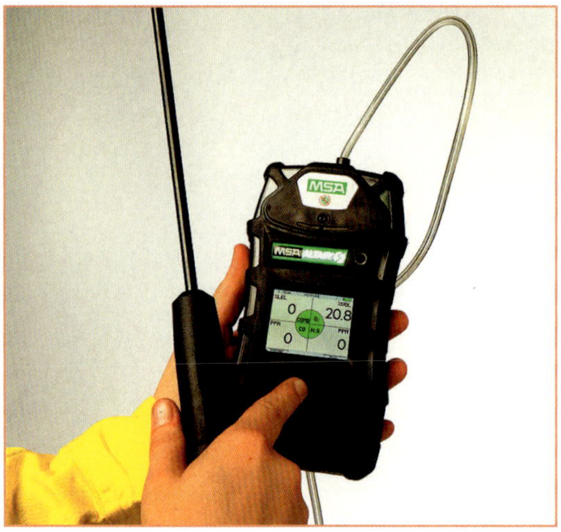

A wide range of portable gas detection equipment is available for flammable and toxic gases; some are specific to one gas (for example, hydrogen sulphide), while others can sample a range of different gases. Such instruments need to be properly calibrated.

9.6.6.1 Continuous monitoring

The initial monitoring and testing must establish that the confined space is safe to enter. Monitoring should then be carried out at intervals to ensure the continued safety of personnel. Tests should be repeated after any breaks (such as lunch or overnight) or after the time limit set out in a permit to work has expired.

It may be necessary to issue individual monitors to people working in a confined space, so as to give them an instant warning of low oxygen, or toxic or flammable gas hazards.

9.6.6.2 Competence of monitors

All atmospheric monitoring must be carried out by persons who are trained and competent to use the instruments and interpret the results. They must have sufficient practical and theoretical knowledge to enable them to make a valid judgement based on the results. They must be fully aware of their responsibilities in permitting an entry into a confined space.

9.6.7 Selection of personnel

Care is required in selecting the right people to work in confined spaces, since conditions can be difficult. They must be physically fit, agile and, most importantly, not be claustrophobic. People who suffer from asthma, bronchitis or other respiratory conditions, or whose immune system has been suppressed, must be assessed by a medical practitioner as to their suitability to work in confined spaces.

Other health conditions that might indicate that a person is not suitable for working in a confined space, or that further checks need to be made before it is allowed, are listed below.

- ☑ High blood pressure.
- ☑ Partial or complete deafness.
- ☑ Lack of mobility through joint problems.
- ☑ Diabetes.
- ☑ Depression or other mental illness.
- ☑ Defective eyesight (which is not corrected by wearing glasses).
- ☑ Sensitivity of the skin to some substances.
- ☑ Taking some types of medication.

Stamina is also required. The wearing of any form of respiratory protection tends to lead to an increase in respiration and a higher use of energy; the amount of work that can be done in confined spaces is less than that expected under normal conditions.

When respiratory protection is to be used, it should be remembered that facial hair and spectacles often prevent a respirator from fitting properly and thus achieving the assumed degree of protection.

Face-fit testing should be carried out to ensure that the chosen mask fits the wearer. This can be achieved quantitatively using a 'portacount' for half or full face masks or qualitatively using bitter/sweet solutions for half or disposable masks.

9.6.8 Communications

Adequate and effective communications must exist between those inside and those outside the confined space, so that, in the event of an incident, a warning can be given and the space evacuated or those inside rescued. The system needs to be fail-safe, ensuring that, if a reply is not received or a scheduled call not made, the procedure for rescue starts immediately.

When a confined space is relatively small, so that the person entering it cannot move far from the entry point and there are no other factors that could hinder effective communication, the method of communication may be relatively simple (such as a prearranged system of tugs on the safety rope, which must be fully understood by all involved). However, if the nature of the confined space, the job to be carried out and other factors necessitate the person travelling some distance from the entry point, a more elaborate communication system might be required.

The following factors could hinder effective communication and may need to be considered in the risk assessment.

- Level of noise inside or outside the confined space, which may or may not be associated with the confined space work.
- Physical nature of the confined space or the presence of substances that could reduce visibility.
- Distance between the point of entry and the place of work.
- Presence of workers with little or no understanding of English.

Depending upon the findings of the risk assessment, prior communication with the emergency services regarding the location and nature of the work might be considered necessary.

All types of respiratory protection affect verbal communication to some degree and, whatever method of communication is chosen, it should be tested and proved outside the confined space before entry is made.

9.6.9 Work equipment

Due to the potential for a flammable or explosive atmosphere in confined spaces, selecting tools and other work equipment with which the work can be carried out safely is essential.

If there is any possibility of flammable gas existing in a confined space, even below the lower explosive limit (LEL), all tools must be of a non-sparking material and all lighting and electrical equipment must carry British Approvals Service for Electrical Equipment in Flammable Atmospheres (BASEEFA) approval. Smoking and naked lights must be strictly prohibited and care must be taken to avoid the generation of static electricity with the consequent risk of sparks.

For further information refer to the BASEEFA website.

9.6.10 Fire safety

Hot works must not be carried out in a confined space unless atmospheric testing has confirmed that flammable or explosive gases are not present and the findings of a risk assessment show that it is otherwise safe to do so.

Where there is still a residual risk of fire, appropriate fire extinguishers may need to be kept in the confined space at the entry point.

Where hot works are being carried out inside a confined space, the operative carrying out the work must also have a suitable and serviceable fire extinguisher at the place of work. In the event of a fire, the local fire service should be called in case the fire cannot be contained or extinguished.

9.6.11 First aid

Appropriate first-aid equipment and trained first aiders should be provided and available for emergencies and to provide first aid until professional medical help arrives.

9.6.12 Rescue

The arrangements for the rescue of persons in the event of an emergency, both in terms of trained persons and equipment, need to be suitable and sufficient. The arrangements must be in place before any person enters or works in a confined space.

In some circumstances (for example, where there are prolonged operations in confined spaces and the risks justify it) there may be advantage in prior notification to the local emergency services (for example, local fire or ambulance service) before the work is undertaken. However, reliance on the emergency services alone will not be sufficient to comply with the regulations. Employers must put in place adequate emergency arrangements before the work starts.

Proper and effective rescue training is quite hard and arduous and is not to be undertaken lightly. Persons selected for such training need to be physically fit and able to adapt to situations as they arise during a rescue.

Injury and collapse

If a person is **injured** in a confined space that has been certified safe to enter without respiratory protection, an entry can be made to rescue and remove them straight away.

If a person **collapses** in a confined space and the cause is not known, irrespective of whether or not the confined space was certified fit for entry without respiratory protection, no-one must enter unless they are wearing breathing apparatus. The collapse may have been due to deterioration in the atmosphere within the confined space. The first duty of any rescuer is to ensure that they do not become a casualty themselves.

Each year, would-be rescuers who are insufficiently trained or equipped die by going into confined spaces where a person has collapsed.

This point is illustrated in the following two case studies.

Open-topped inspection shaft fatalities

At Carsington Reservoir, four men, all aged between 20 and 30 and physically fit, died in an open-topped inspection shaft. Naturally evolved carbon dioxide had displaced the oxygen. No tests were made before entry. The first man down collapsed and the three other men climbed down to their deaths in futile attempts to rescue him.

An HM Inspector of Factories working in the Public Utilities National Industry Group of the Health and Safety Executive (HSE) wrote about this major accident and stressed: 'It should be manifestly obvious that confined spaces working is one activity where shortcuts in safety cannot be permitted. The deaths of these four men will be more tragic if the lessons of this incident are not fully learnt'.

Fatalities in a sewer

When an engineer collapsed in a sewer, a rescuer entered without breathing apparatus and was overcome. A second person made a similarly vain attempt to reach the victims. When the rescue team from the fire and rescue service arrived they had to remove bodies of the two would-be rescuers before they could get to the engineer. By then it was too late and he had died. Had everyone waited for the fire and rescue service, the engineer might have lived and the rescuers would not have needlessly died.

9.6.13 Rescue equipment

Every person entering a confined space wearing breathing apparatus must also wear a safety harness. The harness must be attached to a lifeline, attended by a person outside the confined space.

The harness must be one that is suitable for confined space rescue, in that it must enable an unconscious person to remain in an upright position whilst being hoisted.

An unsuitable harness will allow the unconscious person to bend at the waist, making recovery through a narrow opening difficult or impossible.

This equipment forms part of a safe system of work for any entry into a confined space. Properly used, it may enable a rescue to be carried out successfully without the need for a rescuer to enter the confined space.

Rescue equipment must include some means of lifting or pulling a person up from a confined space, since it is virtually impossible for the average person to achieve this solely by muscular effort. There are a variety of tripods, winches, blocks and tackles which, when used in conjunction with a safety harness, enable a person to be lifted quickly and safely out of a confined space.

If lifting is envisaged as part of a rescue scenario, then the equipment and accessories will be subject to the Lifting Operations and Lifting Equipment Regulations (LOLER). This would mean testing and inspection in accordance with the schedule drawn up by the competent person. In practice, harness, lines and accessories (such as carabiners) should be subjected to a formal thorough examination by a competent person every six months and be checked by the user weekly and before each use. Tripods, hoists and other lifting devices need to be load tested every six months in the same way that a scissor lift used for lifting people would.

Dependent on circumstances, rescue equipment may have to include first-aid equipment, oxygen or resuscitation packs and rescue breathing apparatus. A secure line of communication to the emergency services may also be required.

9.6.14 Respiratory protective equipment

RPE must be selected by a competent person, be CE marked and be suitable for the type of hazard against which it is to protect the wearer.

A wide range of RPE is available from various manufacturers. The equipment functions on the basis of two distinct principles, outlined below.

9.6.14.1 Purifying the air breathed

The air inhaled is drawn through a filter or medium that removes the harmful substance or pollutant. The nature of the filtering agent depends on the type of pollutant to be dealt with. These types are commonly called *respirators*.

The simplest form of respirator is the dust mask, a preformed cup made of filtering material that fits over the nose and mouth to filter out nuisance dust. These masks give no protection against harmful or toxic gases or fumes and the protection factor of the mask may not offer adequate protection against the level of airborne dust that can be experienced in a confined space.

More complex types have filter cartridges that may be general for various types of dust or fume, or specific to a particular substance.

9.6.14.2 Supplying clean air

The air can be supplied straight through an air line via a pump or compressor or, alternatively, the person may carry compressed air in cylinders. These types are known as *breathing apparatus*.

An alternative type of breathing equipment is the self-rescue set. This consists of a small compressed air bottle, the necessary hoses and valves and a facepiece. Self-rescue sets can be carried by operatives who enter confined spaces where the air is initially safe to breathe.

Should the air quality deteriorate, the facepiece is placed over the nose and mouth and the air valve opened. The air bottle supplies fresh air to the operative whilst an escape from the confined space is made. The air bottle of a self-rescue set has a duration of typically 15-20 minutes.

Care must be taken to select the correct type of protection for the conditions. Respirators (as opposed to breathing apparatus) do not protect against oxygen-deficient atmospheres and should not be used in any atmosphere dangerous to life. RPE should not be used unless all other methods of control or protection have been examined and it is established that the use of RPE is the only reasonably practicable solution.

The HSE publication *Respiratory protective equipment at work – A practical guide* (HSG53) sets out the nominal protection factor for each type of respirator and describes their limitations; it should be carefully consulted in cases of doubt.

Respirators can only be used for protection against the gases or dusts for which they are specifically intended. It is important to note that dust masks and canister and cartridge respirators have a limited period of usage before becoming saturated with the contaminant. They may also have a limited shelf life, indicated by a use-by date.

9.6.15 Permits

9.6.15.1 Permit to work

Entries into a confined space can be made under a permit to work, whereby a competent person must be satisfied that all necessary precautions have been taken and provisions made to secure the safety of those entering the confined space, before signing the permit to work. The signed permit thus gives an assurance that work may safely take place.

Permits should only be issued by named, authorised persons, who must sign them. Such persons must be competent, have authority and possess sufficient practical and theoretical knowledge and actual experience of working conditions to enable them to judge whether everything necessary has been done to ensure the safety of personnel. It is quite common for several authorised persons to sign a permit to work, each certifying that they have taken the necessary actions with regard to their own area of responsibility (for example, electrical isolation and atmospheric testing). Where a permit to work system involves the use of padlocks and keys (for example, for locking-off electrical isolators or other sources of energy) the keys must stay with an authorised person until such time as the permit is returned for cancellation.

A permit also ensures:

- that contractors engaged to carry out the work are included
- training and instruction in the issue of permits for operations
- monitoring and auditing, to make sure the permit works as intended.

9.6.15.2 Permit to enter

Depending upon the nature of the confined space and the inherent risks of carrying out the work, some companies may choose to run a separate permit to enter system.

An example of when such a system might be used is where all preparatory work is carried out to meet the requirements of the permit to work and then the permit to enter is issued when final pre-entry checks of the atmosphere have been carried out.

Such a system would cover situations where a single permit to work covers the duration of the whole job, but successive shifts of workers are each authorised to enter the confined space under a newly raised permit to enter.

9.6.15.3 Access and egress

A safe way in and out of the confined space should be provided and, wherever possible, allow quick, unobstructed and ready access (such as a fixed, vertical ladder inside an underground chamber that terminates just below the entry/exit point at ground level).

The means of escape must be suitable for use by the individual who enters the confined space so that, ideally, they can quickly escape in an emergency. However, it must be accepted that in many cases the entry/exit point will be of a restricted size that will not necessarily allow an easy escape route in an emergency, particularly if the person who is escaping is wearing a compressed air cylinder. The means of achieving a prompt escape or rescue must be considered in the risk assessment.

Suitable means to prevent access (for example, a locked hatch) should also be in place when there is no need for access to the confined space. There should be a safety sign that is clear and conspicuous to prohibit unauthorised entry alongside openings that allow for safe access.

9.6.16 Conclusion

For work to be done safely in a confined space, great care has to be taken over the detail of each step of the procedure. Common causes of accidents are shown below.

- Failing to identify confined spaces.
- Inadequate risk assessments.
- Poorly trained and equipped workers.
- Failing to put in place adequate emergency arrangements before work starts.
- Failing to carry out an initial check of air quality.
- Failing to set up a safe system of work, including continuous air monitoring, based around a permit to work system.
- Failing to follow an established safe system of work.
- Deviations in conditions rendering the risk assessment/safe system invalid.
- Incorrectly using RPE.
- Using the incorrect type of RPE.
- Failing to use safety harnesses and lifelines.
- Ill-conceived and badly executed rescue attempts.

All such accidents are avoidable. If an accident does occur, it demonstrates that a breakdown has occurred in the supposed safe system of work.

D
09

9.7 Legislative requirements

In addition to the **Confined Space Regulations** and the **Management of Health and Safety at Work Regulations** the following legislation may also apply.

9.7.1 Construction (Design and Management) Regulations

These regulations place a legal duty on designers, when preparing their designs, to design out risk, so far as it is reasonably practicable.

In the context of this chapter, designers should carry out their design work so that no-one has to enter a confined space during construction work, maintenance or cleaning of the structure or during its demolition. The regulations place a duty on the designer, when preparing their designs, to consider the users of any workplace.

Also, within the context of this chapter, these regulations place legal duties on contractors and principal contractors, where applicable, with regard to the following.

- Safe places of work.
- Excavations.
- Prevention of drowning.
- Prevention of risk from fire, explosion, flooding and asphyxiation.
- Emergency procedures.
- Fresh air.

For further information refer to Chapter A03 Construction (Design and Management) Regulations.

9.7.2 Provision and Use of Work Equipment Regulations

These regulations require that an employer only supplies work equipment that is correct and suitable for the job and ensures that the equipment is maintained and kept in good working order.

Where the use of the equipment involves a specific risk to the health and safety of employees, the use of the equipment must be restricted to specified workers.

9.7.3 Personal Protective Equipment at Work Regulations

These regulations require that, where a risk has been identified by a risk assessment and it cannot be adequately controlled by other means, which are equally or more effective, then the employer must provide and ensure that suitable PPE is used by employees.

In essence, PPE may only be used as a last resort after all other means of eliminating or controlling the risk have been considered and are found to be not reasonably practicable to implement. In practice, however, unless it is possible to carry out the work without entry into the confined space, the wearing of PPE will usually be necessary.

In deciding which type to issue, the employer must take into account the risk that the PPE is being used to protect against, and ensure that the PPE will fit the wearer and allow them to work safely. Where the use of RPE is necessary, face-fit testing to establish the suitability of the RPE for the wearer is required. If more than one item of PPE is being used, the employer must make sure that individual items of PPE are compatible and suitable for the task that is to be undertaken.

Whenever PPE is to be issued, the employer must ensure that employees have been given adequate and appropriate information, instruction and training to enable them to understand the risks being protected against, the purpose of the PPE and the manner in which it is to be used.

Whilst the employer must ensure that PPE is supplied and used, the employee has a duty to properly use the equipment provided, follow the information, instruction and training that they have been given, and know the procedures for reporting losses or defects to their employer.

In the context of this chapter, in addition to the more commonly used PPE, confined space working will often require the use of appropriate RPE and rescue equipment (such as a safety harness and line).

For further information on the Personal Protective Equipment at Work Regulations refer to Chapter B06 Personal protective equipment.

9.7.4 Lifting Operations and Lifting Equipment Regulations

Access to and egress from many confined spaces is made by lowering or raising a person vertically through the entry or exit point, including during practice or actual rescues.

In these circumstances:

- safety harnesses and rescue lines must be regarded as lifting accessories
- the tripod hoist or other type of winch must be regarded as lifting equipment used for lifting persons and, as such, requires thorough examination on a six monthly basis under LOLER.

However, if the rescue involves a sideways or inclined drag along, for example a duct, then there would be no lifting and LOLER would not apply, however the Provision and Use of Work Equipment Regulations (PUWER) would.

For further information on LOLER refer to Chapter C07 Lifting operations.

9.7.5 Other legislation

The following legislation can also have an impact upon how work in confined spaces is planned, organised and carried out.

- Control of Substances Hazardous to Health Regulations *(refer to Chapter B07)*.
- Work at Height Regulations *(refer to Chapter D01)*.
- Dangerous Substances and Explosive Atmospheres Regulations *(refer to Chapter D10)*.

10

Dangerous substances

Contents

Supporting information

G: Checklists and forms

Overview

Dangerous substances are widely used on building and construction sites. The main hazards are fire and explosion, and everything possible must be done to lessen the risks.

Safety is divided into three main areas: the storage of substances, the safe handling and transport of substances and the uses to which substances are put.

10.1 Introduction

This chapter does not cover the storage of explosives, which may be used in the industry for demolition and civil engineering. There are specific requirements under the **Explosive Regulations**. The regulations are supported by guidance which is available from the HSE.

In most cases, the HSE enforces fire safety legislation on construction sites, under the Construction (Design and Management) (CDM) Regulations and the Management of Health and Safety at Work Regulations, although they also have enforcement powers under the Regulatory Reform (Fire Safety) Order or in Scotland under the Fire (Scotland) Act. In Scotland requirements on general fire safety are covered in Part 3 of the Fire (Scotland) Act. The Fire Safety Regulations (Northern Ireland) apply in Northern Ireland.

Local Authority environmental health officers are likely to have a similar role where the work is carried out on a construction project in a premises that they enforce.

The local fire and rescue service (FRS) has responsibilities for the enforcement of fire safety in some circumstances.

Dangerous substances and explosive atmospheres

- **Dangerous substances.** Any substance or mixture of substances that can put people's health or safety at risk from fire and explosion.
- **Explosive atmospheres.** Any substance or mixture of air and one or more hazardous substances in the form of a gas, vapour, mist or dust, which will explode after ignition has occurred.

10.2 Important points

- A risk assessment must be carried out before dangerous substances are stored, transported or used. In some cases, a method statement and/or a permit to work will also be required.
- Important pieces of legislation relating to this chapter are the:
  - Dangerous Substances and Explosive Atmospheres Regulations (DSEAR)
  - Construction (Design and Management) Regulations (CDM)
  - Regulatory Reform (Fire Safety) Order (RRFSO) (England and Wales only)
  - Fire (Scotland) Act
  - Fire Safety (Employees' Capabilities) (England) Regulations
  - Carriage of Dangerous Goods and Use of Transportable Pressure Equipment Regulations (CDG).

Uncontrolled use or storage of explosive materials can have fatal consequences

- DSEAR covers the flammable or explosive properties of dangerous substances used in the workplace.
- There may also be health issues that are covered by the Control of Substances Hazardous to Health (COSHH) Regulations.
- Fire safety legislation will be enforced by the HSE or the local FRS, generally depending upon the location where dangerous substances are stored and used.
- People who use dangerous substances must be fully aware of their hazardous properties, adopt methods of controlling the risks and be trained in the use of portable fire extinguishers.
- Electrical apparatus and naked flames should not be used near flammable or explosive dangerous substances, particularly if they are being sprayed.
- Good ventilation is essential wherever flammable or explosive dangerous substances are used or stored.
- Smoking policies and waste disposal policies must be established and diligently monitored.
- Liquefied petroleum gas (LPG) cylinders are fitted with a spring loaded safety relief valve that will lift and vent gas into the atmosphere if the internal gas (head) pressure valve reaches 26 bar.

D 10

Start by identifying dangerous substances on site and quantities. Use the material safety data sheets and labels to identify these hazards. Also consider processes that may generate dangerous forms of substances.

10.3 Dangerous Substances and Explosive Atmospheres Regulations

10.3.1 Principles of the regulations

The Dangerous Substances and Explosive Atmospheres Regulations (DSEAR) require employers to control the risks to safety from fire and explosions.

The regulations apply at all places of work where a dangerous substance is present (or is liable to be present) at the workplace, or if the dangerous substance could be a risk to the safety of people as a result of fires, explosions or similar energetic events.

Dangerous substances are:

- a substance or mixture of substances that is classified as explosive, oxidising, extremely flammable, highly flammable or flammable
- any dust, whether in the form of solid particles or fibrous materials, which can form an explosive mixture in air.

In the construction industry, many dangerous substances are used, or created by work. Some examples are shown below.

- The storage and use of solvents, adhesives and paints.
- The storage and use of flammable gases (such as oxygen and acetylene) during cutting and welding.
- The storage and use of LPG for work processes, heating or cooking.
- The creation of large quantities of airborne dust (for example, as a result of wood-machining or sanding) and the handling and storage of bulk waste dust.
- The storage and decanting of vehicle fuels and lubricants.
- The storage and handling of liquid flammable wastes (such as fuel oils).
- Many hot works (such as the hot-cutting of tanks and drums that have contained flammable materials).

www. **Further guidance is available on the HSE website.**

10.3.2 Employers' duties under DSEAR

DSEAR places duties on employers (and the self-employed, who are considered employers for the purposes of the regulations) to assess and eliminate or reduce risks from dangerous substances. Complying with DSEAR involves the responsibilities shown below.

10.3.2.1 Assessing risks

Before work is carried out, employers must assess the fire and explosion risks that may be caused by dangerous substances. This should be an identification and careful examination of:

- dangerous substances in the workplace
- work involving those substances
- ways in which those substances and work could harm people.

The purpose is to help employers to decide what they need to do to eliminate or reduce the risks from dangerous substances. If there is no risk to safety from fires and explosions, or the risk is low, no further action is needed. If there are risks then employers must consider what else needs to be done to comply fully with the requirements of DSEAR. If an employer has five or more employees, the employer must record the significant findings of the risk assessment. This is the same risk assessment required under the Management of Health and Safety at Work Regulations. There is no requirement to carry out two risk assessments, as long as the requirements of both sets of regulations are met.

10.3.2.2 Preventing or controlling risks

Employers must put control measures in place to eliminate risks from dangerous substances, or reduce them as far as is reasonably practicable. Where it is not possible to eliminate the risk completely employers must take measures to control risks and reduce the severity of the effects of fire or explosion.

The best solution is to eliminate the risk by replacing the dangerous substance with another substance, or using a different work process. In DSEAR, this is called substitution.

In practice, this may be difficult to achieve. However, it may be possible to reduce the risk by using a less dangerous substance (for example, by replacing a low flashpoint liquid with a high flashpoint one). In other situations, it may not be possible to replace the dangerous substance. For example, it would not be practical to replace petrol with another substance at a filling station.

10.3.2.3 Control measures

Where the risk cannot be eliminated, DSEAR requires control measures to be applied in the following priority order.

1.	Reduce the quantity of dangerous substances to a minimum.
2.	Avoid or minimise releases of dangerous substances.
3.	Control releases of dangerous substances at source.
4.	Prevent the formation of a dangerous atmosphere.
5.	Collect, contain and remove any releases to a safe place (for example, through ventilation).
6.	Avoid ignition sources.
7.	Avoid adverse conditions (for example, exceeding the limits of temperature or control settings) that could lead to danger.
8.	Keep incompatible substances apart.

These control measures should be proportionate to the degree of risk as highlighted in the risk assessment and be appropriate to the nature of the activity or operation.

10.3.2.4 Mitigation

In addition to control measures, DSEAR requires employers to put mitigation measures in place. These measures should be consistent with the risk assessment and appropriate to the nature of the activity or operation, and include the following.

- Reducing the number of employees exposed to the risk.
- Providing explosion-resistant plant.
- Providing explosion suppression or explosion relief equipment.
- Taking measures to control or minimise the spread of fires or explosions.
- Providing suitable PPE.

10.3.2.5 Preparing emergency plans and procedures

Arrangements must be made to deal with emergencies. These plans and procedures should cover safety drills and suitable communication and warning systems, and should be in proportion to the risks. If an emergency occurs, workers tasked with carrying out repairs or other necessary work must be provided with the appropriate equipment to allow them to carry out this work safely.

The information in the emergency plans and procedures must be made available to the emergency services to allow them to develop their own plans if necessary.

10.3.2.6 Providing information, instruction and training for employees

Employees must be provided with relevant information, instructions and training, which will include the following.

- The dangerous substances present in the workplace and the risks they present, including access to any relevant safety data sheets and information on any other legislation that applies to the dangerous substance.
- The findings of the risk assessment and the control measures put in place as a result, including their purpose and how to follow and use them.
- Emergency procedures.

Information, instruction and training need only be provided to other people (non-employees) where it is required to ensure their safety. It should be in proportion to the level and type of risk.

The contents of pipes and containers must be identifiable to alert employees and others to the presence of dangerous substances. If the contents have already been identified in order to meet the requirements of other legislation this does not need to be done again under DSEAR.

10.3.2.7 Places where explosive atmospheres may occur

DSEAR places additional duties on employers where potentially explosive atmospheres may occur in the workplace. In relation to construction site work, this could include bottled gas/petrol storage areas. These duties include the following.

- Identifying and classifying (zoning) areas where potentially explosive atmospheres may occur.
- Avoiding ignition sources in zoned areas, in particular those from electrical and mechanical equipment.
- Where necessary, identifying the entrances to zoned areas by the display of signs.
- Providing appropriate anti-static clothing for employees.
- Before they come into operation, verifying the overall explosion-protection safety of areas where explosive atmospheres may occur.

Decisions on the zoning of areas and the appropriate actions to take must be made by someone who has been trained and is competent to do so.

(The above summary of DSEAR is reproduced from the HSE website under licence from The Controller of Her Majesty's Stationery Office.)

Further guidance on DSEAR is available on the HSE website.

Whilst the employer must, as far as possible, ensure that any PPE supplied must be worn, the employee in turn must ensure that they wear the equipment provided and know the procedures for reporting loss or defect to the employer.

In the context of this chapter, the relevance of these regulations includes the prevention of:

- inhalation of fumes and vapour given off by dangerous substances
- skin contact with dangerous substances
- eye injuries resulting from splashes of dangerous substances.

For further information on the Personal Protective Equipment at Work Regulations refer to Chapter B06 Personal protective equipment.

10.4 Carriage of Dangerous Goods and Use of Transportable Pressure Equipment Regulations, and the European agreement

The CDG and ADR are highly prescriptive and deal with the carriage of dangerous goods and their purpose to protect everyone, either those directly involved (such as consignors or carriers) or those who might be harmed (such as members of the public or the emergency services). ***Note:*** *ADR comes from the French abbreviation **A**ccord Européen relatif au transport international des marchandises **D**angereuses par **R**oute.*

Dangerous goods are liquid or solid substances, and the articles containing them, that have been tested, assessed and given a classification. Dangerous goods are given different classes depending on their predominant hazard.

If goods being carried by rail or road are dangerous there is a risk of spillage leading to fire, explosion, chemical burn or environmental damage if there is an incident. The regulations place duties upon everyone involved in the carriage of dangerous goods to ensure they know what they have to do to minimise the risk of incidents and guarantee effective responses.

Many duty holders will need to appoint a dangerous goods safety advisor.

10.4.1 Carriage of Dangerous Goods and Use of Transportable Pressure Equipment Regulations

These regulations were substantially restructured in 2009, with direct referencing to ADR for the main duties, with amending regulations made in 2011. CDG now cross-references almost totally to ADR; it is ADR that contains the detailed requirements.

CDG sets the legal framework in the UK – ADR has no provision for enforcement. They include a number of exemptions and make substantial changes to ADR requirements for the domestic carriage of many explosives.

10.4.2 ADR structure

Each part of ADR is sub-divided into chapters, with each chapter further divided into sections and paragraphs.

Part number	Description
1.	Introduction – setting out high-level aims and duties, together with exemptions. This part includes the need for a dangerous goods safety advisor.
2.	Classification.
3.	The dangerous goods list.
4.	Packing and tank provisions.
5.	Consignment procedures, including documentation and vehicle marking.
6.	Construction and testing of packages, intermediate bulk containers, large packages and tanks.
7.	Carriage – loading, unloading and handling.
8.	Vehicle crews, equipment, operation and documentation.
9.	Construction and approval of vehicles.

Further information on the requirements of CDG and ADR can be found on the HSE website.

10.5 Control of Substances Hazardous to Health Regulations

The Control of Substances Hazardous to Health (COSHH) Regulations do not apply to dangerous substances by virtue of their explosive or flammable nature. However, they may apply if these substances also possess certain other hazardous properties. This would be identified as part of the COSHH assessment carried out on the substance.

For further information refer to Chapter B07 Control of substances hazardous to health.

10.6 Storage of dangerous substances

On most building or construction sites, dangerous substances will be used at some time during the construction phase.

Safe and secure storage

Depending upon the nature of the work to be undertaken it may be necessary to store bulk quantities of dangerous substances, either in an external, secure, purpose-built compound, where site conditions allow, or in a suitable, secure internal storeroom if, because of the nature of the site, external storage is not possible.

Alternatively, small quantities (for example, 200 ml containers upwards) will often be taken to the place of work by the person doing the job.

Where small quantities of dangerous substances for daily use are required in the workplace, metal lockable bins may be used.

10.6.1 Storage in the open air

Where it is necessary to store dangerous substances in bulk, a store should be built to the following requirements.

- ☑ On a concrete sloping pad with a sump to catch any leaks or spills.
- ☑ With a low sill all around, sufficient to contain the contents of the largest can or drum stored, plus 10% (in other words, bunded).
- ☑ Surrounded by a 1.8 m high wire fence.
- ☑ So that it is protected against direct sunlight.
- ☑ At least 2 m away from nearby buildings or boundaries, except that, where the boundary of the store forms part of a solid wall, cans or drums may be stacked up against that wall up to one metre from the top.

Cans or drums should be stored so that their contents can be easily identified and removed in the event of any leak or damage. They must also be stored on their sides and chocked to prevent movement.

Stores or bins must be kept locked and only sufficient amounts for each day's requirements should be removed, as and when needed.

They may be marked with suitable signs, such as 'Flammable liquid' or 'Flammable gas'.

Additionally, if an assessment under DSEAR shows that an explosive atmosphere may be present in a particular area, appropriate numbers of the illustrated sign must be displayed.

The sign comprises a yellow background and black graphics. Signs must conform to the Health and Safety (Safety Signs and Signals) Regulations and *Safety signs and colours* (BS 5499). All signs purchased from reputable suppliers will be to these specifications.

Naked flames, smoking, matches or lighters must not be allowed in the area of the store, and proper prohibition signs must be clearly displayed, as well as other signs already indicated.

Any lighting within a store must be flameproof to the appropriate standard, and under no circumstances should electrical sockets be permitted.

Where there is a need for electrical apparatus (other than lighting) within a store, the supply must be permanently wired in using intrinsically safe equipment.

Example of a secure storage area

Other points to be noted.

- Stores should not be built below ground level because the vapours from spills and leaks will not be able to disperse (they are heavier than air).
- Adequate cross-ventilation at both high and low level is necessary.
- The store should always be kept locked when unattended.
- A door sill of approximately 150 mm in height should be provided to catch any leaks or spills in order to retain the liquids inside the building.
- A quantity of absorbent material, to soak up any spilt liquids, and a suitable container for the collection and safe disposal of the contaminated absorbent, should be provided at the store.
- The use of mobile phones in or immediately adjacent to the store should be prohibited. Notices to this effect should be provided and prominently displayed.
- Any shelves or racking in the store should be of a non-ferrous metal or other non-combustible construction.

10.6.2 Storage inside a building

A separate building should be provided, if possible, solely for the storage of dangerous substances where security or protection from the weather is required. Ideally, it will be constructed from fire-resisting materials and it should be at least 2 m away from other buildings or boundaries.

A risk assessment should be carried out to determine whether the risks of storing dangerous substances in such a location are acceptable. If not, either additional control measures must be put in place or alternative arrangements made for storing the substances.

Where a separate building cannot be provided, and the store forms part of an existing structure, the surrounding walls and roof of the store must be fire-resisting and the door should be of the fire-resisting type and open outwards.

It is recommended that the maximum quantities that may be stored in cabinets and bins are no more than 50 litres for highly flammable liquids (and flammable liquids with a flashpoint below the maximum ambient temperature of the workroom/working area) and no more than 250 litres for other flammable liquids with a higher flashpoint of up to 55°C.

Other points to be considered.

- Stores should not be built below ground level, because the vapours from spillages and leaks will not be able to disperse.
- Adequate cross-ventilation at both high and low level is necessary.
- The store should always be kept locked when unattended.
- When not in use, containers of flammable liquids needed for current work should be kept closed and stored in suitable cabinets or bins of fire-resisting construction, which are designed to retain spills (110% volume of the largest vessel normally stored in it).
- A quantity of absorbent material, to soak up any spilt liquids, and a suitable container for the collection and safe disposal of the contaminated absorbent, should be provided at the store.
- Signs should be positioned on or near the store stating, for example, 'Highly flammable' or 'Flashpoint below 32°C'. All signs should conform to the Health and Safety (Safety Signs and Signals) Regulations and *Safety signs and colours* (BS 5499).
- Naked flames, smoking, matches or lighters must not be allowed in the store, and signs stating this must be clearly displayed.
- The use of mobile phones in or adjacent to the store should be prohibited. Notices to this effect should be provided and prominently displayed.
- Any lighting or other electrical apparatus must conform to BS EN 60079-14.
- Any shelves or racking in the store should be of a non-ferrous metal or other non-combustible construction.

10.7 Handling and use of dangerous substances

The use of any dangerous substance, including decanting small quantities for daily use from bulk containers, must be the subject of a risk assessment.

The findings of the risk assessment will indicate the maximum quantity of the dangerous substance that can be taken to the place of work and the safe working practices to be observed once it is there and being used.

Generally, only enough of the dangerous substance to enable the work in hand to be carried out should be taken to the place where it is to be used.

The HSE recommends that only the minimum quantity needed for frequently occurring work, or that required for use during a half day or one shift, should be present in the workroom/working area.

Handle flammable liquids with care

Clearly, actual quantities will depend on the work activity and also the organisational arrangements for controlling the fire risks in the workroom/working area.

Decanting, mixing or sampling should not be carried out in a store. It should be done in the open air or in a separate room constructed of fire-resisting materials.

Funnels should be used to prevent spillage whilst decanting is taking place and drip trays should be used to catch any spillage that may inadvertently occur.

Any spillage should be soaked up using proprietary absorbents, dry earth or dry sand.

Metal bins with lids should be provided for any used absorbents to be placed in and these should be emptied regularly and carefully.

Consideration must be given to the disposal of any waste as it may well be classified as hazardous waste. Such waste must be transported by a registered carrier to a licensed landfill site. Depending on how much waste is produced the Environment Agency (England), Natural Resources Wales (Wales), or the Scottish Environment Protection Agency (Scotland) may need to be notified.

In general, where work involves the use of a dangerous substance that has the potential to create an explosive atmosphere inside a room, all electrical power should be turned off unless all electrical fittings are intrinsically safe by design. If space heating is needed, it should be flameproof and incapable of causing the ignition of any vapours present in the atmosphere.

The build-up of concentrations of vapours must be avoided and dispersed, if necessary, by natural or mechanical ventilation. If mechanical ventilation is necessary, a flameproof motor, not in the ventilation trunking, should be used.

Other points to be considered.

- Naked flames, welding and heating torches, and smoking materials should be prohibited in any area where an explosive atmosphere may be present.
- Metal bins with lids must be provided for offcuts, waste or rags, and should be emptied regularly.
- A suitable container with a lid should be used for any brushes or scrapers that require soaking to remove residues of dangerous substances. This should be placed in a safe area well away from any possible source of ignition.

10.7.1 Spraying of dangerous substances

New covering materials (such as paints, varnishes and lacquers), and the techniques for applying them, have been developed, and extensive use of spray painting equipment can now be seen on construction sites.

Using a spray gun for spraying dangerous substances is most likely to introduce an airborne explosive mist into the workplace, creating a hazard both to the user and to other workers in the area. Such work must only be undertaken by fully trained and competent employees and in a situation where all appropriate precautionary measures are in place.

A risk assessment must be carried out and other controls, including permits to work and/or permits to enter (for those people involved in the job, by implication, excluding all others), implemented as necessary.

Other points to be considered.

- Identify the material carefully and always follow the manufacturer's instructions on preparation, use and application.
- Always use the correct type of spraying equipment. Never make do, just because the proper equipment is not immediately to hand.
- If alternative control measures are not available or adequate, protective clothing and respiratory protective equipment must be used.
- Always use the hygiene and washing facilities provided.
- Do not introduce ignition sources into the working area.

- Do not smoke or use naked flames in the working area.
- Always place warning signs in approaches to the area where the work is being carried out, and at entrance points to areas where dangerous substances are being used. Use physical barriers, if necessary, to stop unauthorised persons entering the area.

10.7.2 Empty tanks and containers

Do not cut or heat any empty tanks, containers or drums unless they have been certificated as being free of flammable vapours that could explode. Current opinion recommends reducing the length of time that such certification is valid for. Under most circumstances, the cutting work should be planned to start as soon as the gas-free certificate is issued.

Special care is necessary when demolishing or dismantling disused bulk tanks. By disturbing the tank or heating the residues left inside, you may cause an explosive concentration of vapours.

Entry into any disused tank or vessel that may be regarded as a confined space should be avoided by doing the work from outside, if possible. Often, there will be a need to clean residues and if entry to a confined space is unavoidable, a safe system of work must be followed and the work carried out under a permit to work system.

Further advice on permit to work systems and entry into confined spaces is contained in the Approved Code of Practice (ACoP) and guidance notes that support the Confined Spaces Regulations (L101) and HSE leaflet *Safe work in confined spaces* (INDG258).

There are a number of factors to consider when the work involves large tanks. The first would be what the contents were. Oil storage tanks may have held so-called heavy fuel oil and these will undoubtedly have been insulated. It is quite likely that the insulation system will have been asbestos. If the tanks once held petrol, it may have been leaded fuel. This means that the exposure to lead fumes during cutting should be considered.

It is normal for large tanks, whether above or below ground, to be emptied and cleaned by a specialist contractor before dismantling. The contents are generally removed by a large vacuum tanker and then the inside of the tank is steam cleaned. Most of this work can be carried out from the outside and it is only to carry out the final clean that entry is required. Operatives carrying out this final clean must be trained in confined space working and provided with all the normal gas detector, rescue equipment and personal protective equipment (PPE) that would be expected for confined space working.

Having been cleaned, the tank is tested and a gas-free certificate issued. It should then be cut up as soon as possible. The risk of not doing so is that it is practically impossible to completely clean a tank, particularly where its construction incorporates internal ribs, welds and other internal features that could harbour residue of the content. These may well become fumes and if the concentration becomes high enough then the atmosphere inside the tank may become explosive if ignited.

It is important to be aware that even cold-cutting techniques (such as hydraulic shears) may cause sparks and, therefore, leaving the cutting even until the next day is simply not an option.

10.7.3 Industrial gas cylinder colours

While the cylinder label is the primary means of identifying the properties of the gas in a cylinder, the colour coding of the cylinder body provides a further guide.

The colour applied to the shoulder, or curved part at the top of the cylinder, signifies the European standard colour coding.

The aim of the new standard (EN 1089-3), which has replaced the old cylinder colour scheme (BS 349), is to help improve safety standards within the gases industry.

Cylinder identification colour coding and labelling requirements (Technical information sheet 6) can be downloaded for free from the British Compressed Gas Association website.

Operators should obtain a cylinder identification chart from their supplier, as different gas suppliers may paint the body of a cylinder different colours. For example, a BOC oxygen gas cylinder has a black body with a white shoulder whilst an air products cylinder has a grey body with a white shoulder.

10.8 Liquefied petroleum gas

Liquefied petroleum gas (LPG) is a mixture of hydrocarbons that are a gas or vapour under normal conditions of temperature and pressure, but can be turned into a liquid by either the application of pressure or the reduction of temperature.

LPG can be found in numerous locations, in various sizes of cylinder, and can be put to a variety of uses on building and construction sites. Uses range from the heating of bitumen boilers, site huts and offices to providing a fuel for hand tools and cutting equipment.

If used properly and safely, LPG is a convenient and valuable source of energy. Misuse or carelessness can cause serious accidents.

Important points about liquefied petroleum gas

- In some cases, the Regulatory Reform (Fire Safety) Order will only be relevant where LPG is stored off site (for example, at company premises and builders' yards). However, it will also apply to some construction sites where LPG is used in conjunction with a work process.
- LPG is normally found as a compressed liquid, usually of commercial butane or propane.
- LPG is a colourless, odourless liquid that floats on water but vaporises to form a gas that is heavier than air. A stenching agent is normally added.
- A release or spillage of LPG can form a large vapour cloud of flammable gas capable of ignition from some distance.
- LPG is stored on site in fixed tanks, refillable cylinders or non-refillable disposable cylinders (cartridges).
- Storage should be in secure, non-combustible, well ventilated areas away from other risks and sources of ignition.
- There are special requirements for vehicles and drivers covering the transportation of LPG.
- In site huts all LPG cylinders and regulators for use with fixed heaters, cookers and lighting must be kept outside and piped in using rigid copper piping.
- Staff who work with LPG must be suitably trained in the hazards and use of LPG (such as not rolling cylinders).
- In the event of a leak, do not attempt to operate electrical apparatus or switches.
- If a fire breaks out that involves LPG cylinders:
  - immediately inform the FRS of the whereabouts of all cylinders on site, including details of whether they are full or empty
  - if in any doubt as to the safety of the overall situation, evacuate the site and put a security cordon in place.

LPG and commercial butane and propane

- **Liquefied petroleum gas.** Means any commercial butane, commercial propane or a mixture of the two.
- **Commercial butane.** This is usually stored in blue cylinders. It consists mainly of butane and butane isomers. The remaining components are predominantly propane and propane isomers, pentane and pentane isomers. Because of the low vapour pressure, butane cylinders are not generally used outside.
- **Commercial propane.** This is usually stored in vessels or in red cylinders. It consists mainly of propane and propane isomers. The remaining components are predominantly butane and butane isomers, ethane and ethane isomers.

D 10

10.8.1 Properties

LPG is a colourless, odourless liquid or gas that normally has a smell or stench added before distribution.

As a liquid, it is lighter than water and will float before evaporating.

As a gas, it is approximately twice as heavy as air and will sink and flow into sumps and underground excavations or workings. It will also sink into drains but, because its density is approximately half that of water, it will not flow through drains that are water-trapped.

As a gas, it is capable of ignition at some distance from the original leak. The resulting flame can travel back to the source of the leak.

Any release of liquid under pressure into the atmosphere results in its rapid conversion to gas. This gas has a volume of about 230 (butane) and 270 (propane) times that of the liquid.

The expansion, during a rapid release of pressure, results in a rapid drop of temperature, which for propane can approach its boiling point of -45°C. Leakage of liquid LPG will result in the release of large volumes of highly flammable gases.

For example, one litre of liquid propane spilt in a workplace will evaporate to make approximately 270 litres of gas. If it is diluted with air to 2%, this will give 13,750 cubic litres of an explosive gas/air mixture – enough to fill a room 3 m x 2.3 m x 2 m.

Property	Commercial butane	Commercial propane
Density in comparison to water.	0.57	0.5
Density in comparison to air.	2	1.5
Litres per tonne.	1,745	1,995
Boiling point.	-2°C	-45°C
Pressure at 15°C.	1.5 bar	7.0 bar
Expansion ratio.	1:230	1:270
Levels of flammability.	1.9% – 8.5%	2.0% – 10.9%

The use of LPG equipment in confined spaces, and small, poorly ventilated spaces (such as basement and sub-basement boiler houses, toilets and kitchens) can give rise to a highly flammable or explosive atmosphere, if the equipment should leak.

10.8.2 Flammability

Following mechanical failure of LPG equipment, or any other event that causes the release of LPG, the resulting gas will form a flammable mixture with air at gas concentrations between approximately 2% and 10%.

Ignition of released LPG, where the concentration exceeds 2%, can result in fire or, if confined, an explosion. If a leak does not ignite immediately, and the LPG and air mixture drifts from the point of release, it will gradually become more diluted.

However, should the concentration still exceed 2% and ignition occur, this could cause a flash or cloud-fire back to the point of release.

A leak of LPG may sometimes be noticed either by the smell or the noise of the gas escaping. There may also be condensation or frosting on the outside of the cylinder.

All LPG systems must be leak tested each time prior to use. An approved leak detection fluid (not soapy water) should be applied to all joints and connections. The presence of bubbles indicates that the system is not gas tight and should not be used. If a leak is discovered the system should be shut down, safely de-pressured and the leak rectified. LPG leaks must never be traced with a lighted match or flame.

If it is suspected that LPG has leaked inside a building, no attempt should be made to touch any electrical apparatus. Do not turn light switches, sockets or any other electrical appliance either on or off.

Open all doors and windows, if it is safe to do so, and leave immediately. Do not re-enter the building until advice has been sought and you are told that it is safe to do so.

10.8.3 Health issues

10.8.3.1 Workplace exposure limits

The maximum levels of exposure, as stated in EH40 under the heading LPG, are:

- 1,000 ppm (0.1%) for long-term exposure (reference period eight hours)
- 1,250 ppm (0.125%) for short-term exposure (reference period 15 minutes).

During any maintenance work involving release of pressure, especially in confined spaces, care must be taken that these exposure limits are not exceeded.

10.8.3.2 Inhalation

LPG gas is not toxic, but at concentration levels above about 10,000 ppm (1%) in air, propane becomes a slight narcotic. At higher levels, it becomes an asphyxiant by displacing oxygen.

In a sufficiently high concentration, a person will suffocate and die.

10.8.3.3 Cold burns

The release of liquid propane onto unprotected skin will cause cold burns. This is due to the rapid vaporisation of the liquid, withdrawing heat from the affected area of the body.

The release of liquid, or significant amounts of gas at vessel pressure, can also cause the adjacent fittings to cool. This may be sufficient to cause cold burns if the fittings are subsequently touched by unprotected hands.

Suitable skin and eye protection must be worn whenever there is the possibility of a release of liquid LPG.

In the event of a cold burn, treat as for a burn from a hot object. Flush with copious amounts of tepid water and seek medical help (call 999).

10.8.4 Environmental hazards

A small, unignited release of LPG would not pose a serious danger to the environment.

The gas, being heavier than air, will roll and sink to the lowest point (such as a basement or excavation). This may result, if in the flammable range, in a fire or explosion, even if a naked source of flame is a considerable distance from the original leak.

A fire and explosion would be instantaneous on ignition and would be limited to immediate damage. The fire might devour only escaping LPG and then the danger will have passed with no lasting environmental damage.

The fire will burn fast and the explosion will be intense, but both may be over very quickly.

D 10

10.8.5 Storage

LPG can be stored on construction sites in one of three ways.

- ☑ Fixed storage tanks.
- ☑ Refillable cylinders.
- ☑ Non-refillable cylinders (that is, disposable cylinders).

10.8.5.1 Fixed storage tanks

Whilst most LPG used on construction sites can be found in cylinders, on some larger sites there may be a need for bulk storage. In view of the large capacity, it is essential that the positioning of any storage tank is carefully planned and discussed with the local fire prevention officer and the HSE.

LPG tanks should be positioned on a level concrete base to provide a stable foundation. For short-term installations it may be satisfactory to stand the tank on concrete slabs, but advice must be sought from the tank or gas suppliers. Consideration also needs to be given to any pipework that may run from the tank to the application.

Tanks should not be sited close to any ditches, cellars or drains, and delivery and emergency vehicles must easily reach them.

If the bulk tank is used as a supply vessel for filling LPG cylinders on site then reference should be made as to how this procedure can be undertaken safely.

All access roads must be clear of obstruction and the entire area kept free from weeds and other vegetation.

Tanks over 2,250 litres liquid capacity should be electrically bonded and earthed.

All bulk storage tanks must have good, all-round ventilation. On non-secure sites, tanks should be protected against vandalism by a chain-link fence at least 2 m high.

Motorway-type crash barriers should surround the installation to minimise damage by motor vehicles.

Installations must be clearly labelled 'Highly flammable LPG. No smoking or naked lights'.

Signs must conform to the Health and Safety (Safety Signs and Signals) Regulations and *Safety signs and colours* (BS 5499). Signs purchased from reputable suppliers will be to these specifications.

Adequate separation must be maintained between bulk storage tanks and adjacent buildings or boundaries. As a guide, the separation distances for bulk LPG tanks, detailed in the table below, should be followed.

Gas capacity	Water capacity		Minimum distance*
Tonnes	Litres	Gallons	Metres
Under 0.2	450	99	2.5
0.2 – 1	451 – 2,250	100 – 495	3
1 – 4	2,251 – 9,000	496 – 1,980	7.5

* Minimum distance from boundaries, buildings or sources of ignition.

Where possible, LPG storage areas should not be positioned under power cables. Where this is unavoidable, the **minimum** distances between the extremities of the vessel or cylinders to the nearest cable should be:

- ☑ up to 1 kV – 1.5 m
- ☑ 1 kV or above – 10 m.

10.8.5.2 Refillable cylinders

A level base of compacted earth, concrete or paving slabs should be provided and surrounded by a secure chain-link fence at least two metres high. A hard standing should be provided for the delivery and dispatch of cylinders. The area should be kept weed and vegetation free. If the compound is more than 12 metres square, two exits should be provided in opposite corners of the compound. The emergency exits should be fitted with a panic bar so that they can be easily opened in an emergency. If it is less than 12 metres square, one gate will suffice. Gates should open outwards and always be left unlocked when someone is in the compound. There should be sufficient shelter to prevent cylinders from being exposed to extremes of weather.

D 10

LPG store

Signs must be clearly displayed indicating the presence of LPG, and prohibiting smoking and the use of any naked flame in the area of the store.

LPG cylinders must be stored with their valves uppermost. They must be stored away from oxygen, highly flammable liquids, oxidisers, toxic or corrosive gases or substances. A distance of at least three metres must be kept between LPG cylinders and other such substances, although they may be kept in the same compound.

Any store for refillable LPG cylinders must be located away from boundaries, buildings, fixed sources of ignition or electrical equipment by at least the distances detailed in the table below.

LPG storage (including empties)	Separation from building/boundary
Below 50 kg	1 m
50-1,000 kg	3 m
1,001-4,000 kg	4 m

The store must be sited at least three metres away from any cellars, drains or other excavations into which a leak of gas would collect.

If only a small compound is used (3 m^2 for example) cylinders may be stored against the inside of the compound fencing, providing this fence is not within three metres of any boundary.

Empty cylinders must be stored with their valves securely closed to prevent any residue of gas escaping, or air being drawn into the cylinder. Full cylinders (including part-used) must be stored separately from empty cylinders in properly identified areas.

Stocks should be grouped in batches of not more than 1,000 kg and batches separated by a minimum 1.5 m gangway. However, if there is less than 50 kg of LPG these may be stored with other gases.

Where lighting is necessary, it should be mounted well above ground level and not less than two metres above the cylinders.

Any equipment not in use (such as portable hand equipment) should be isolated so as not to be easy to get to for trespassers. Any cylinders not required should be returned to the storage compound or other secure position.

10.8.5.3 Non-refillable cylinders

Non-refillable LPG cylinders for use with small portable equipment (such as blowlamps) may be stored in a clearly identified, lockable, metal container, adequately ventilated, to prevent a build up of LPG gas.

Care should be taken when changing cylinders to ensure that connections are correctly made and that there are no leaks.

Always dispose of empty containers safely and in accordance with the manufacturer's recommendations. Do not, under any circumstances, puncture or throw empty cylinders onto a fire.

Small refillable cylinders (for example, primus) should also be stored in the same way as non-refillable cylinders. Although only containing small quantities of gas, they must not be stored in occupied site huts.

They should be kept in a secure, non-combustible, well-ventilated external enclosure. The store should have warning signs 'Highly flammable – LPG', and prohibition signs 'No smoking/naked lights'.

The disposal of cartridges after use requires care as they still contain gas. Under no circumstances should cartridges be thrown on fires. All empty cartridges should be disposed of by a specialist waste contractor. Larger quantities should be disposed of by a specialist waste contractor.

Small refillable cylinders should be kept and returned to the supplier when empty.

10.8.6 Cylinders

10.8.6.1 Handling

Care must be taken when moving cylinders around the site, especially by hand or on rough ground. A full 47 kg cylinder has a total mass of about 90 kg and, before moving by hand, requires an assessment under the Manual Handling Operations Regulations of the method to be used. Cylinders must not be rolled, even when empty.

Cylinders should be handled with care and, wherever reasonably practicable, moved using suitable equipment. They should not be moved unprotected in dumper trucks or on forklift trucks. The valve on a cylinder should not be used for lifting or to lever the cylinder into position. Damage to the valve can result in a non-controllable release of LPG under high pressure. Throwing cylinders from any height or dropping them is prohibited, as in such circumstances damage to the valve, shroud and cylinders is even more likely.

10.8.6.2 Damaged cylinders

Before use, cylinders should be examined. Any damaged or faulty cylinder should **not** be used. The cylinder should be labelled and the supplier immediately requested to collect the cylinder.

If a cylinder is found to be leaking (usually from the valve) and the leak cannot be stopped, the cylinder should be carefully removed to a well-ventilated, open space, free from sources of ignition. It should be left with the leak uppermost, marked faulty, and notices displayed prohibiting smoking or other naked lights. General access should be prevented by barriers or otherwise. The supplier of the cylinder and, if necessary, the FRS, should be informed immediately.

Under no circumstances should attempts be made to dismantle or repair defective cylinders.

10.8.6.3 Orphaned compressed gas cylinders

Whilst this advice applies to abandoned LPG cylinders, it is also valid for compressed gas cylinders that have held other gases.

Empty compressed gas cylinders may still contain some of their original content. They are abandoned for a variety of reasons and then appear at metal recyclers or council waste disposal sites, neither of which welcomes their presence. It is thought that cylinders are often abandoned for the following reasons.

- They are empty and are too troublesome to return to the supplier.
- The owner/supplier cannot be identified.
- They are damaged and therefore not returnable.
- They are at the end of their useful life.

Within the UK there is a cylinder retrieval system co-ordinated by the Liquid Petroleum Gas Association. Five major companies own around 90% of all UK compressed gas cylinders. Each company has arrangements in place to collect their own cylinders.

For details of collection companies refer to Appendix A.

10.8.7 Carriage of dangerous goods

This section details the requirements of legislation for people who occasionally carry LPG cylinders in a van, truck or similar vehicle. This is covered by the CDG which implements the European agreement on carriage of dangerous substances by road, hereafter referred to as 'ADR' (from the French abbreviation ***A****ccord Européen relatif au transport international des marchandises* ***D****angereuses par* ***R****oute)*.

10.8.7.1 Transportation

Acetylene, LPG and other gases are commonly carried by tradespersons (such as welders, plumbers and motor vehicle repair technicians). Flammable gases are in transport Category 2. Oxygen and gases (such as carbon dioxide and argon) are in transport Category 3. Usually small load threshold exemptions will apply.

The parts of ADR which apply are shown below.

- The driver will have received general awareness, function-specific and safety training (ADR 1.3). A record of such training must be kept.
- The vehicle must be equipped with at least one 2 kg dry powder fire extinguisher, which is kept in good working order.
- The load must be properly stowed.

Note that special provisions CV 9, 10 and 36 all apply in the case of these gases. In particular, CV 36 specifies:

> **... packages shall preferably be loaded in open or ventilated vehicles or open or ventilated containers. If this is not feasible and packages are carried in other closed vehicles or containers, the cargo doors of the vehicles or containers shall be marked with the following, in letters not less than 25 mm high: 'WARNING: NO VENTILATION, OPEN WITH CAUTION'.**

The HSE has published a leaflet *Working with acetylene* and the British Compressed Gases Association (BCGA) has a useful leaflet on the topic of carrying gas cylinders in vehicles, as well as a wider range of publications that may be helpful. The Liquid Petroleum Gas Association (LPGA) has also published its *Carriage of LPG cylinders by road* (Code of Practice 27).

D 10

10.8.7.2 Small load exemptions (ADR 1.1.3.6)

Small load exemptions relate to the total quantity of dangerous goods carried in packages by the transport unit (usually the van or lorry, but also any trailer). It is the transport category (TC) that determines the load limits (thresholds). Many substances are assigned a packing group but these are not synonymous in all cases with the TC. The TC is given in Column 15 of Table A in ADR (Chapter 3.2). If this is not available, the table at ADR Part 1.1.3.6.3 needs to be consulted. References to load limits for the different transport categories are given in the table below. For convenience this has been amended in accordance with Regulation 19 but it needs to be used with care.

Vehicle/load	Driver training	ADR reference
All vehicles except those carrying packages under the load limit.	General training plus ADR training certificate. The certificate may be endorsed for different classes of dangerous goods or different modes (in tanks or other than tanks).	8.2.1
Any vehicle carrying packaged dangerous goods under the small load limit.	General training.	8.2.3 *(refers to Chapter 1.3).* ADR 1.1.3.6
Vehicle with small tank (up to 1 m^3).	General training.	8.2.1.3 8.2.3

If a vehicle is carrying dangerous goods under the small load threshold, many of the requirements of ADR are not applicable. Some care needs to be taken, as 'what is not exempted is still required'. In most cases the remaining obligations are as follows.

- General training for driver (ADR 1.3.2) a record of the training should be kept (ADR 1.3.3).
- Carry one 2 kg dry powder fire extinguisher or equivalent (ADR 8.1.4.2).
- Stow the dangerous goods properly (ADR 7.5.7).

Note that use of these exemptions is optional. For example, a carrier may choose to display the orange plates as long as the vehicle is carrying dangerous goods.

All vehicle marks (orange plates) must be removed when dangerous goods are not being carried. An important aspect is that packaging has to comply with the relevant standards.

e.g.

Small load application

- LPG. This is in transport Category 2. The small load threshold is 333 kg and LPG is LQ0. The result is that all cylinders count towards the load limit, but if that is less than 333 kg, the minimum ADR requirements apply.
- Section 8.2 of the ADR details mandatory training for drivers. There should be a record of their training, which must be carried at all times. The level of training required depends upon the load.

10.8.7.3 General transportation of LPG cylinders

When loaded onto vehicles, cylinders must be kept upright and secured. Vehicles must be equipped with two dry powder extinguishers (nominally a 6 kg and a 2 kg) and a first-aid kit. They must also display warning notices.

Ideally, LPG should not be carried on vehicles with other flammable substances (such as paints and solvents). Where this is unavoidable, the other materials should be kept in a steel chest and away from the LPG cylinders. Drivers carrying more than two LPG cylinders must have received training in what to do in an emergency and carry a transport emergency card containing details of the load carried.

If a cylinder leaks during a journey, close the valve immediately. If this is not possible, move the vehicle to open ground, away from buildings and people, and inform the emergency services.

www.

For information on fire extinguisher requirements when carrying dangerous goods refer to the HSE guidance.

10.8.8 Safe use and handling of LPG

Everyone with any responsibility for the storage and transportation of LPG must understand the characteristics and hazards of the LPG product they are using.

They should understand the fundamentals of fire-fighting and control of leakages. They should also have knowledge of the procedures for dealing with emergencies.

It is not possible to cover all aspects of the use and application of LPG, but the following checklist gives the main points for its safe use and handling. Please note that this list should not be regarded as exhaustive.

Safe use and handling of LPG

- Never use or store a gas cylinder on its side, unless it is a special cylinder for use on LPG-fuelled plant and vehicles. Liquefied gas may escape, causing concentrations of gas, and operatives may suffer frostbite because of the very low temperature of the escaping liquid.
- Propane cylinders must never be stored indoors because any leakage will lead to large concentrations of explosive mixtures.
- Only hoses suitable for use with LPG installations or appliances should be used and these should be inspected frequently for wear. Hoses fitted with worm drive screws should not be used.
- Cylinders must not be dropped during handling, nor brought into violent contact with other cylinders or adjacent objects.
- After use, valve protection caps and plastic thread caps or plugs should be fitted to prevent accidental leakage.
- LPG cylinders should not be used below ground level as any leakage of gas will collect at the lowest point and will not disperse.
- Regulators must be handled with care. Damaged regulators should not be used, but should be replaced or sent for specialist repair. The regulator should also be labelled for the type of gas it is designed for, comply with European Standards and be in date.
- Hoses and fittings should be examined before use. Damaged items must be replaced.
- LPG cylinders are fitted with a left-hand thread or push-on connection. Union nuts and couplers have grooves on the outside corners of the nuts confirming this. Always use the correct size spanner to tighten or loosen connections. Hand-tight connections will permit leaks. Over-tightening will damage threads and cause leaks.
- Checks for leaks should be carried out using a proprietary detector. **Never use a match or other naked flame.**
- Before connecting any LPG cylinder to equipment, it is essential that all fires, flames or other potential sources of ignition, including any smoking materials, are extinguished. Where it is reasonably practicable to do so, cylinders should be changed in the open air.
- If a leak is found, the gas supply must be turned off at the cylinder immediately.
- Flexible hoses should be in good condition and be protected or steel braided if they are likely to be subjected to damage by abrasion. Hoses must conform to the *Specification for flexible rubber tubing, rubber hose and rubber hose assemblies for use in LPG vapour phase and LPG air installations* (BS 3212).
- Before use, inspections should be carried out on all LPG appliances and equipment. The inspection should cover testing for leaks, cleaning, adjusting, checking hoses, hose clips and ferrules.
- Empty cylinders should always be treated as new ones and returned to a properly designated central storage area for collection. Under no circumstances should an LPG cylinder, either full or empty, be left around the site or buried during site operations.

10.8.9 Regulators

LPG regulators should be suitable for the equipment with which they are to be used. They should be suitable for either propane or butane and be set to the correct pressure. They should be capable of passing the correct flow capacity.

It is dangerous to use regulators set at the incorrect pressure.

Cylinders should not be transported with the regulators and hoses attached, unless on a purpose designed trolley or carrier.

Before assembling regulators and fittings ensure that the cylinder valve outlet is clean, dry and free from damage and dirt. This will help to prevent the ignition of components. Oxygen regulators should be kept free from oil or grease and be suitable for the maximum cylinder pressure being used. Oxygen cylinder valves should be opened slowly.

Before attaching a regulator to a cylinder the following checks should be made.

- The regulator is within its expiry date. (All regulators have a lifespan, on expiry of which they require either replacement or refurbishment.)
- The gas inside the cylinder is correctly identified and the regulator is suitable for that specific gas.
- The maximum cylinder pressure.
- The regulator is suitable for the maximum cylinder pressure (regulator inlet pressure).
- The regulator has a suitable outlet pressure for the application.
- The regulator is in a serviceable condition.
- The gauges are not damaged and do not show signs of over pressurisation.
- The cylinder valve outlet thread is mechanically compatible with the regulator inlet connection and is clean and free of dirt. A lint free cloth can be used to clean the outlet.
- The regulator outlet thread is in good condition.
- The regulator has the manufacturer's or supplier's name clearly visible.
- The regulator can be fitted at a suitable orientation.

- ☑ The regulator pressure adjusting screw is set to zero pressure position by turning the control knob fully anti-clockwise.
- ☑ Only the correct sized spanner is used.
- ☑ The inlet connection should be inspected for damage. If an 'O' ring is fitted to the inlet, check for damage and replace, if necessary, with an 'O' ring recommended by the regulator manufacturer.

Jointing paste or tape should never be used between the regulator and cylinder valve.

10.8.10 Bitumen boilers and cauldrons

Work with a bitumen boiler should always be supervised by a competent person.

The majority of, if not all, bitumen boilers or cauldrons are fuelled by LPG to melt the block bitumen. Such a boiler or cauldron must be sited on a level non-flammable base, away from areas where site traffic may damage hoses or gas cylinders. If avoidable, bitumen boilers should not be taken onto roofs.

Ensure that any LPG cylinder is at least three metres away from the boiler or cauldron to which it is attached. Full cylinders, not attached, should be kept at least six metres away from the boiler or cauldron and protected from heat.

Supply hoses should be checked for crushing, damage to the metal braiding or impregnation with bitumen. Any unserviceable hose must be replaced.

The sequence for lighting is as follows.

1.	Remove the burner from the boiler or cauldron.
2.	Have the source of ignition ready before turning on the gas.
3.	Light the burner, ensuring that the gas is turned on slowly.
4.	Replace the burner beneath the boiler or cauldron.

If frost forms on the outside of the cylinder, the gas flow rate is too high. Either use a smaller burner or couple two or more cylinders together by means of a manifold.

Never leave a bitumen boiler or cauldron unattended when the burner is alight, and never move a bitumen boiler or cauldron with the burner alight.

If a bitumen boiler or cauldron is overfilled, overflows or boils over, the LPG cylinder valves must be turned off immediately. Any spillage should be contained using dry sand or earth and then left until cool. No attempt should be made to remove or recover any spillage of hot bitumen.

A dry powder extinguisher, of a minimum 4.5 kg in size, should be provided whenever a bitumen boiler or cauldron is used.

10.8.11 Gas-operated hand tools and equipment

There are two types of LPG cylinder available for use with portable tools: disposable and refillable.

These cylinders come in various shapes, sizes and colours, depending on the manufacturer. They range in size from the very small (0.5 kg) to the very large (47 kg).

All LPG cylinders used with portable equipment should be positioned upright and secured (if possible). Cylinders used with cutting equipment should always be placed on purpose-made trolleys.

- ☑ Before changing a cylinder, always make sure that all valves are closed.
- ☑ Hoses must never be kinked to try to shut off gas when changing torches. It does not work and can lead to a gas escape.
- ☑ Always replace valve protection caps and plastic thread caps.
- ☑ Flames from portable tools must not be allowed to play on LPG cylinders.
- ☑ When work has been completed, turn off the cylinder valves and allow the flame from the portable torch to burn out.
- ☑ Closure of torch valves rather than cylinder valves will retain gas in hoses which, if damaged, will allow gas to escape.
- ☑ Hoses and torches must never be put into site toolboxes while still attached to the cylinder.
- ☑ Manufacturers' operating pressures must be strictly observed and must never be exceeded.
- ☑ Do not interfere with preset pressure regulators.

10.8.12 Gas-powered fixing tools

Many of the principles for the safe use of cartridge-operated tools also apply to gas-powered fixing tools, which use a canister of pressurised gas (a fuel cell) as a propellant. Generally, gas-powered fixing tools are used for firing fixings into softer materials (such as timber). However, in untrained hands they can be as dangerous as cartridge-operated tools.

Example of a gas-powered tool

The implications of a misfire when using a gas-powered fixing tool are not as serious as when using a cartridge-operated tool and it is usually safe after a misfire to attempt to make the next fixing immediately. The battery and fuel cell must be removed prior to attempting to remove a blockage.

However, it is important to store and dispose of canisters safely. *(Refer to 10.6 Storage of dangerous substances.)*

10.8.13 LPG for use in site huts and other small buildings

All LPG cylinders and regulators for use with fixed heaters, cookers and lighting within site huts must be kept outside and the gas supply piped in using rigid copper piping. The use of flexible hosing is permitted only between the cylinders and changeover valves or manifolds, and for the final connection to appliances, but this must be kept as short as possible.

All pipework should be exposed and easy to get to for inspection, but located to prevent accidental damage. Any work on LPG pipework or other parts of a fixed installation, including testing, must only be carried out by appropriately trained (Gas Safe registered) persons.

Ventilation for heaters and cookers must be permanent and adequate. It should be divided equally between vents at high and low level.

A two-burner cooker in a site hut needs approximately 150 mm x 150 mm ventilation. A 3 kW convector heater needs approximately 225 mm x 225 mm ventilation.

Inspections of all appliances must be carried out before use. If soot forms or smells occur do not use or allow the appliance to be used. Find out the reasons for the problem and ensure that it is corrected.

10.8.14 Enclosed spaces

Before using LPG equipment in an enclosed space, it is essential to carry out a risk assessment under the Management of Health and Safety at Work Regulations. It is essential to ensure that there is adequate ventilation, which may have to be forced. This is necessary to ensure full combustion and also to make certain that the products of combustion, other fumes and excess oxygen from any cutting apparatus are removed. Proper safety precautions and atmospheric monitoring should be considered.

Wherever practicable, cylinders used with operations in confined spaces should be located in a safe area, preferably in the open air. The supply pressure should be reduced to the lowest practicable level on leaving the source of supply.

Where cylinders are used below ground level, the number must be kept as small as possible. All cylinders and hoses should be removed as soon as work has finished or if it is interrupted for a substantial period, for example overnight.

LPG cylinders must not be taken into confined spaces, as defined in the Confined Spaces Regulations, unless exceptional safety precautions are taken.

10.9 Fire

Fires involving flammable liquids usually fall into one of two categories.

- ☑ Flowing liquid fires.
- ☑ Contained liquid fires.

Powder extinguishers are the most suitable type for tackling a flowing liquid fire. The use of foam or carbon dioxide extinguishers may be effective on a small, flowing liquid fire.

Foam extinguishers are the most suitable type for use on contained liquid fires. Powder or carbon dioxide extinguishers may also be used, but operators should be aware of the short duration of small carbon dioxide extinguishers and the possibility of reignition of any residual vapours being given off when an ignition source is still present.

Do not use a water extinguisher for any fire involving highly flammable liquids, because the water will cause a violent reaction and make the liquid overflow.

Suitable portable fire extinguishers should, wherever possible, be sited in pairs (so as to minimise the risk of failure) and in strategic positions adjacent to the store.

10.9.1 Colour of fire extinguishers

With the introduction of the British Standard *Portable fire extinguishers* (BS EN 3) there are now two colour coding systems for portable fire extinguishers.

It is important that staff who may be called upon to use a fire extinguisher have a clear understanding of the colour coding.

This standard states that the body of all fire extinguishers should be red with zones of colour covering not more than 5% of the surface area of the extinguisher, fixed to the extinguisher body and denoting the extinguishing agent or medium it contains.

Colour coding by agent or medium (see below) enables a trained person to rapidly identify the type of extinguisher needed in an emergency.

Extinguishing medium	Colour of panel
Water	Red
Foam	Cream
Powder (all types)	Blue
Carbon dioxide	Black
Wet chemical	Yellow

Other information concerning its use may also be displayed on the body of the extinguisher.

The requirements of the standard are not retrospective. Fire extinguishers conforming to the older standard, BS 5423, which has been withdrawn, will continue to be found on premises and they can remain in use and be refilled until they need to be replaced. When replaced, the new extinguishers must be to BS EN 3. The one exception is vaporising liquid extinguishers (body colour green). These contained halogenated hydrocarbons (halons), which are known to be environmentally damaging. All vaporising liquid extinguishers should have been removed and properly disposed of during 2002.

The full body colour coding of the older extinguishers is the same as is listed in the table above. In addition, a small number of extinguishers are bright silver or self-coloured metal with a designated panel stating the medium they contain. The colour coding of the panel is the same as the above.

Training in the correct type of extinguisher to use and the safe way to operate fire-fighting equipment is essential and should be undertaken by all staff who work with dangerous substances. The use of the wrong extinguisher in the wrong way would have serious consequences.

Advice on training can be obtained from extinguisher manufacturers or the local fire station.

10.9.2 Enforcement of fire safety legislation

The responsibility for the enforcement of fire safety legislation is split between the following organisations.

- HSE, or possibly the Local Authority on small sites, either of which would usually take enforcement action under the Construction (Design and Management) Regulations (CDM) or the Management of Health and Safety at Work Regulations (MHSAWR). However, the HSE also has enforcement powers under the RR(FS)O.
- FRS, which would enforce their powers under the Regulatory Reform (Fire Safety) Order (England and Wales) or the Fire (Scotland) Act (Scotland only).

In most circumstances, fire safety legislation will be enforced by the following organisations.

- HSE on construction sites, including on-site offices and other on-site accommodation.
- FRS where work other than construction is taking place, for example where:
  - one floor of an office block is being refurbished but the other floors remain occupied
  - part of a department store sales floor is a cordoned-off construction site but the public have access to the sales floor outside of the hoarding.

In circumstances such as those described, it is usual for the HSE to enforce fire safety legislation within the confines of the site and the FRS to enforce it outside the hoardings.

However, the responsibility for the enforcement of fire safety legislation may not always be as clear cut as this. For example, the FRS is likely to take an interest in any construction site where there is a significant fire loading or there are other factors that significantly increase personal risk. Some examples are shown below.

- Where the flammable nature of the partly finished structure is considered to pose a significant risk should it catch fire.
- The flammable (or highly flammable) nature and quantities of materials and substances stored and used on the site (for example, LPG).
- The vulnerability of adjacent premises should a fire start on site.
- If there is a large on-site multi-floor administrative complex.

This aspect of fire safety is considered to be particularly relevant to this chapter if significant quantities of flammable or highly flammable substances are stored on site.

For further information on legislation and other resources, including guidance and incident reports, refer to the HSE website.

10.9.3 Liquefied petroleum gas

10.9.3.1 Action in an emergency

Instructions for dealing with incidents involving LPG will vary for each situation. The most important thing is to avoid endangering anyone's life. The following actions should be taken by anyone discovering a fire.

- In case of fire, **no matter how small**, call the FRS.
- Whilst waiting for the FRS to arrive, (if it can be done safely) turn off all cylinder valves to cut off the fuel supply and remove the cylinders from the area.
- If this action cannot be completed safely (which would starve the fire of further LPG), evacuate the site and impose a cordon to stop anyone inadvertently entering the area.
- Never attempt to use a water extinguisher to put out an LPG fire. Dry powder extinguishers are the most suitable type to use. The use of the wrong extinguisher in the wrong way could have serious consequences.
- Training in the correct type of fire-fighting equipment to use, and the safe way to operate it, should be undertaken by all staff who work with LPG. These staff must be trained to recognise when the situation is getting out of control and know when to evacuate the area.
- When the FRS arrives, inform the fire officer of the situation including:
  - the location and contents of all cylinders
  - details of any security cordon that you have implemented
  - confirmation that all people who were known to be in the area have been accounted for or details of anyone that is unaccounted for
  - if possible and required, offer them the data information sheet relating to the cylinder(s) involved.

10.9.3.2 Remember

- Cylinders fitted with pressure relief valves can produce gas jets that will extend a considerable distance.
- If cylinders are exposed to a severe fire or are engulfed in flames, no attempt should be made to fight the fire. **Evacuate everyone from the area.**
- Where a flame from a leaking gas cylinder is extinguished but the valve is still open, gas will continue to escape and there will be a danger of a gas cloud forming and the risk of an explosion.
- Any cylinder involved in a fire should be clearly labelled that it has been involved in a fire and removed from the area to a safe place. Telephone the suppliers – they will give advice and arrange for the cylinder(s) to be collected.

Instructions concerning emergency procedures should be clearly displayed and all employees should be made aware of them.

Data information sheets are available from product manufacturers giving advice in case of an accident involving LPG cylinders. A copy of each sheet should be available for inspection and those sheets relating to the cylinders involved should be given to the fire officer.

10.9.4 Fire-fighting equipment

Selected and suitable employees should be trained in the use of fire-fighting equipment.

Advice on the training of staff can be obtained from the LPG supplier or the FRS.

Portable fire extinguishers, sited in pairs to minimise the risk of failure, should be positioned at strategic points wherever LPG is stored or used. As a general guide, no fewer than two 4.5 kg dry powder extinguishers or equivalent should be provided for every 20 large cylinders (47 kg) stored.

10.9.5 Training

Most accidents involving LPG are due to ignorance of basic safety precautions.

All persons using LPG cylinders, tools or equipment should be suitably instructed in the hazards associated with LPG, and the precautions to be taken in its use.

For an LPG safety questionnaire refer to Section G: *Checklists and forms.*

10.10 Legislative requirements

10.10.1 Construction (Design and Management) Regulations

These regulations specify the measures to be taken to prevent the risk from fire, explosion or any substance likely to cause asphyxiation and include the measures that should be taken to detect and fight fires, which could occur on a construction site.

In practice, the HSE is likely to use this legislation for any enforcement action.

For further information refer to Chapter A03 Construction (Design and Management) Regulations.

10.10.2 ATEX and explosive atmospheres

ATEX is the name commonly given to the two European Directives for controlling explosive atmospheres.

1. Directive 99/92/EC (also known as ATEX 137 or the ATEX Workplace Directive) on minimum requirements for improving the health and safety protection of workers potentially at risk from explosive atmospheres.
2. Directive 94/9/EC (also known as ATEX 95 or the ATEX Equipment Directives) on the approximation of the laws of member states concerning equipment and protective systems intended for use in potentially explosive atmospheres.

In Great Britain the requirements of Directive 99/92/EC were put into effect through Regulations 7 and 11 of the Dangerous Substances and Explosive Atmospheres Regulations (DSEAR).

The aim of Directive 94/9/EC is to allow the free trade of ATEX equipment and protective systems within the EU by removing the need for separate testing and documentation for each member state.

In Great Britain, the requirements of the directive were put into effect through BIS Equipment and Protective Systems Intended for Use in Potentially Explosive Atmospheres Regulations (SI 1996/192).

The regulations apply to all equipment intended for use in explosive atmospheres, whether electrical or mechanical, and also to protective systems.

Manufacturers/suppliers (or importers, if the manufacturers are outside the EU) must ensure that their products meet essential health and safety requirements and undergo appropriate conformity procedures. This usually involves testing and certification by a third-party certification body (known as a notified body) but manufacturers/suppliers can self-certify equipment intended to be used in less hazardous explosive atmospheres. Once certified, the equipment is marked by the 'EX' symbol to identify it as such.

Certification ensures that the equipment or protective system is fit for its intended purpose and that adequate information is supplied with it to ensure that it can be used safely.

10.10.3 Competence and training

All the above sets of regulations stipulate the need for a degree of competence in assessing certain workplace situations.

In most cases it will be necessary for the employer to provide employees with adequate information, instruction, training and supervision to enable them to carry out any work task safely and without risk to their health.

Appendix A – Retrieval of orphaned compressed gas cylinders

The cylinder retrieval arrangements in place for the major national companies are listed below.

Parent company	Collection company	Contact
Calor Gas	CylinderCare	www.wastecare.co.uk/services/cylindercare Tel: 0808 274 3977
BP	Synergy Asset Services Ltd	www.synergyassetservices.co.uk/regulations.asp Tel: 01304 827 277 www.cylinder-recycling.co.uk/ Tel: 0845 199 0144
Flogas	In-house collection by own staff	Tel: 01132 497 140
BOC	In-house collection by own staff	Tel: 0800 111 333

Orphaned cylinders

1. If a cylinder is no longer needed, it should be returned to the local dealer of the company owning the cylinder.
2. Where the original owner of a compressed gas cylinder cannot be identified, contact CylinderCare.
3. Until such time as they are collected, orphaned cylinders should be stored in a safe and secure manner.
4. If it is not known which company owns an LPG cylinder, the table of LPG cylinder fillers should be viewed in the 'who knows who' guidance table (available online).
5. In extreme circumstances, where all attempts to trace the owner of a cylinder have failed, the Local Authority waste disposal sites may offer a disposal service.

Index